PERIODIZATION OF STRENGTH:

THE NEW WAVE IN STRENGTH TRAINING

Prof. TUDOR O. BOMPA, Ph. D.
York University
4700 Keele St.
Toronto, ON Canada M3J 1P3

Edited by
Orietta Calcina

VERITAS PUBLISHING INC.
P.O. Box 58031
3089 Dufferin St.
Toronto. ON M6A 3C8
Canada
Phone: (905) 889-8228
Fax: (905) 881-8552

PROGENEX
574 East Alamo Drive
Suite #80
Chandler, AZ 85225
USA
Phone: 1-800-PROGENEX
602-813-0713
Fax: 602-813-0920

Copyright © 1993 by Tudor O. Bompa
First Printing April 1994
Second Printing February 1995

ISBN:0-9697557-0-8

Published by:

VERITAS PUBLISHING INC.
P.O. Box 58031
3089 Dufferin St.
Toronto. ON M6A 3C8
Canada
Phone: (905) 889-8228
Fax: (905) 881-8552

PROGENEX
574 East Alamo Drive
 Suite #80
Chandler, AZ 85225
USA
Phone: 1-800-**PROGENEX**
          602-813-0713
Fax: 602-813-0920

Printed in Canada by: **COPYWELL**
1999 Leslie Street, Don Mills, Ontario, M3B 2M3
Canada
Phone: **1-416-COPYWELL**

Table of Contents

PART 3: TRAINING METHODS AS APPLIED TO PERIODIZATION OF STRENGTH

THE FOUNDATIONS OF STRENGTH TRAINING

The effectiveness of a strength program relies on science and methodology.

Do you want to be successful?

You must understand the strength training!

CHAPTER ONE

TRAINING AND STRENGTH TRAINING

WHAT IS TRAINING?

Training is usually defined as a systematic process of repetitive, progressive exercises, having the ultimate goal of improving athletic performance.

The key to improved athletic performance is a well-organized system of training. A training program must follow the concept of periodization, be well-planned and structured, and be sport specific, so as to adapt the athlete's energy systems to the particular requirements of the sport. For further information on these topics, the reader can refer to *Theory and Methodology of Training* (Bompa, 1994).

An athlete is a trained individual who excels in a particular form of physical activity following a period of extensive physical and psychological training. In order to optimize the athlete's abilities, the athlete has to be trained in such a way that the body will be prepared for optimum response to the physical demand of competitions. In fact, **through training the athlete is conditioned, is modeled, not only to match, but more importantly, to overpass the special demand of the chosen sport, and the specific requirements of the athletic competitions**. In order to reach that state the athlete tries to reach higher training levels and to constantly challenge his/her state of adaptation. If a given state of adaptation is not overpassed, performance would hardly be improved.

WHAT IS STRENGTH TRAINING?

In simple terms, strength is defined as the ability to apply force. Its development should be the prime concern of anyone who attempts to improve the athletes' performance. Although strength development in primitive forms was employed by athletes preparing to compete in the ancient Olympic games, there are still many coaches who do not take advantage of its benefactory role. The utilization of some methods of strength development seems to lead to a faster growth, by up to 8–12 times, as compared to expecting to improve strength just by practising the skill of a sport. For instance a volleyball player will develop faster jumping abilities for spiking by using strength training rather than by just resorting to performing several spikes during a volleyball practice. Therefore, strength training has to be seen as the most important ingredient in the process of "making" an athlete.

There is strong evidence that strength training enhances performance and that it is used with success not only in rehabilitation, but in preventing injuries as well. Strength training has also become an important part in fitness for both men and women.

WHY "PERIODIZATION OF STRENGTH: THE NEW WAVE IN STRENGTH TRAINING?"

The market is almost saturated with strength, or weight training books. However, almost all can be classified as very "traditional", without visible difference between them. Almost all discuss some basic physiology, showing various exercises, and make references to some training methods. Planning is rarely discussed. As for periodization, it is not referred to, simply because its comprehension is very limited. Therefore a strength training novelty is rarely seen.

In order to overcome the fact that there are very few new strength training ideas, many authors introduce "magic" methods with "incredible results", especially in the bodybuilding journals! However, ever since this author has created the "Periodization of Bodybuilding" (and introduced it to the readers of *Ironman* magazine as the "Ironman Training System"), bodybuilders started to experience better performance without the typical exhaustion (please refer to the series of articles written, in *Ironman* 1991-1993).

The purpose of any training method or technique should be to prepare an athlete for competition-the ideal test of an athlete's abilities, skills, and psychological readiness. In doing so the athlete is exposed to phase-specific variations of training. These phases are planned according to the competition schedule and each of them have a specific goal. Ultimately, the whole training program aims at **peaking** for the most important competitions of the year.

Strength training is an ingredient of paramount importance in athletes' development. It is used to enhance athletes' abilities, to use specific methods for different training phases in order to reach peak performance at the time of the main competition(s) of the year. Therefore the employment of the term **periodization** is purposefully selected to specifically emphasize this novelty in strength training. Strength training does not mean just lifting weights with no plan, or specific purpose.

Why use the term "strength" and not "weight" or "resistance" training? The answer is quite simple: strength development is possible by more than just applying force against resistance or by lifting weights. Gains in strength is the result of increasing the tension in the muscles, by activating a quick and powerful contraction. (Activation is used to mean: to spur into action, or to favour the growth, in this case gains in strength). As such, muscle tension, or muscle activation, can also be induced by utilizing electrical stimulation or plyometric exercises. Therefore, strength training seems to be the most comprehensive term which incorporates all the possible elements of development, methods, and techniques available.

One of the major objectives of this book is to demonstrate that strength training is not just a standard method of "lifting every day as much as possible", irrespective of the scope of a given training phase, or in disregard of the intricate methodology of peaking for competitions.

Furthermore, **the ultimate objective of strength training is to develop power, or muscular-endurance,** or both of these combinations, depending on the specifics of a given sport. To produce such a combination just before the competitions begin is a must, because it **represents the main physiological foundation athletes' performance** rely on. But the road to either or both of these strength combinations is the result of specific plans as well as phase-specific specialized training methods.

To achieve such a goal means to **utilize the concept of periodization** (please refer to chapter 10). It means to shake-up the whole tradition of strength training which is still in place, and replace it with this **"new wave of strength training".** This is a revolutionary idea which was tested by this author, and which has demonstrated the best results in strength gains with athletes in football, track and field, bodybuilding, rowing, swimming, etc. The rate of improvement is incomparable with anything utilized in athletics today.

Although some terms employed may not be very familiar to some readers, periodization of strength is not that complicated. Everyone will understand it and be able to apply it successfully. Specific examples and plans will assist the reader to comprehend and apply it. **Performance will improve better than ever, and peak performance will overpass those achieved in the past.**

This "new wave in strength training" will be examined, and hopefully, adopted by the vast majority of coaches, instructors, and fitness fans. They will do that simply because it is more scientific, methodical, and logical.

To put it straight forward: it is superior to everything used today in strength training. And equally important: it is less exhausting!

For the enthusiastic follower, this book is designed to equally address: coaches, training specialists, and fitness instructors. It can be used by coaches who train athletes from beginners to international class levels of performance. Athletes whose goal is high performance, nationally or internationally, will experience improvements not only in strength gains, but in overall performance as well.

The topic of strength is discussed from many angles, making the attempt to simplify the complexity of strength training. Examining several scientific elements, those which are crucial for reaching a higher level of knowledge, forms the basis for the foundation. To be involved in strength training without the understanding of muscle structure, the process of muscle contraction, adaptation to training, fatigue, methodology of training, detraining etc., is like being a seafarer without the understanding of how the compass works.

This book is more concerned with addressing the theory behind training than in discussing and illustrating specific exercises, or techniques. It is assumed that most exercises are known, or are very easy to find. Good strength training coaches/instructors will always be ready to assist anyone in selecting appropriate exercises.

CHAPTER TWO

STRENGTH AND ITS RELATIONSHIP WITH THE OTHER BIOMOTOR ABILITIES

Almost all physical activities incorporate one or more of the elements of force, quickness, duration, and the range of motion. When a given exercise is required to overcome resistance it is called a strength exercise. When quickness and high frequency is maximized it is referred to as a speed exercise. If distance, duration, or the number of repetitions are high, an endurance exercise is performed. On the other hand, if the range of motion is maximized a flexibility movement is being performed. And finally, when in a given exercise a high degree of complexity is required, this is known as a coordination exercise. Some athletes are more capable than others of performing such exercises. They are said to have "talent" for that type of activity. But this talent is largely genetic; it is inherited from one's family. **Strength, speed, and endurance are inherited abilities** which play the most important role in one's chances of reaching high levels of performance. Therefore they are called **dominant motor, or biomotor abilities**. The term **"motor"** refers to movement, whereas the prefix **"bio"** is added to illustrate the biological importance of these three abilities.

When a skill, or a sport, requires a higher contribution from one of the three biomotor abilities to perform it, it is said that such an ability is dominant. For instance, in long distance running the dominant ability is endurance. However, most sports are rarely dominated by only one ability. On the contrary, the performance of the vast majority of sports is often the product of at least two abilities. For instance, for sports such as football, baseball, sprinting, throwing, and jumping events in track and field, the dominant ability is power. Figure 1 illustrates the interdependence between the main biomotor abilities, and the possible combinations between them.

Figure 1 exemplifies clearly that when **strength and endurance combined together the result is muscular-endurance**, or the ability to perform many repetitions against a given resistance for a prolonged period of time, such as in rowing, mid and long distance swimming, and canoeing. When **maximum strength and speed are integrated the outcome is power**, the ability of performing an explosive movement in the shortest period of time such as batting, spiking, pitching, tackling in football,

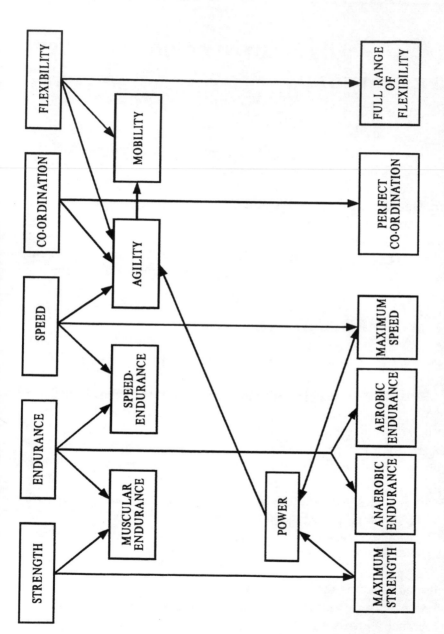

FIGURE 1. An illustration of the interdependence between the biomotor abilities.

8

throwing events, and starting in sprinting.

The combination between **endurance and speed** (events between 20 seconds and one minute) is called **speed--endurance**. The highly acclaimed **agility** is the product of a complex combination between speed, coordination, flexibility, and power (gymnastics, wrestling, and many skills performed in football, soccer, volleyball, baseball, boxing, diving, and figure skating). And, finally, when **agility and flexibility join together** the result is called **mobility**, or the quality of covering a playing area quickly as well as being well timed and co-ordinated such as in team sports, diving, some floor exercises in gymnastics, karate, and wrestling.

Among strength, speed and endurance there is a relationship of high methodical importance. During the initial years of involvement in training, all abilities have to be developed in order to build a solid foundation for specialized training. This latter phase is specific to national level and elite athletes whose program aims for a precise, specialized training effect. Thus, as a result of employing specific exercises, the adaptation process occurs in accordance with one's specialization. For elite class athletes the relationship between the magnitude of strength, speed and endurance, as the three more determinant biomotor abilities, are dependent upon the particularities of the sport and the athlete's needs.

Figure 2 illustrates such a relationship, where in each example **strength or force (F), speed (S), or endurance (E)** is dominant. In each case when one biomotor ability is strongly dominant the other two do not share or participate to a similar extent. However, the above example is just pure theory, which may only be directly applied to very few sports. In the vast majority of sports the amalgamation between the three biomotor abilities leads to a different outcome in which each ability has a given input. Figure 3 exemplifies a few sports where the circle represents the dominant composition between strength, speed and endurance.

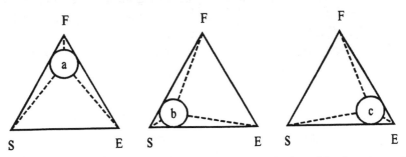

Figure 2. A graphical illustration of the relationship between the main biomotor abilities, where strength (a), speed (b) and endurance (c) are dominant.

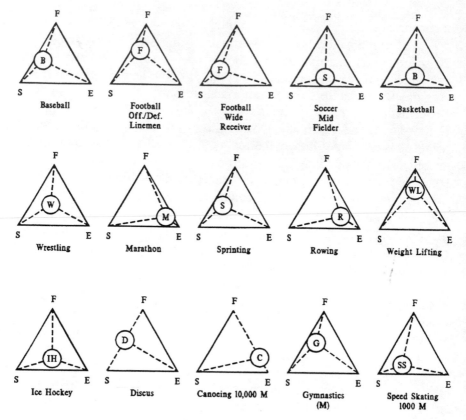

FIGURE 3. The dominant composition between the biomotor abilities for various sports.

Considering figure 3 as a model, please try the following exercise:

1. using figures 2 and 3 as models and the pertinent discussion, try to define the combination between the dominant abilities for your sport (if not provided above). Place a circle where you feel it is appropriate, or the most ideal place (figure 4);
2. to the best of your abilities, try to evaluate your own/or your athlete(s) dominant abilities, and place the circle where appropriate (figure 4), and;
3. if the last circle you have placed is in another area than the ideal combination for your own sport, that tells you what you have to train in order to shift the circle to match the dominant combination of biomotor abilities of your sport.

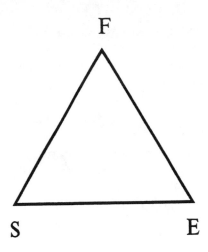

Figure 4. Use this triangle for the suggested exercise.

THE EFFECT OF STRENGTH TRAINING ON THE OTHER BIOMOTOR ABILITIES

The development of a biomotor ability has to be specific and very methodical. When a dominant ability is developed (e.g., strength), it has a direct or an indirect effect upon the other abilities (speed and endurance). Such an effect depends strictly on the degree of resemblance between the methods employed and the specifics of the sport. Thus, the development of a dominant biomotor ability may have a positive or in rare occasions, a negative transfer. When an athlete attempts to develop strength there may be a positive transfer to speed, and to a certain degree even to endurance. On the other hand, a strength training program designed to develop maximum strength only, may have a negative transfer to the development of aerobic endurance such as the one required in marathon running (e.g. by adding extra mass on the athlete). Similarly, a training program aiming exclusively at developing aerobic endurance, under certain circumstances (i.e., training for a marathon) may have a negative transfer to strength and speed. Since strength is one of the crucial abilities in athletics, it has to always be trained along with the other abilities so that their overall improvement will lead to a better performance.

For far too long some misleading theories, with dubious foundation, have suggested that strength training, especially maximum loads, slows down the athletes, and affects both the development of endurance and flexibility. Both empirical and research data do not concur with such unproven theories. Furthermore, the result of recent research studies

11

definitely discredit any such theories (Atha, 1981; MacDougall et al., 1987; Hickson et al., 1988; Dudley and Fleck, 1988; Micheli, 1988; Sale et al., 1990; Nelson et al., 1990). These studies concluded that combined strength and endurance training does not affect improvement (i.e. no negative transfer) of aerobic power, or muscular strength. Similarly, strength programs do not have any risk of loss in body flexibility. Therefore endurance related sports, such as rowing, cross-country skiing, canoeing, and swimming can safely perform concurrent work on strength and endurance. The same is true for sports requiring strength and flexibility. No one can represent a better proof for such a reality than the athletes in gymnastics, weight lifting, and wrestling, who are both very strong and flexible. As for wrestlers they are both strong, and flexible, but also fast and have a great aerobic capacity.

For sports where speed is the dominant ability, power represents a great source of speed improvement. One would never see a fast sprinter without he/she being strong as well. High acceleration, fast limb movement, and high frequency could not be developed without strengthening the muscles to contract fast and powerfully. However, in extreme situations, maximum loads may momentarily affect speed. If speed training is performed after an exhausting training with maximum loads, then quite expectedly high velocity would be affected. But such an approach would be faulty anyways, since speed training should always be performed before strength (please refer to short-term planning).

SPORT-SPECIFIC COMBINATIONS BETWEEN STRENGTH, SPEED, AND ENDURANCE

The above discussion can be followed by a more sport-specific analysis regarding the combination between the dominant biomotor abilities. Most of the actions and movements in sports are slightly more complex than the above analysis, and as such, the role of strength in sports should be viewed as the mechanism required to perform skills, and athletic actions.

The development of strength is not made just for the sake of being strong. On the contrary, **the scope of strength development is to serve the specific needs of a given sport, to develop specific strength, or its combinations, in order to increase athletes' performance** to the highest possible level. Figure 5 illustrates the complexity and the types of combinations possible between the biomotor abilities necessary to be developed in order to successfully perform an athletic action.

As already defined, the combination between strength (F) and endurance (E) results in muscular-endurance (M–E). But there are quite a few sports requiring M–E, some being of longer, while others of shorter duration. Since the type of M–E requirements between them is so drastically different, it is necessary to make a clear distinction between sports and the required kind of M–E. Knowing this distinction the coach will be able to determine the type of strength to train, for each sport category. The sport-specific strength combinations will be exemplified in the chapters for planning and training methods.

Before actually referring to a specific discussion on the topic, a brief clarification is necessary regarding the terms **"cyclic"** and **"acyclic"**. For the purpose of this discussion sports skills can be classified into two main categories: cyclic and acyclic. A **cyclic** skill is composed of cyclic movements which are repeated continuously, such as running, walking, swimming, rowing, skating, cross-country skiing, cycling, and canoeing. As soon as one cycle of the motor act is learnt, the others can be repeated with the same succession.

An **acyclic** skill, on the other hand, is made out of actions which constantly change without being similar to most others, such as in throwing events, gymnastics, wrestling, fencing, and many technical elements in team sports.

With the exception of sprinting events, cyclic sports are endurance-related. That means that endurance is either dominant or has a very important contribution to perform in the sport. On the other hand acyclic sports can often be related to speed-power. However, many other sports are more complex, requiring speed, power, and an important component of endurance, such as basketball, volleyball, soccer, ice hockey, wrestling, boxing, etc. Therefore the following analysis may often refer to some skills of a given sport, and not just the sport as a whole.

Figure 5 is used as a reference for the analysis of various combinations of strength. The discussion will be made clockwise, starting with F–E axis, or the strength-endurance axis.

The reader will observe that each combination of strength has an arrow pointing to a certain part of the axis between two biomotor abilities. An arrow placed closer to F indicates that strength plays a dominant role in the performance of a sport, or a composing skill. As the arrow is placed closer to the mid-point of the axis, that indicates an equal, or an almost equal contribution of both biomotor abilities. The further away from F, the less importance it has, thus suggesting that the other ability becomes more dominant. However, even for such situations, strength still has a role in that sport.

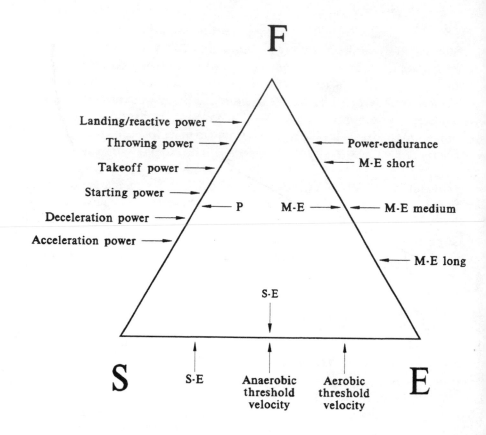

FIGURE 5. An illustration of the sport-specific combinations between the dominant biomotor abilities.

The F–E axis refers to sports where M–E (muscular-endurance) is the dominant strength combination (the inner arrow). But not all the sports require an equal contribution from both strength and endurance. If reference is made to swimming events, the range is from 50–1500 m. While the 50 m event is speed-power dominant, from 100 m on M–E becomes more important as the distance increases.

Power-Endurance is placed on top of the F–E axis because of the importance of strength for activities such as a rebounding jump in basketball, a spike in volleyball, a jump to catch the ball in Australian football, rugby, or a jump to hit the ball in soccer. All these actions are typical of power-dominant movements. The same is true for some skills in tennis, boxing, wrestling, and all the martial arts. But to conclude that

14

in order to be successful in such actions throughout the game or match, one has to train power only, will be a training error since they are performed between 100–200 or more times per game or match (the average number of jumps for spiking and blocking in volleyball is around 200 for national class players). While it is definitively important to jump high to rebound a ball, say 60 cm (24 inches), it is equally important to duplicate such a jump 200 times per game. Consequently for the above mentioned sports both power and power-endurance have to be trained.

M-E of Short Duration, refers to the type of M–E necessary for events of short duration (40 seconds–2 minutes). If one intends to analyze the 100 m swimming event, the start itself is a power-type of action (please refer to "take-off power"), and so is the first 20 strokes. From the second part of the race on M–E becomes at least equally important to power. In the last 30–40 m, the crucial element is the ability to duplicate the force of the arms' pull so that the velocity does not decrease, but instead is maintained the same, and increased at the finish. For events such as 100 m in swimming, 400 m in running, 500–1000 m in speed skating, and 500 m in canoeing, M–E has a strong contribution to the final result.

M-E of Medium Duration is typical of cyclic sports performed over 2–5 minutes, such as: 200 and 400 m in swimming, 3000 m in speed skating, middle distance running in track and field, 1000 m in canoeing, wrestling, martial arts, figure skating, synchronized swimming, and cycling pursuit.

M-E of Long Duration, represents the ability to apply force against a relative standard resistance for a longer period of time, such as in: rowing, cross-country skiing, road racing in cycling, and long distance running in track and field, swimming, speed skating, and canoeing. Considering the purpose of this book the S–E (speed-endurance) axis is mentioned just in passing.

Speed-Endurance refers to the ability to maintain or repeat a high velocity (e.g. football, baseball, basketball, rugby, soccer, or power skating in ice hockey). In the latter group of sports the same type of speed is necessary to be repeated several times per game. As such, players belonging to the aforementioned sports need to train, and display a speed-endurance capacity.

The remaining two types of speed-endurance alters their combination and proportion between speed and endurance, as the distance increases. Therefore in the first case sports required to train a velocity around the **anaerobic threshold**, (4 mmol of lactate, or approximately a heart rate around 170 beats per minute), while in the other, around the **aerobic threshold** (2–3 mmol of lactate, or a heart rate around 125–140 beats per minute).

The F–S (**strength-speed**) axis concerns mostly the strength-speed sports where power is the dominant ability.

Landing And Reactive Power is a major concern for several sports, from figure-skating to gymnastics and several skills in team sports. Quite a few injuries occur in these sports for the lack of specific skills in landing, but most of them for improper training.

Most coaches are training their athletes only on the take-off part of a jump, but are not concerned whether they have the power to perform a controlled and balanced landing. Although in **landing** there is also a technical component, the physical/power element plays a more important role particularly for advanced athletes. An athlete will never be able to "stick" a landing or have the power to absorb the shock, and maintain a good balance in order to be able to continue the routine, or perform another move immediately unless he/she is trained eccentrically.

The power required to control landing depends on the height of the jump, the athlete's own body weight, and whether landing is performed by absorbing the shock or with the joints flexed but stiff. As revealed by testing performed to provide the data for this book, for shock absorbing landing one is using a resistive force of 3-4 times the athlete's own body weight. If landing is performed with the joints stiff one requires a force of 6–8 times own body weight. If a person's mass is 60 kg (132 lbs) the power required to absorb the shock of landing is 180–240 kg (403–537 lbs). However, if the same subject is landing with the leg joints stiff, the power recorded at the instant of landing is 360–480 kg (806–1072 lbs).

The theory that through specific/skill training one develops the power required at the instant of landing is far from being acceptable. It is known that strength training can do that better, faster, and with a much higher consistency. Specific power training for landing can generate much higher tension in the muscles of the legs than performing an exercise with only your own body weight. Higher tension means improvements of landing power. In addition, through specific power training for landing, especially through eccentric training, one can build a **"power reserve"** for landing, that is a force higher than the power required to have a correct and controlled landing. The higher the power reserve the safer and better controlled landing.

If landing is performed with one leg, such as in figure skating, the force displayed at the instant of landing is 3-4 times own body weight for shock absorbing, and 5–7 times for landing with stiff leg joints.

Reactive power refers to the ability to generate the force of jumping immediately following landing (therefore "reactive"). This kind of power is also necessary to quickly change the direction of running, such as in football, basketball, and tennis. Similarly, reactive power is necessary in martial arts, wrestling, and boxing. One of the most effective training methods for reactive training are plyometric exercises, briefly mentioned in this book, but extensively explained in **"Power Training for sport: Plyometrics for Maximum Power Development"** (Bompa, 1993).

The force necessary to perform a reactive jump depends on the height of the jump, the athletes body weight, and leg power. For instance, for reactive jumps a force equal to 6–8 times own body weight is required. Higher reactive jumps, made from a platform of 1 m (3.3 feet), requires a reactive force of 8–10 times own body weight.

Throwing Power. In events in which the athletes apply force against an implement, such as in throwing the ball in football, the speed of release is determined by the size of muscular force exerted at the instant of release. At first the athlete has to defeat the inertia of the implement, which is proportional to the mass of the implement (important only in throwing events). Then the athlete concentrates to continuously accelerate through the range of motion, maximum acceleration being achieved at the instance of release. The force and acceleration of release depends directly on the force and speed of contraction applied against the implement. The power required to maximize athletes' ability employs various methods and is developed according to the process of periodization.

Take-off Power is a crucial element in all the events in which the athlete attempts to project the body at the highest point, to either jump over a bar (e.g. high jump), or to reach the best height in order to catch a ball (e.g. rebound), or spike it. The height of a jump directly depends on the athletes vertical force applied against the ground in order to defeat the pull of gravity. In most cases the vertical force performed at the instance of take-off is at least twice as much as the athlete's weight. The higher the jump the more powerful the legs should be. Leg power is developed through periodized strength training as explained in chapters 10 and 14.

Starting Power. Many sports, from sprinting to all team sports, requires a high speed to cover a given distance in the shortest possible time. This is achievable only if at the beginning of a muscular contraction the athlete has the capacity to generate maximum force in order to create a high initial speed. A fast start, both from low start in sprinting, and from different positions in team sports, including tackling in football, depends on the reaction time and power the athlete can exert at that instant.

Decelerating Power. From soccer to basketball and from football to ice and field hockey, just to mention a few sports, the athletes run fast, constantly changing their direction with quickness and agility. Such an athlete is an exploder, and accelerator, but also a decelerator. The dynamics of the game changes so abruptly that as the athlete runs very fast in one direction, he/she may have to quickly change direction with the least loss of speed, and accelerate back to the direction he/she came from.

If one accepts that in order to accelerate fast a great deal of leg and shoulder power is required, the same is true for deceleration. The same muscles used for acceleration (i.e. quadriceps, hamstrings, and calves) are used for deceleration, except that they are **contracting eccentrically**. Therefore in order to enhance the ability to decelerate fast, in order to quickly move in another direction, decelerating power must be trained.

Accelerating Power. In 2–3 seconds after the start of the run the athlete is attempting to reach the highest acceleration possible. This sprinting speed, or acceleration, depends on the power and quickness of muscle contraction to drive the arms and legs to the highest stride frequency, shortest contact phase when the leg reaches the ground, and the highest propulsion when the leg pushes against the ground for a powerful forward drive. The capacity of the athlete to accelerate depends both on the arm and leg force. Specific strength training for high acceleration will benefit most team sport athletes, from wide receivers in football to a winger in rugby or a striker in soccer.

All the fast athletic performances, from throwing events to sprinting are more difficult to achieve without a specialized and periodized strength training program.

TABLE 1

Sports-Specific Strength Required to be Developed in Sports/ Events

No.	Sport/Event	Types of Strength Required
1	Athletics:	
	Sprinting	Reactive power, starting power, acceleration power, power-endurance
	Middle Distance Running	Acceleration power, M-E medium
	Distance Running	M-E long
	Long Jump	Acceleration power, take-off power, reactive power
	Triple Jump	Acceleration power, reactive power, take-off power
	High Jump	Take-off power, reactive power
	Throws	Throwing power, reactive power

No.	Sport/Event	Types of Strength Required
2	**Baseball**	Throwing power, acceleration power
3	**Basketball**	Take-off power, power-endurance, acceleration power, deceleration power
4	**Biathlon**	M-E long
5	**Boxing**	Power-endurance, reactive power, M-E medium/long
6	**Canoeing/Kayaking:**	
	500 m	M-E short, acceleration power, starting power
	1000 m	M-E medium, acceleration power, starting power
	10,000 m	M-E long
7	**Cricket**	Throwing power, acceleration power
8	**Cycling:**	
	Track 200 m	Acceleration power, reactive power
	4000 Pursuit	M-E medium, acceleration power
	Road Racing	M-E long
9	**Diving**	Take-off power, reactive power
10	**Driving**	Starting power, reactive power
11	**Equestrian**	M-E medium
12	**Fencing**	Reactive power, power-endurance
13	**Figure Skating**	Take-off power, landing power, power-endurance
14	**Field Hockey**	Acceleration power, deceleration power, M-E medium
15	**Football (American):**	
	Lineman	Starting power, reactive power
	Line Backers; Quarterbacks; Running Backs; Inside Receivers	Starting power, acceleration power, reactive power
	Wide Receivers; Defensive Backers; Tail Backs	Acceleration power, reactive power, starting power

No.	Sport/Event	Types of Strength Required
16	**Football (Australian)**	Acceleration power, take-off power, landing power, M-E short/medium
17	**Gymnastics**	Reactive power, take-off power, landing power
18	**Handball (European)**	Throwing power, acceleration power
19	**Ice Hockey**	Acceleration power, deceleration power, power-endurance
20	**Martial Arts**	Starting power, reactive power, power endurance
21	**Rhythmic Sportive Gymnastics**	Reactive power, take-off power, M-E short
22	**Rowing**	M-E medium and long, starting power
23	**Rugby**	Acceleration power, starting power, M-E medium
24	**Sailing**	M-E long, power-endurance
25	**Shooting**	M-E long, power-endurance
26	**Skiing:**	
	Alpine	Reactive power, M-E short
	Nordic	M-E long, power-endurance
27	**Soccer:**	
	Swippers; Full Backs	Reactive power, acceleration/deceleration power
	Midfielders	Acceleration/deceleration power, M-E medium
	Forwards	Acceleration/deceleration power, reactive power

No.	Sport/Event	Types of Strength Required
28	**Speed Skating:**	
	Sprinting	Starting power, acceleration power, reactive power
	Middle Distance	Acceleration power, M-E medium, power-endurance
	Long Distance	M-E long
29	**Squash/Handball**	Reactive power, power-endurance
30	**Swimming:**	
	Sprinting	Starting power, acceleration power, M-E short
	Middle Distance	M-E medium, power-endurance
	Long Distance	M-E long
31	**Synchronized Swimming**	M-E medium, power-endurance
32	**Tennis**	Power-endurance, reactive power, acceleration/deceleration power
33	**Volleyball**	Reactive power, power-endurance, M-E medium
34	**Waterpolo**	M-E medium, acceleration power, throwing power
35	**Wrestling**	Power-endurance, reactive-power, M-E medium

CHAPTER THREE

MUSCLES, MUSCLE CONTRACTION AND STRENGTH

HOW MUSCLES WORK?

The musculo-skeletal frame of the body is an arrangement of bones attached to one another by a series of ligaments at structures called joints (which allow the motion of articulating bones), and a number of muscles crossing the joints, which provide the force necessary for the body's movements.

The spinal column represents a mechanism which gives the body stability, support for the weight of the body, and more importantly, acts as a shock absorber for many athletic movements. This amazing mechanism is the core of many effective functions, all produced by the muscle contractions.

The muscles arranged along the skeletal frame of the body, the skeletal muscles, always act as a group rather than contracting individually. Consequently, the movements performed about a joint are produced by several muscles, with different roles, such as:

AGONISTS or *SYNERGISTS* are called the muscles working together as a team, which cooperate together to perform a movement.

ANTAGONISTS are the muscles that during a motion act in opposition to the agonists, often just in a passive resistance. In most cases, especially for skilled athletes, the antagonists are relaxed, thus allowing the motion to be performed with ease. Therefore, athletic movements are directly influenced by the interaction between agonists and antagonists. A motion which looks rough, or is rigidly performed, can possibly be the result of an improper interaction between the two groups. Only by concentrating on the antagonists to relax, one may improve the flow and smoothness of an athletic movement.

PRIME MOVERS is the term referring to the muscles which are primarily responsible for producing a strength movement or a technical skill. In the case of elbow flexion (bending the elbow) the prime mover is the bicep muscle. The triceps, as an antagonist, should be relaxed in order to facilitate an easier and smoother flexion.

The *LINE OF PULL,* for strength training, represents an imaginary line, crossing the muscle longitudinally, (longitudinal axis) and connecting the two extreme heads of a muscle. The highest physiological and

mechanical efficiency of a muscle contraction is achi⟨
performed along the line of pull. An example using the b
make this point easier. Elbow flexion can be performe⟨
being held in different positions. When the palm is turne⟨
of pull is direct, therefore having highest efficiency. On ⟨⟨⟨ ⟨⟨⟨
the palm is facing down this is not the case anymore since the tendon of
the bicep muscle wraps around the bone radius. As such the line of pull is
not direct, mechanical efficiency decreases, and as a result a good portion
of the force of contraction is wasted.

120°

An almost similar situation occurs with squats. If feet are shoulders'
width apart and the toes pointing forward, muscle quadriceps have a better
line of pull. The opposite is true when the feet are far apart, and the toes
pointing diagonally-forward. Therefore, if one looks for maximum strength
gains, and especially for optimal muscle efficiency, strength exercises have
to be selected and performed along the line of pull.

STABILIZERS or *FIXATORS,* are usually smaller muscles which
contract isometrically to anchor, or steady, a bone so that the prime movers
have a firm base to pull on. Although this subject will be more extensively
addressed later, it is important to mention that other muscles of some limbs
act as stabilizers so that another limb can perform a motion. Take the case
of batting: the leg muscles are contracted isometrically to stabilize the
lower body firmly so that the arms and trunk can perform the action easier.
And one more example, in "preacher's curls" (elbow flexion, with the
upperarms' rested on a firm support) the shoulders, upper arm, and
abdominal muscles are contracted isometrically, to stabilize the shoulders,
so that the biceps have a stable base to pull.

TYPES OF MUSCULAR CONTRACTION

Skeletal muscles perform two things: contraction and relaxation.
As the muscle is stimulated by a motor impulse it contracts, when the
impulse is discontinued the muscle relaxes.

During athletic performance, muscles perform three types of
contractions: isotonic, isometric and isokinetic. Isotonic contractions are
performed in three variations such as concentric, eccentric, and plyometric.

ISOTONIC, or *DYNAMIC,* is the most familiar type of muscle
contraction, and the term means same tension (from the Greek
"isos" = equal, and "tonikos" = tension or tone). As the term implies,
during an isotonic contraction the tension should be the same throughout
the entire range of motion. However, as illustrated by figure 6, the tension
of muscle contraction is angle related, the highest contraction being around

and the least around 20°.

CONCENTRIC (from the latin "com-centrum", having a common centre) refers to contractions in which the muscle length shortens. Concentric contractions are possible only when the resistance, be it the force of gravity (in free weights) or a machine, is bellow the athlete's potential. Concentric is also known as "positive" contraction.

The peak force for concentric contraction is reached around an angle of 120° and the lowest force is close to 20° of the angle joint (figure 6). Highest tension is achieved at a more open angle because that corresponds with the early part of the contraction (refer to chapter 5), the sliding action of the actin and myosin filaments. In their early part of overlapping they have a higher pulling force, creating a higher tension in the muscle. As the sliding of filaments approaches their limits, force production diminishes.

ECCENTRIC, or "negative" contraction refers to reversing the process of concentric action, returning the muscles back towards their original starting point. During an eccentric contraction the muscles are either yielding to the force of gravity (as in free weights), or to the force of pull of a machine. Under such conditions the actin filaments are sliding outward, away from the myosin, the muscle lengthens as the joint angle increases, releasing a controlled tension.

In both concentric and eccentric, the contractions are performed by the same muscles. Elbow flexion is a typical concentric contraction performed by the bicep muscle. As the forearm returns to its original position the eccentric contraction is performed by the same muscle, the biceps.

ISOMETRIC or "static" refers to the type of contraction in which the muscle develops tension without changing its length (isos = equal, or same, and "meter" = unit of measurement).

A muscle can develop tension, often higher than that developed during a dynamic contraction, via static or isometric contraction. The application of an athlete's force against specially built immobile frames, or objects that will not yield to the force generated by the athlete, makes the muscle develop high tension without altering its length. Since there is no visible muscle shortening the actins remain in the same position.

ISOKINETIC is defined as a contraction with constant speed over the full range of motion (iso = same, kinetic = motion). Sports, such as rowing, swimming, and canoeing, are good examples of a stroke where the drive through the water is performed at a near constant speed (although the intent is constant acceleration).

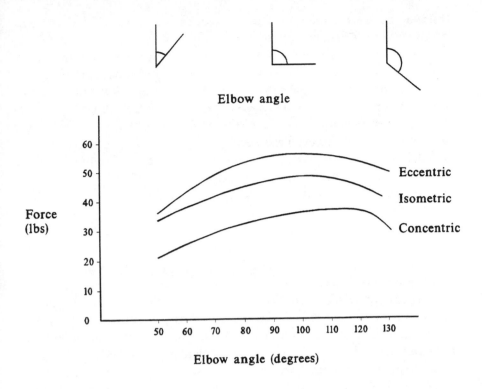

Elbow angle

Figure 6. The force of all three types of contraction is angle-related.

Special equipment is designed to allow a constant speed of motion, irrespective of load. During the movement which combines both concentric and eccentric contraction, the machine provides a resistant equal to the force generated by the athlete. The speed of movement in most isokinetic devices can be preset, having also read-out devices for recording muscle tension. In this way the athlete can monitor training during a training session.

TYPES OF STRENGTH AND THEIR SIGNIFICANCE IN TRAINING

There are various types of strength which one has to be aware of in order to conduct a more effective training. For instance, the ratio between body weight and strength has an important consequence to the extent that it allows comparison between individual athletes, and indicates whether or not an athlete has the ability to perform certain skills. Therefore, the following types of strength should have important meaning to a coach.

GENERAL STRENGTH refers to the strength of the whole muscular system. As this aspect is the foundation of the whole strength program, it must be highly developed, with a concentrated effort during the preparatory phase, or during the first few years of training beginner athletes. A low level of general strength may be a limiting factor for the overall progress of an athlete (please refer to chapter 9).

SPECIFIC STRENGTH is considered to be the strength of only those muscles that are particular to the movement of the selected sport (concerns the prime movers). As the term suggests, this type of strength is characteristic for each sport, therefore any comparison between the strength level of athletes involved in different sports is invalid. Specific strength, which has to be developed to the maximum possible level, should be progressively incorporated toward the end of the preparatory phase for all advanced class athletes.

MAXIMUM STRENGTH refers to the highest force that can be performed by the neuromuscular system during a maximum voluntary contraction. This is demonstrated by the highest load that an athlete can lift in one attempt, and it is expressed in percentage of maximum, or 100%. Because maximum strength refers to highest load lifted in one repetition, it is often called **one repetition maximum**, or **1RM**. As suggested in the planning section, it is very important in training to know maximum strength, since it is the basis for calculating the load for any type of strength development.

MUSCULAR ENDURANCE is usually defined as the muscle's ability to sustain work for a prolonged period of time. It represents the product of stressing in training both strength and endurance.

POWER is the product of two abilities, strength and speed, and is considered to be the ability to perform maximum force in the shortest period of time.

ABSOLUTE STRENGTH (AS) refers to the ability of an athlete to exert maximum force regardless of own body weight (BW). In order to be successful in some sports (shot put, heaviest weight categories in weight lifting and wrestling) absolute strength is required to reach very high levels. Considering that an athlete follows a systematic training, absolute strength increases parallel with gains in body weight.

RELATIVE STRENGTH (RS) represents the ratio between an athlete's absolute strength and his/her body weight. Thus:

$$RS = \frac{AS}{BW}$$

Relative strength is very important in sports such as gymnastics, or in sports where the athletes are divided in weight categories (i.e., wrestling, boxing). For instance a gymnast may not be able to perform the iron cross on the rings unless the relative strength of the muscles involved is at least 1.0, which means that the absolute strength must be at least sufficient to offset the athlete's body weight. But gains in body weight changes this proportion: as the body weight increases relative strength decreases.

STRENGTH RESERVE. Although at this point in time it is inadequately investigated, strength reserve is regarded as the difference between absolute strength of an athlete and the amount of strength required to perform a skill under competitive conditions. For instance, strength gauge techniques utilized to measure rowers' maximum strength per stroke unit revealed values of up to 106 kg while the mean strength per race was found to be 56 kg (Bompa et al., 1978). The same subjects were found to have an absolute strength in power clean lifts of 90 kg. Subtracting the mean strength per race (= 56 kg) from absolute strength (90 kg) results in the strength reserve being 34 kg. The ratio of mean strength to absolute strength is 1:1.6. Similarly, other subjects were found to have a higher strength reserve with a ratio of 1:1.85. Needless to say, the latter subjects were capable of achieving higher performances in rowing races, thus allowing one to conclude that an athlete with a higher strength reserve is capable of reaching higher performance. Although the concept of strength reserve may not be meaningful to all sports it is hypothesized to be significant in sports such as swimming, canoeing, rowing, jumping, and throwing events in athletics.

CHAPTER FOUR

ENERGY SOURCES FOR MUSCULAR CONTRACTION AND THE RESTORATION FROM EXERCISE

Energy should be viewed as the capacity of an athlete to perform work. Work is nothing else but the application of force; the contraction of muscles to apply force against a resistance.

Energy is a necessary prerequisite for the performance of physical work during training and competitions. Ultimately, energy is derived from the conversion of food stuffs at the muscle cell level into a high energy compound known as adenosine triphosphate (ATP) which is stored in the muscle cell. ATP, as its name suggests, is composed of one molecule of adenosine and three molecules of phosphate.

Energy required for muscular contraction is released by the conversion of high energy ATP into ADP + P (adenosine diphosphate + phosphate) (Mathews and Fox, 1976). As one phosphate bond is broken ADP + P is formed from ATP and energy is released. There is a limited amount of ATP stored in the muscle cells thus ATP supplies must be continually replenished to facilitate continued physical activity.

ATP supplies may be replenished by any of three energy systems, depending on the type of physical activity being undertaken. They are as follows: 1) the ATP—CP system, 2) the lactic acid system and 3) the oxygen (O2) system. The first two systems replenish ATP stores in the absence of O2 and is therefore known as the anaerobic system. The third is known as an aerobic system due to the presence of O2.

THE ANAEROBIC SYSTEM

THE ATP—CP SYSTEM (ANAEROBIC ALACTIC OR PHOSPHAGEN SYSTEM). Since only a very small amount of ATP can be stored in the muscle, energy depletion occurs very rapidly when strenuous physical activity begins. In response to this, creatine phosphate (CP) or phosphocreatine, which is also stored in the muscle cell, is broken down into creatine (C) and phosphate (P). The process releases energy which is used to resynthesize ADP + P into ATP. This can then be transformed once more to ADP + P causing the release of energy required for muscular contraction. The transformation of CP into C + P does not release energy that can be used directly for muscular contraction. Rather, this energy must be used to resynthesize ADP + P into ATP.

Since CP is stored in limited amounts in the muscle cell, energy can be supplied by this system for about 8–10 seconds. This system is the chief source of energy for extremely quick and explosive activities such as 100 m dash, diving, weight lifting, jumping, and throwing events in track and field, vaulting in gymnastics and ski jumping. Strength training of short duration, such as power and maximum strength also employs this source of energy.

RESTORATION OF PHOSPHAGEN. Through restoration the body attempts to recover and replenish the energy stores to the pre-exercise conditions. The body, with its biochemical means, attempts to return to the state of a physiological balance (homeostasis), when it has the highest efficiency.

Phosphagen restoration occurs quite rapidly (Fox et al., 1989):

- in the first 30 seconds it reaches 70%, and
- in 3–5 minutes it is fully restored (100%).

THE LACTIC ACID SYSTEM (ANAEROBIC LACTIC OR ANAEROBIC GLYCOLYSIS). For events of slightly longer duration, up to approximately 40 seconds, which are still very intensive in nature (200 m, 400 m in sprinting, 500 m speed skating, some gymnastics events), energy is provided at first by the ATP—CP system and continued after 10–20 seconds by the lactic acid system. The latter system breaks down glycogen which is stored in the muscle cells and the liver, releasing energy to resynthesize ATP from ADP + P. Due to the absence of O2 during the breakdown of glycogen, a by-product called lactic acid (LA) is formed. When high intensity work is continued for a prolonged period of time, large quantities of LA accumulate in the muscle causing fatigue, which eventually leads to a cessation of physical activity.

The LA system is also employed in strength training, mostly when training for the development of M-E of short duration. As such, longer sets (25-30 repetitions) use the LA system to provide the necessary energy.

RESTORATION OF GLYCOGEN. Full restoration of glycogen requires longer time, even days, depending on the type of strength training and diet.

For intermittent activity, typical of strength training (say 40 seconds of work, three minutes of rest) restoration takes:

- 2 hours to restore 40%
- 5 hours to restore 55%, and
- 24 hours for full restoration (100%)

If the activity is continuous, typical of endurance related activities, but of higher intensity (M-E of long duration), restoration of glycogen takes much longer:

- 10 hours to restore 60%
- 48 hours to achieve full restoration (100%)

From the above information (Fox et al., 1989) it can be observed that continuous activity needs twice the amount of time necessary for the restoration of glycogen following intermittent activity. The difference between the two can be explained by the fact that intermittent work consumes less glycogen, restores part of it during the rest interval, and as such, a shorter time is required for the resynthesis of glycogen.

Following a demanding training session, liver glycogen decreases considerably. For a normal, or carbohydrate-rich diet, it takes approximately 12–24 hours to replenish the liver glycogen stores.

During strength training there can be a LA accumulation in the blood, which has a fatiguing effect on the athlete. Before returning to a balanced resting state, LA has to be removed from the systems. However, it takes some time before this will be achieved (Fox et al., 1989):

- 10 minutes to remove 25%
- 25 minutes to eliminate 50%, and
- 1 hour and 15 minutes to remove 95%.

The normal biological process of LA removal can be facilitated by 15–20 minutes of light aerobic exertion, such as jogging or using a rowing machine. The benefit of such an activity is that sweating continues, and the elimination of LA and other metabolic residues is maintained.

Fitness level is also another element which facilitates recovery. The better the fitness level the faster the recovery.

THE AEROBIC SYSTEM

The aerobic system requires approximately 60–80 seconds to commence producing energy for the resynthesis of ATP from ADP + P. The heart rate and respiratory rate must be increased sufficiently to transport the required amount of O2 to the muscle cells in order that glycogen may be broken down in the presence of oxygen. Although glycogen is the source of energy used to resynthesize ATP in both the lactic acid and aerobic systems, the latter breaks down glycogen in the presence of O2 and thus produces little or no lactic acid, enabling the athlete to continue the exercise for a longer period of time.

The aerobic system is the primary source of energy for events of duration between 2 minutes and 2–3 hours (all track events from 800 m on, cross-country skiing, long distance speed skating etc.). Prolonged work in excess of 2–3 hours may result in the breakdown of fats and proteins to replenish ATP stores as the body's glycogen stores near depletion. In any of these cases, the break down of glycogen, fats or protein produces the by-products carbon dioxide (CO_2) and water (H_2O), both of which are eliminated from the body through respiration and perspiration.

The rate at which ATP can be replenished by an athlete is limited by his/her aerobic capacity, or the maximum rate at which one can consume oxygen.

This is an essential element in both fitness as well as training. Mobilization of fatty acids from the body-fat stores should represent a major objective for anybody intending to loose body fat. Only a continuous activity of over 20 minutes, of medium intensity, enhances weight reduction (please refer to the methodology of developing muscular-endurance).

Figure 7 illustrates a comprehensive chart regarding the energy systems, or the energy systems continuum.

In the top part of the figure, the energy pathway is illustrated, the source of energy, and the fuel used against the duration of sporting activities, from 10 seconds to 2–3 hours. Below the duration segment, there are columns for some of the most competitive sports, showing their approximate duration of performance, and the system which is used to supply energy.

In the bottom of the chart there are different strength combinations (as per figure 5), and their corresponding energy system, as well as the approximate sports benefiting from their development.

Energy Pathway	Anaerobic Pathway		Aerobic Pathway		
	Alactic	Lactic			
Primary Energy Source	ATP Produced Without the Presence of O_2		ATP Produced in the Presence of O_2		
Fuel	Phosphate system. ATP/ CP Stored in Muscle	Lactic Acid (LA) System Glycogen →LA Byproduct.	Glycogen Completely Burned in the Presence of O_2	Fats	Protein
Duration	0 sec. 10 sec.	40 sec. 70 sec.	2 min. 6 min.	25 min. 1h 2h 3h	
Sports/ Events	·Sprinting, 100 Dash. ·Throws ·Jumps ·Weight Lifting ·Ski Jumping ·Diving ·Vaulting In Gymnastics	·200-400M ·500 Speed Skating ·Most Gym Events ·Cycling Track ·50M Swimming / ·100M Swimming ·800M Track ·500 Canoeing ·1000 Speed Skating ·Floor Ex. Gym. ·Alpine Skiing ·Cycling Track: 1000M and Pursuit	·Middle Dist Track, Swimming, Speed skat. ·1000M Canoeing ·Boxing ·Wrestling ·Martial Arts ·Fig. Skating ·Synch. Swim. ·Cycling, Pursuit	·Long Distance: Track, Swimming, Speed Skating, Canoeing ·Cross Country Skiing ·Rowing ·Cycling, Road Racing	
	Most Team Sports / Raquet Sports / Sailing				
Combinations of Strength	·Landing Power ·Throwing " ·Take-off " ·Starting "	·Acceleration power ·Deceleration power / ·P-E ·M-E Short	·M-E Medium	·M-E Long	

FIGURE 7. Energy sources for competitive sports, and their corresponding combination of strength.

32

CHAPTER FIVE

MUSCLE STRUCTURE:
THE BASIS FOR CONTRACTION

For any serious student of strength training, the improvement of knowledge in the area should start with understanding muscle physiology in order to comprehend the muscle's structure and its main function: muscle contraction.

The human body is constructed around a bony skeleton. When two or more bones meet together they form a joint, which is held together by tough bands of connective tissue called **ligaments**.

The skeleton frame is covered with approximately six hundred muscles which represent about forty percent of the total body weight.

At each end a muscle is continued with a dense connective tissue, called **tendon**, which serves as the attachment of the muscle on a bone. Since the muscle fibers themselves do not come in direct contact with a bone, the entire tension developed in the muscles is directed to the bone through this tendinous linkage. As such, limbs perform movements as a result of the muscle pull against a bone. The higher the tension, the more powerful the pull, and as a result the more powerful or quicker the limb's movement.

Each muscle is supplied with blood vessels, arteries and veins, which enter the muscle along the connective tissue. At the muscle level they branch into a fine network of small vessels called **capillaries**, where the exchange between blood and tissue occurs. Through this capillary network the blood supplies the muscle with oxygen and fuel for energy, removing at the same time the waste products. The amount of blood required by muscles is proportional to the intensity and duration of activity, often being as much as 100 times higher than during rest.

Along with blood vessels, the muscle is also supplied with two types of nerves: **motor**, or efferent (which conveys **motor impulses** from the central nervous system—CNS—to the muscle), and **sensory**, or afferent (which sends **sensory impulses** from the muscle to the CNS). Each motor nerve has a point of termination on a muscle fiber, called a motor endplate. A stimulated motor nerve causes the muscle to contract, and as such to perform work.

THE STRUCTURE OF THE MUSCLE CELL. A muscle is made of special cells called **fibers**, ranging from a few inches to over a yard, and as such extending over the entire length of the muscles. A muscle is a collection of fibers made up of cells and grouped in bundles. Each bundle (fasciculus) is separately wrapped in a sheath that holds it together (perimysium).

Each muscle fiber contains many thread like **myofibrils** (protein strands), which hold the contractile units, called **sarcomere**. The sarcomere itself contains two kinds of muscle filaments: thick ones, or **myosin**, and thin ones, called **actin**. The ability of the muscles to contract is determined by the muscle design, the sarcomere arrangement, the cross-section of the muscle, the muscle fiber length, as well as their number. The latter is determined genetically, therefore not being affected by training. However, as a result of training these filaments increase their thickness, thus increasing the force of contraction.

Each myosin is surrounded by six or more actins. The myosins have some very small extensions towards the actins, the so called **cross-bridges**, which play such an important role in muscle contractions.

MUSCULAR CONTRACTION. The basic theory on how contraction occurs is called the **sliding filament theory**, since some filaments slide over the others, resulting in the shortening of the muscles.

During contraction the actin and myosin filaments do not change but rather slide over each other. When an impulse from the motor nerve reaches the motor endplate it stimulates the generation of impulses (action potentials) which quickly covers the entire fiber. As this occurs, chemical reactions create electrostatic forces between actin and myosin, causing them to attract to each other. This in turn promotes the sliding process, causing the muscles to shorten, and as such to contract and produce force. When the impulse is over, the muscle contraction ceases, and thus the muscle is in a state of relaxation.

A repeated impulse recharges the myosin **cross-bridges** resulting in a new contraction. The nerve impulse travels at a very high velocity, approximately 5 meters (16 feet) per second, reaching both ends of a short muscle (say 10 cm; 4 inches long) in a record time of one hundred of a second. It is therefore quite obvious that a nerve impulse stimulates a muscle fiber in an extremely short period of time, being able at the same time to perform tenths of contractions per second.

The force of contraction, among others, depends on the length the muscle is stretched before contraction. The optimal length for muscle contraction is its normal length (resting length or full length) without overstretching. The force of a muscle is weakened if it starts the contraction from a shorter or over-stretched position. Similarly, as the muscle shortens

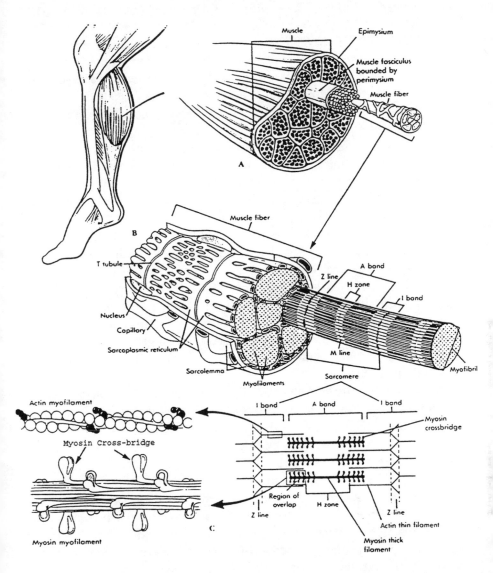

FIGURE 8. Muscle physiology. A. Muscle is composed of muscle fasciculi, which are composed of bundles of individual muscle fibres (muscle cells). B. Each muscle fibre contains myofibrils in which the banding patterns of the sarcomeres are seen. C. The myofibrils are composed of actin myofilaments and myosin myofilaments, which are formed from thousands of indvidual actin and myosin molecules (From Prentice, W.E, Rehabilitation Techniques in Sports Medicine. Time Mirror/ Mosby CollegePublishing, 1990).

its strength of contraction decreases. therefore the force of a muscle is angle related, the highest force output of a muscle being around 110-120 degrees.

THE MOTOR UNIT. The motor nerves entering a muscle can innervate, can reach and activate, up to 150 or even more muscle fibers. All the muscle fibers innervated by the same motor nerve reacts together to its impulses. The muscle fibers contract and relax together and at the same time. Therefore a single motor nerve and the muscle fibers it serves is called a **motor unit**.

A muscle contracts as a result of a stimulation of a motor nerve. The impulse sent to the muscle spreads either completely or not at all. Therefore an impulse, whether strong or weak, provokes the same tension in a motor unit, and the same contraction force (the so called **"all-or-none-law"**).

Since a muscle has several motor units not all are stimulated at the same time. The number of motor units involved in a contraction depends on the load. If the load is low the work is carried out by a certain number of motor units. If the load increases, more motor units are recruited in order to perform the task (McDonagh and Davis, 1984). Customarily, the same motor units are recruited to perform a lighter task, and always the same units are engaged in lifting a heavier load. The same is true for a maximum load. Therefore a muscle exerts force of **graded strength** (Fox et al., 1989). If one intends to train the entire muscle he/she must expose it to maximum loads.

The force performed by a muscle does not depend only on the number of motor units involved in contraction but also on the number of muscle fibers within a motor unit. This number can vary between 20–500, the average number of fibers being around 200. The more fibers per motor unit, the higher the force output. But since the number of fibers are genetically determined, it explains why some people have more talent, or are genetically-inclined for strength-related events than others.

When a motor unit is stimulated by a nerve impulse it responds by giving a **twitch**, or a very quick contraction followed by relaxation. If another impulse reaches the motor unit before it has the time to relax the two twitches **summate** (fuse), as a result the tension produced is greater than the one produced by a single twitch. A high frequency of impulses results in continuous summation, fusion, (called **tetanus**), which can result in a tension 3–4 times higher than a single twitch.

The summation of motor units depends on the load employed. During maximum loads, all the muscle fibers involved in a contraction summate in **synchronization**, whereas for medium loads some motor units are twitching while others are relaxing (synchronous summation). This is one of the main reasons heavy loads lead to higher gains in maximal strength.

36

MUSCLE FIBER TYPES

Although all the motor units behave as explained above, not all the muscle fibers have the same biochemical (metabolic) functions. While all muscle fibers can function under both anaerobic and aerobic conditions some are physiologically more effective to perform work under anaerobic, whereas others under aerobic conditions.

The aerobic-type fibers are called **type I**, red, or **slow-twitch** (ST), whereas the anaerobic-type fibers, the white fibers, are called **type II**, or **fast-twitch** (FT). These latter fibers are further subdivided into **FT IIa** (or fast-oxidative glycolytic) and **FT IIb** (or fast-glycolytic). The proportions of these three types of fibers are roughly 50 percent ST, 25 percent FT IIa and the remaining 25 percent FT IIb (Wilmore and Costill, 1988; Fox et al., 1989). The innervation of muscle fibers determines whether they are FT or ST, depending on how many muscle fibers are connected to each motor nerve. A FT motor unit is made out of a larger nerve cell and innervates some 300 to well over 500 fibers. A ST motor unit on the other hand normally has a smaller nerve cell and connects some 10–180 fibers. It is therefore quite obvious that since FT motor units connects such a large number of fibers their contraction is faster and more powerful. Successful athletes in speed-power dominated sports are genetically equipped with a higher proportion of FT fibers but they also fatigue faster. On the other hand individuals with higher numbers of ST are more successful in endurance dominated sports, being able to perform work of lower loads (intensity) for a longer period of time.

Although the FT fibers are used in shorter and faster activities it is not the speed of contraction but rather the **force** of the muscle that **causes the motor nerves to recruit the FT fibers** (Wilmore and Costill, 1988). To a high degree, this explains why speed-related athletes (e.g. sprinters, football and baseball players) have to increase their power. The high power movements performed by these athletes activate the FT fibers and as a result one is capable to perform explosive and fast actions.

Recruitment of muscle fibers are intensity-related. During below-medium, low intensity activity ST are recruited as work horses. As the load increases FT IIa fibers get involved to perform muscle contractions. And if the load increases to maximum, FT IIb are recruited to successfully cope with the task.

The distribution of fiber types can vary within the same muscle and between muscles as well. Generally speaking, the arms tend to have a higher percentage of FT fibers as compared to legs: the biceps 55%, triceps 60%, whereas soleus (calves) just 24% FT (Fox et al., 1989).

37

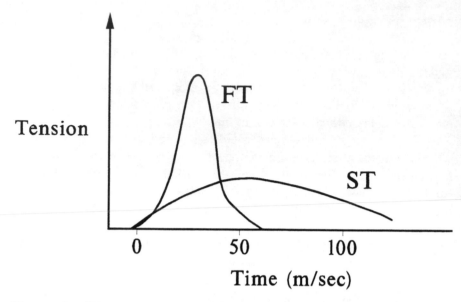

FIGURE 9. Illustrates the twitch response of FT and ST fibers to the same intensity of stimulus. (Based on data from Golnick et al, 1974: Komi et al, 1979, and Costill, 1986)

At the same time differences in muscle fiber type distribution is visible between athletes involved in various sports. Figures 10 and 11 illustrate a general profile of FT fibers percentage for some sports. Please note the drastic differences between sprinters and marathon runners, which clearly suggests that success in some sports is at least partially determined by muscle fiber composition.

Although sprinters and jumpers are expected to have the highest percentage of FT fibers (61%), what is surprising is that the untrained group is very close (56%). Yet, if testing the two groups in both power or maximum strength, the difference in their capacity is very large. Which may lead to the conclusion that **training can significantly increase the ability to display power and maximum strength** (Golnick et al., 1972; Costill et al., 1976; Komi et al., 1977).

The peak power generated by an athlete is also related to the fiber-type distribution. The higher the FT fibers distribution the greater the power generated by the athlete. Similarly, the percentage of distribution of FT fiber in the muscles is also velocity related. The greater the velocity displayed by an athlete the higher the percentage distribution of FT fibers. Such individuals make great sprinters and jumpers, and as much as possible individuals with such natural talent should be channelled to speed-power dominated sports. It would be a waste of talent to attempt to make such an

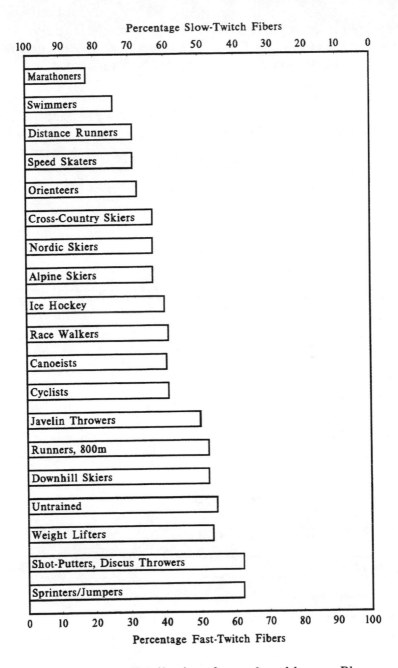

FIGURE 10. Fiber type distribution for male athletes. Please note the dominance in ST fibers for athletes from aerobic dominant sports, and FT for speed - power sports. (Based on data from Golnick et al, 1972; Costill et al, 1976; Komi et al, 1977; Thorstensson et al, 1977)

individual a distance runner. He/she would not be anything but a mediocre runner, when in reality he/she could be an excellent sprinter, baseball, or football player, just to mention a few speed-power related sports.

There are no clear differences in muscle fiber distribution between female and male athletes. Therefore, irrespective of sex, the percentage of fiber type is determined genetically. What is inherited can represent, as compared to others, a good start in the race to high performance. However, taking this genetic quality alone should not give the basis for a risky prediction on future athletic success. To gamble in making predictions one must look to other variables beyond genetic profile.

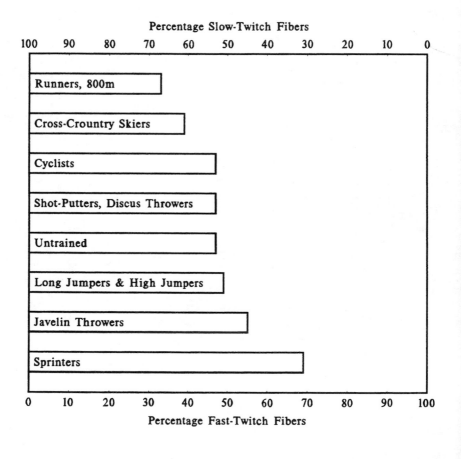

FIGURE 11. Fiber type distribution for female athletes (please refer to the remarks made on figure 10).

CHAPTER SIX

STRENGTH TRAINING AND MUSCLE ADAPTATION

Adaptation to training is the sum of modifications brought about by the systematic repetition of exercise. These structural and physiological changes are the result of a specific demand placed upon the body by the specific activity pursued, and are dependent on the volume, intensity and frequency of training. Physical training is beneficial only as long as it forces the body to adapt to the stress of physical work. If the load is not sufficient to challenge the body, then no adaptation occurs.

A high level of performance is the result of many years of well planned, methodical and hard training. During all this time the athlete tries to adapt his/her organs and functions to the specific requirements of the chosen sport. The level of adaptation is reflected by performance capabilities. The greater the degree of adaptation, the better the performance.

Adaptation occurs only when a stimulus, a training load, is proportional to the individual's capacity. For trained athletes low loads, below 30%, do not result in challenging the athlete's level of adaptation (**adaptation threshold**), and as such training effect is nil or at best minimal. Only higher intensity, heavier loads, initiate such adaptation.

HYPERTROPHY. One of the most visible signs of adaptation to higher loads is the enlargement of muscle size, the increase of cross-sectional area of individual muscle fiber. This increase in the diameter of muscle fiber is called **hypertrophy**. A reduction in size as a result of inactivity is referred to as **atrophy**.

Customarily, gains in muscle size are often paralleled by strength increments, except in bodybuilding, where such an analogy is not always the case. The reason has to be associated with training objectives, intensity, and training methods.

The hypertrophy of muscle fiber is credited to physiological factors such as: increase in the size and number of myofibrils per muscle fiber, increase of the amount of protein in the myosin filament, and increase in capillary density per muscle fiber. However, there are some other mechanisms related to strength gains than just hypertrophy. These mechanisms, very complex and not completely understood, refers to muscle structure, the nervous system, and neuromuscular coordination (learning).

Hypertrophy, as a physiological adaptation to training is of two kinds. **Transient** hypertrophy, as its name implies, lasts only for few hours and is the result of the "pumping-up" effect typical of bodybuilding training. Largely the result of fluid accumulation (edema) in the muscle, transient hypertrophy is provoked by the increase of water in the intracellular spaces of the muscle, and is returned to the blood a few hours following training. If not stimulated by daily workouts such hypertrophy does not have a lasting effect. For this reason bodybuilders look big and strong, but their strength is far from being proportional to their muscle size.

Chronic, or constant, hypertrophy typical for trained athletes, results from structural changes at the muscle level. It can be explained by either an increase in the number of muscle filaments or their growth in size.

The number of fibers an individual has is an inherited quality. It is called a "quality" because individuals with larger numbers of fibers tend to be stronger. This number remains the same throughout one's life. However, a controversial theory suggests that heavy loads in strength training results in the **"muscle splitting"** in two halves, or **hyperplasia**, and as such hypertrophy is induced also by a possible increment in the number of muscle fibers. This theory, however, is based only on animal research, and the results have not yet been duplicated in research involving human subjects.

Another theory regarding hypertrophy suggests that **testosterone**, a male sex hormone (**serum androgen**, a substance that has masculinizing properties) is also responsible for muscle hypertrophy. While testosterone seems to promote muscle growth, there is still not sufficient scientific proof that it alone determines the size of the muscle. Although there are no physiological differences between the muscles of women and men, male athletes usually have larger and stronger muscles. This difference is attributed to testosterone content which is approximately tenfold greater for men than for women.

Strong evidence suggests that individual fiber hypertrophy accounts for most of muscle hypertrophy. The increase in the muscle fiber size and filaments, especially the myosin, has been demonstrated by research (Gordon, 1967; Goldberg et al., 1975; MacDougall et al., 1975, 1976, 1977, and 1979; Costill et al., 1979; Dons et al., 1979; Gregory, 1981, Fox et al., 1989). In the case of myosin, heavy training increases the number of cross-bridges, which increases not only the cross-sectional area of the fiber but also results in visible gains in the force of maximum contraction.

Fiber type composition, the proportion of FT fibers, also plays an important role in power-speed related sports. The higher the proportion of FT fibers the quicker and more powerful the contraction. The ability to change a type of muscle fiber to another one, as a result of training, is critical for gains in strength, and yet still controversial. However, recent studies suggest that a shift in fiber type may be possible as a result of prolonged, high intensity training. The long term adaptation seems to result in some conversion of ST into FT, that the proportion of FT increases at the expense of ST (Jacobs et al., 1987, and Abernethy et al., 1990).

ANATOMICAL ADAPTATION. Research in the area of anatomical adaptation suggests that as a result of constant and extensive high intensity loads the material strength of bones decreases (Matsuda, 1986). This can mean that if the load does not change from time to time, varying from low to maximum, the decrease in material strength may make the athlete prone to bone injuries. The mechanical properties of bones are not strictly dependent on chronological age, as is often believed, but rather on the mechanical demand in training. In other words, an injury-prone athlete is not necessarily a young one, but one who in training exposes the bones to an abrupt mechanical stress without a proper progression, and as such without a long and progressive adaptation.

Low intensity training, at an early age, may have a positive, stimulating effect on long bones, and on their length and girth increase. High intensity heavy loads, on the other hand, may restrict bone growth (Matsuda, 1986). These realities should make one think very carefully of how to work with young athletes, what kinds of loads to use, as well as to understand that a long term plan, where the load is progressively increased over several years, is the most appropriate approach in training.

For mature athletes a well monitored load increment has a positive effect, resulting in increase of bone density, which allows the bone to better cope with mechanical stress, typical of many athletic actions.

Bone adaptation to exercise is also believed to be a function of age. Immature bones are more sensitive to heavy load changes than are more mature bones. For instance, long bone growth is suppressed after training. On the other hand physical training accelerates the maturation process, causing permanent suppression of bone growth (Matsuda, 1986). Therefore the purpose of training should be to stress the body in such a way that it should result in adaptation and not aggravation.

Training specialists should be at least equally concerned regarding the adaptation to strength training of muscles' attachment on bones. Muscles do not attach on bones directly, but rather through their extension, called tendons. The ability of a muscle to pull forcefully against a bone, and as a result to perform a movement depends on how strong the muscle's tendons are. The adaptation of tendons is a long-term proposition. It takes a longer time to adapt a tendon than to train the muscle to perform powerful contractions. Therefore, before the muscles are strengthened the athlete should work on the tendon's adaptation (pleas refer to

Anatomical Adaptation in the planning section).

NERVOUS SYSTEM ADAPTATION. Gains in muscle strength can also be explained by the pattern of motor units recruitment, and by the synchronization of the motor units to act in unison. Motor units are controlled by different nerve cells, called **neurons**, which have the capacity to produce **excitatory** (stimulating) as well as **inhibitory** impulses (restraining or decreasing the electrical activity).

Although excitation is a necessary process to stimulate the contraction of a motor unit, inhibition is proposed to be a mechanism which prevents the muscles from exerting more force that can be tolerated by the connective tissue (tendons) and even by bones. In such a case these two nervous system processes perform a sort of balancing role regarding the intensity, and the degree of stimulation on a muscle.

The CNS has the ability to initiate and send inhibitory impulses to the muscle to check the degree of muscle excitation. It is theorized that as a result of training, inhibitory impulses can be counteracted, enabling the muscle to contract more powerfully. The force outcome of the athlete depends on how many motor units will contract or be in a state of relaxation. If the excitatory impulses exceed the inhibitory impulses, a given motor unit will be stimulated and participate in the overall contraction and production of force. If the opposite is the case, that particular motor unit will stay relaxed. Consequently, it is fair to say that to a high degree gains in strength are the result of gains in the ability to recruit more motor units to participate in the overall force of contraction. Such an adaptive response is facilitated only by a combination of high intensity (speed) and maximum loads in strength training.

ADAPTATION OF NEUROMUSCULAR COORDINATION results from the many repetitions of movements an athlete performs. The precision of movements are related to learning, to one's ability to coordinate the sequence in which muscles are involved in performing a lift. This is categorically enhanced by the ability of the athlete to concentrate on relaxing the antagonistic muscles, so that unnecessary contractions of these muscles do not affect a correct performance of a skill. A highly coordinated group of muscles consume less energy. As a consequence, improved coordination means more economical utilization of energy stores. Normally, this translates into superior performance.

Athletes come in different sizes, age, and potential. The greatest difference in muscle coordination can be found among beginners and juniors. Since these young athletes were not involved in organized training they lack skills and muscle coordination in performing a movement against resistance. Hypertrophy cannot be expected since they do not have the background in strength training. If a group of young athletes are exposed to strength training, in the course of 4–6 weeks visible strength increments can be seen. Puberty, or prepuberty athletes, can make strength gains even without increasing their muscle size. How is it possible to gain in strength without muscle hypertrophy? The answer is **neural adaptation**, or the increase in the nervous coordination of the muscles involved. As a result of training the young athletes have learned to use their muscles effectively and economically. This motor learning effect seem to be of major importance in the early stages of strength training. Growth in muscle size cannot be expected prior to mid puberty, since hypertrophy is not possible without increasing the testosterone levels. As children grow, from puberty on they develop their sexual organs, and as a result, the testosterone concentration. Therefore strength developments during growth and development parallels sexual development.

Neural adaptation to strength training is reflected in the increased ability to activate the prime movers, the chain of muscles involved in lifting, and in improved coordination of agonists and antagonists. The normal outcome is increased strength of the intended movement.

Power training, the explosive actions of the muscles in a short period of time, increases the neural contribution of the nervous system, its synchronization of motor unit firing pattern, without much gains in hypertrophy.

Figure 12 illustrates neural and muscular adaptation in strength training. While strength gains steadily occurs over time, early improvements are the result of neural adaptation. Benefits of hypertrophy are visible after several months of training. From this point on gains in strength are related to both hypertrophy as well as the neural adaptation (depending on the load and training method employed).

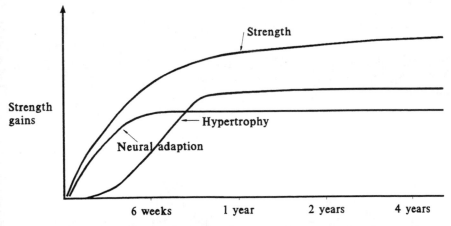

FIGURE 12. An illustration of gains in strength as a result of neutral adaptation and hypertrophy.

45

CHAPTER SEVEN

TRAINING PRINCIPLES AS APPLIED TO STRENGTH TRAINING

The process of training is a complex activity, governed by several principles and methodical guidelines. These principles and guidelines assist the coach in selecting the best avenues to higher performance, the methods to be considered, and the best progression to be employed.

Training principles are a series of necessary guidelines that fulfil a given training goal. Their understanding and application in strength training will ensure a superior organization, with the least possible errors. The presentation of training principles will be as condensed as possible, and reference will be made only to those which have relevance in strength training. One of the leading principles in strength training—overloading—is strongly deemphasized and incorrectly used. Therefore, the principle of **"progressive increase of load in training"** will be presented as the crucial method which will lead to better adaptation, and as a result to improved strength gains.

PRINCIPLE OF VARIETY

Contemporary training is a very demanding activity requiring many hours of work from the athlete. The volume and intensity of training are continuously increasing and exercises are repeated numerous times. In order to reach high performance, the volume of training must surpass the threshold of 1,000 hours per year. A world class weight lifter performs 1200–1400 hours of heavy work per year. Any athlete who is serious about training has to dedicate 6–8 hours of strength training per week, in addition to technical, tactical, and other elements of general and specific conditioning. Therefore under these conditions it is quite obvious that boredom and monotony can become an obstacle to motivation and improvement.

In order to overcome such a possible negative occurrence, variety in training is the best medicine. To insure that, the instructor or coach, has to be well versed in the area of strength training and thus being required to know as many exercises as possible.

Variety in training is necessary to improve training response in order to reflect positively upon the athletes' mental and psychological well-being. It is hoped that the following suggestions will assist the coach/instructor to enrich the variety in strength training:

- alternate as often as necessary exercises designed to develop the prime movers. This should be a concern especially prior, and during the competitive phase, where normally exercises should be reduced in number in order to have the highest number of sets per prime movers;
- variation of loading system, as suggested by the principle of progressive increase of load in training;
- variation in the type of muscular contraction, especially between concentric and eccentric;
- variation in the speed of contraction (slow, medium, and fast). However, this is mostly valid during the preparatory phase. As periodization requests mostly heavy loads with high Application of force, explosive actions, slow and even medium speeds of contraction might not be possible too often;
- variation in equipment (if possible), from free weights to heavy implements, isokinetics, etc.;
- variation between training phases (please refer to the planning section);

Do not forget: the lack of variety can result in limiting further improvements.

PRINCIPLE OF INDIVIDUALIZATION

Individualization in training is one of the main requirements of contemporary training and refers to the fact that each athlete, regardless of the level of performance, must be treated individually according to ability, potential and strength training background.

Individualization should not be perceived only as a method of correcting individual technical deficiencies, or the specialization of an individual in an event or position played in a team, but rather a means by which an athlete is evaluated objectively and observed subjectively. The coach may then assess the athlete's strength training needs in an attempt to maximize his/ her abilities.

However, much too often, in their quest for easy gains, some coaches slavishly follow training programs of successful athletes, completely disregarding the athlete's particular needs, experience and abilities. What is even worse, such programs are sometimes inserted into junior athletes' training schedules. These athletes are not ready, both physiologically and psychologically, of following such programs, especially the high intensity components.

Prior to designing a training program, the coach should analyze the athlete's training potential development, in order to determine the limits of tolerance to work. Often the individual's working capacity depends on the following factors:

1. **Training background,** or the age at which the athlete began participation in sports and strength training. The work demand should be proportional to experience. Although the rate of improvement of some athletes may be different, the coach still has to be cautious with regard to the load which may be undertaken. Similarly, when athletes of different backgrounds and experiences are assigned to train in the same group, the coach should not ignore their individual characteristics and potential.

2. **Individual capacity for work and performance.** Not all athletes who are capable of the same performance have the same work capacity. There are several biological and psychological factors which determine the individual's work abilities. Therefore, in determining the amount of work, the load, and the type of strength training, the instructor should consider the work ability of an individual. Gains in performance would just be a natural training outcome.

3. **Training load and the athlete's rate of recovery.** When planning and evaluating the work in training, the coach must take into consideration factors outside of training which may place a high demand on the athlete. Heavy involvement in school, work, or family, and distance to travel to school or training can affect the rate of recovery between training lessons. By the same token, the athlete's lifestyle and emotional involvement should also be known by the coach. These factors must be properly assessed in planning the content and stress of training.

4. **The anatomical structure and biological differences between genders** requires specific consideration in the design of strength training programs. In general, strength training for women should be rigorously continuous, without long interruptions. As far as plyometric exercises are concerned, a careful progression should be observed over a longer period of time.

As compared to men, women's total body strength is 63.5% of men's strength, with the major difference being in the upper extremity's strength, an average of 55.8% of men. In the lower body the difference is much lower: only 71.9% (Laubach, 1976).

Women tend to have lower hypertrophy levels as compared to men. This is mostly due to a lower testosterone level, which is ten times lower than that for men (Wright, 1980). Therefore female athletes should not be overly concerned with building excessive bulky muscles. This should make females conclude that their strength training programs do not have to be different from their male counterparts. Without any concerns, women can apply the same loading pattern, apply the same training methods, and follow similar planning.

Strength training for women is as beneficial as for men. Furthermore, strength gains occur at the same rate or even at a greater rate then for men (Wilmore et al., 1978). And since women, in general, tend to be weaker than men, visible gains in future performance will come from improved and increased strength training.

PRINCIPLE OF SPECIFICITY

In order to be effective and achieve a higher adaptation, training has to be aimed specifically at developing the type of strength dominant in a given sport or event. Of similar importance is that the selected strength training program must be suitable to the specific physical demands of the sport. As such, a strength training program and the selected training method(s) should consider:

1. **The dominant energy system** in that sport. The selected strength program must compliment other elements of training, and as such result in performance improvement. For instance, to select a bodybuilding method for endurance dominated sports, such as rowing, long distance swimming, canoeing, or speed skating will be at least a fallacy. Muscle-endurance training would be the most appropriate training method for the above mentioned sports (please refer to training methods and periodization of strength).

2. **The specific muscle groups** involved as well as the movement patterns characteristic of the selected sport. Thus, strength exercises have to mimic as much as possible the key movement patterns, the dominant skills of the sport, and improve the power of the prime movers, the muscles required to perform a specific technical movement. Normally, gains in power have a positive transfer to improvement in skill.

SPECIFICITY VS. A METHODICAL APPROACH

By attempting to develop an optimal strength training program some coaches suggest that the program has to be specific. This concept was then developed by some physiologists (i.e., Matthews and Fox, 1976) into a principle of training. By strictly following this principle throughout an athletic career, the athlete has to simulate the movement pattern used while performing a skill and develop to perfection only that type of strength which is dominant in the selected sport.

This concept is correct if applied only to advanced athletes and during the competitive phase. If the same rule is followed by children and beginners from their first day of training throughout their entire athletic career and throughout all training phases, then the principles of training are misunderstood and violated. In this case this principle is either a faulty one or wrongly applied.

An exaggerated specificity results into an asymmetrical, and non-harmonious body development, where the antagonistic and stabilizer muscles are completely neglected. This is not only a incorrect approach but it can also hamper the development of prime movers and result in injuries. An exaggerated specificity can result into a narrow development of the muscles and a one-sided specialized function of the muscles. Therefore, compensation strength exercises should always be used in training, especially during the preparatory phase of the annual plan. The compensation exercises are necessary to balance the force of agonistic and antagonistic muscles.

Often, training principles such as specificity, are misunderstood and misused. According to this principle a specific exercise, or type of training results in the fastest adaptation, and as a result, it yields faster performance. And, although, on a short term basis this might be true, on a long term approach, the outcome can result in overuse, overtraining, and sometimes burn-out. Such programs can be too stressful, boring, lacks variety and fun, and contradicts the concept of periodization of training, the main training law guiding planning.

Specificity of training is a very important principle, but one which has to be viewed on a long-term base. Such a program should have three main phases (Figure 14):

1. **General and multilateral strength training**, during which the coach develops all muscle groups, ligaments and tendons of a child, thus strengthening and developing the base for future heavy loads and specific training. Such an approach is not only desirable from the methodology of training point of view but would also be more likely to lead to any injury-free athletic career. The duration of this phase may be between 2–4 years,

depending on the athlete's age and abilities. Throughout this phase the coach's patience is a desirable attribute. To look for a quick return in training is an unhealthy approach.

The multilateral, overall development is a basic requirement necessary to reach a highly specialized level of training.

2. **The specific phase.** Following the development of the foundations of strength training the coach may start the specific phase which will be considered for the rest of the athlete's career. However, this does not mean that a strength training program specific to the needs of the sport will be followed throughout all phases of an annual training plan. Rather, it has to consider the concept of periodization of strength training, which always starts with a build-up, or Anatomical Adaptation phase (see the periodization of strength). Depending on the age of the athlete, this phase can be 2–3 years long.

3. **High performance phase**, considers athletes at the national and international level of performance. During this stage of athletic development specificity prevails during the latter part of the preparatory and throughout the competitive phase. This phase is terminated when the athlete stops competing.

FIGURE 14. A suggested long term approach to specificity of strength training.

Another aspect of specificity is that improvements are angle-specific (Logan, 1960; Bompa, 1978; Lindh, 1979). This means that if an athlete trains at a certain angle, often typical of isometric training, training effects will be visible at, and around that particular angle. Consequently, it makes physiological sense to train at all the angles, throughout the whole range of motion.

PRINCIPLE OF PROGRESSIVE INCREASE OF LOAD IN TRAINING

The progression of increasing the load in training has been known and used since ancient times. According to Greek mythology, it is said that the first person to apply it was Milon of Croton, a pupil of the famous mathematician Pythagoras (580–500 BC), who himself was an Olympic wrestling champion. In his teens, Milon decided to become the strongest man in the world. Consequently, he started to lift and carry a calf everyday. As the calf became heavier Milon became stronger. When the calf developed into a full grown bull, thanks to a long-term progression, Milon became the strongest man on earth.

Improvement of performance is a direct result of the amount and quality of work achieved in training. From the initiation stage right up to the elite performance stage, workload in training has to be increased gradually, in accordance with each individual's physiological and psychological abilities.

The physiological basis of this principle rests on the fact that as a result of training the body's functional efficiency and thereby its capacity to do work, work gradually increases over a long period of time. Similarly, any drastic increase in performance requires a long period of training and adaptation (Astrand and Rodahl, 1986). The body reacts anatomically, physiologically and psychologically to the demands of the increased training load. Consideration must also be given to the fact that improvement in the functions and reactions of the nervous system, in neuro-muscular coordination and the psychological capacity to cope with the stress resulting from heavy training loads, also occurs gradually. The process requires time and competent technical leadership.

The principle of progressive increase of load in training is the basis for planning all athletic training, and should be followed by all athletes regardless of their level of performance. The rate at which performance improves depends directly on the rate and manner in which the training load is increased.

In several sports the load in training is maintained the same throughout the year. This should be called a **standard load**. For instance in most team sports the number of hours of training is maintained the same throughout the year; approximately 6–12 hours. In many cases strength training is poorly planned without applying the concept of periodization of strength. A similar situation exists in many clubs in track and field. If power is the dominant ability in some events, then power training, using similar exercises and loads, are used throughout the preparatory phase (during the competitive phase this is decreased). In both cases coaches use standard loading.

It should be clearly stated that the repetition of standard loading results in improvements in the early part of the annual plan followed by a plateau and detraining during the competitive phase (Figure 15). As a result, not only may performance deteriorate during the latter part of the competitive phase, since the physiological basis of performance has decreased, but the expected improvements from year to year will not occur as well. Only constant increments of training load from year to year will create superior adaptation, and as such superior performance.

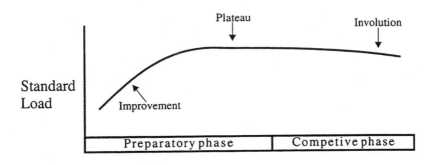

FIGURE 15. A standard load does result in improvements only in the early part of the actual plan.

The **overload** principle represents another traditional approach used in strength training. According to the original proponents of this principle, strength and hypertrophy will increase only if muscles work at their maximum strength capacity against workloads that are above those normally encountered (Lange, 1919; Hellebrant and Houts, 1956). It is also suggested that the load in strength training should be increased throughout the course of the program (Fox et al., 1989). As such the curve of load increment is constantly going up, as illustrated by figure 16.

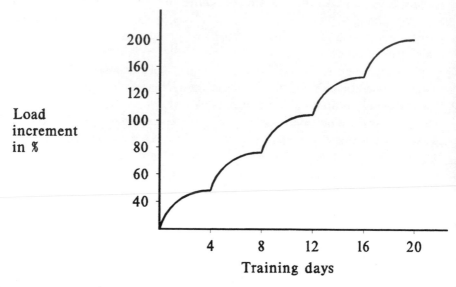

Figure 16. An illustration of load increments according to the overloading principle. (Based on data from Hellebrant and Houtz, 1956, Fox et al, 1989)

The proponents of overloading suggest two methods to increase strength: 1) brief maximum contractions which should result in high activation of the muscles involved, and 2) submaximum contractions to exhaustion, which induces hypertrophy. The latter approach is very popular among bodybuilders. There is great ground for questioning, for challenging the merits of this principle. It may work in a laboratory environment, where the duration of research is short. But it is categorically impractical in athletics. It is certainly necessary to increase the load if improvement is expected. But, in laboratory experiments overloading occurs only over 4–6 weeks, where as in athletics this must be done over one, or in most cases over several years. It is also quite difficult to expose an athlete to exhaustion over several years. Such a physiological and psychological drainage will certainly result in high levels of fatigue, exhaustion, and overtraining. Overloading in strength training is also not applicable because a training program follows the concept of periodization, with specific training goals for each phase of training, leading to the major competitions of the year, when a peak performance is expected.

An athlete cannot just grind out the same old method of lifting to exhaustion day in and day out. Overloading, as compared to the "**step type approach**" is found to be less effective. Improvements in the athletes' ability to tolerate heavy loads is the result of adaptation to such stressors applied in strength training (Counsilman, 1968; Harre, 1982; Bompa, 1983).

54

In contrast to overloading, the **step type** method fulfills the physiological and psychological requirement that a training load increase must be followed by a phase of unloading during which the body adapts and regenerates, thus preparing for a new increase. The recurrence of the increase in training load must be determined in accordance with each individual's needs, rate of adaptation and competitive calendar. A very abrupt increase in training load may go beyond the athlete's capacity to adapt, thereby affecting the physiological balance. Ultimately, such an approach may result in symptoms of overtraining and even injuries.

The **step type** approach (Figure 17) to elevating the training load should not be interpreted as a steady increase in each training session through the arithmetical addition of equal quantities of work. A training session is insufficient to cause visible changes in the body. To achieve such an adaptation, it is necessary to repeat the same type of training loads several times. Often, training sessions of the same type may be planned for an entire week, followed then by another increase in the training load.

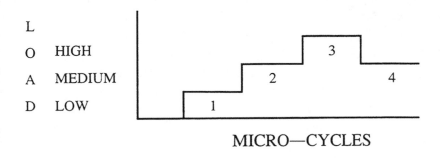

Figure 17.   The increase of training load in steps.

Figure 17 illustrates how the load in training is increased in a **macrocycle**, which is a phase of 2–6 weeks, usually four weeks. Each vertical line represents an increase in load, while the horizontal line represents the phase of adaptation required by the new demand.

Let the horizontal line be a week, or a microcycle of training. Let us also assume that the new load is increased on Monday. Following the new increase, the body is in a state of fatigue, a physiological crisis, since it was not used to such a stress. If similar load levels were maintained throughout the week, by Wednesday the body might get used to it, adapt to the load in the following two days, and by Friday the athlete will feel really good, being capable to even lift heavier loads. This demonstrates that following the crisis of fatigue, there is a phase of adaptation, followed by a physiological rebound, or improvement. This new level is called a new **ceiling of adaptation.** By Monday the athlete feels very comfortable, both physiologically and psychologically. As such, the previous level of adaptation has to be challenged again, so that constant improvements occur from step to step. Following the third step there is a lower step, or an **unloading phase,** allowing the body to **regenerate.** The purpose of regeneration is to allow the body to remove part of the fatigue accumulated in the first three steps, to replenish the energy stores, and to psychologically relax. In this way the body accumulates new reserves in anticipation of further increases in the training load. **Training performance usually improves following the regeneration phase.**

The fourth step in this example, the unloading phase, represents the new lowest step for another macrocycle. However, since the body has already adjusted to the previous loads, the new low step is not of the same magnitude as the previous low, but rather equal to the medium one.

There is a direct relationship between the length and height of the step. The shorter the length of the adaptation phase, the lower the height, or the amount of increase in training load. A longer adaptation phase may allow a higher increase.

Although the increase of training load progresses in steps, in a training plan of longer duration the training load curve appears to have an undulatory shape which is enhanced by the continuous alternations of increase and decrease of the components of training (Figure 18).

The increase in training load should also be governed by the rate of improvement of performance in a sport. The quicker the rate of performance improvement, the greater the training loads required. Otherwise, the athlete will never catch up with contemporary performance.

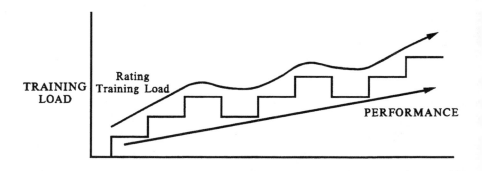

Figure 18. The curve of rating the training load appears to be undulatory while the performance improves continuously (the arrow).

THE FOUR BASIC LAWS OF STRENGTH TRAINING

The aforementioned principles of training represent a general guideline for training in general, with specific applications for strength training as well. However, because of the specific particularities of strength training it is important to refer to the four basic laws which should govern any comprehensive program.

The applicability of these basic laws is a necessity especially for junior athletes and beginners in general, since all four regulations are meant to ensure the anatomical adaptation of a young body before exposing it to the strain of strength training. If the instructor intends to produce an injury-free athlete, the four basic laws of strength training represent important assets for such a goal.

LAW #1: Before developing muscle strength develop joints flexibility. Most strength training exercises, especially those employing free weights, utilize the whole range of motion of major joints, especially knees, ankles and hips. In some exercises (e.g. deep squats), the weight of the barbell compresses the knees to such acute degrees that if the athlete does not have good flexibility at the knee joints, strain and pain can result.

In a low squat position, the lack of good ankle flexibility forces the performer to stay on the ball of the feet and toes, rather than on the flat of the foot, which ensures a good base of support and balance. Therefore, the development of ankle flexibility (plantar flexion, or to bring the toes toward the calf) for all the athletes, especially for beginners must be a major concern. As such, flexibility development is not sought only for its own merits, but also for its injury prevention quality. Its development must start during prepubescence and pubescence so that in the latter stages of athletic development it just has to be maintained.

LAW #2: Before developing muscle strength develop the muscles' attachments to the bone (tendons). Muscle strength always improves faster than the abilities of tendons to withstand tension, and the resistance of ligaments to preserve the integrity of the bones forming the joints. Because of misusing and faulty utilization of the principle of specificity, the lack of a long-term vision, many training specialists and coaches constantly stress just the specific exercises for a given sport. Consequently they do not pay attention to the overall strengthening of ligaments, especially at an early age, when time is not pressing.

The strengthening of tendons and ligaments is achieved through a program designed to attain anatomical adaptation.

Tendons attach the muscles to bones. Their main function is to transmit the pull, the force generated by muscle contraction to the bone, the result being a movement at a given joint. Vigorous strength training, without a base, without a proper anatomical adaptation of tendons and ligaments, can result in injuries of the muscle attachments (tendons) and joints (ligaments).

Tendons and ligaments are trainable, the result of it being the enlargement (increase the diameter) of tendons and ligaments, thus increasing their ability to withstand tension and tear.

LAW #3: Before developing the limbs develop the core of the body. The result of misunderstanding the principle of specificity, is that most of the attention of training specialists is directed towards the development of the arms and legs. After all, most sports are played with the arms and legs!! Therefore attention should be directed towards strengthening these two segments of the body. The stronger they are the more effective!

Although it is true that legs and arms should be viewed as the performers of all athletic skills, it should not be forgotten that the trunk represents the link between them. The legs and arms are only as strong as the trunk is. A poorly developed trunk will represent a weak support for the hard working arms and legs.

Strength training programs, therefore, should not revolve only around the legs and arms but should first focus on strengthening the "**core**" area of the body: the abdominals, the lower back and the spinal column musculature. Consequently, when preparing training programs for young athletes, one should start from the core section of the body and work towards the extremities. In other words, before strengthening the legs and arms, concentrate on developing the link between them, the support, the core muscle groups of the trunk.

The abdominals and back musculatures provide the trunk with an array of muscles whose bundles run in different direction surrounding the core area of the body with a tight and powerful support for a wide range of physical moves.

Back Muscles, the long and short muscles, run along the vertebrae column, and along with rotators and diagonal muscles are working together as a unit, taking part in sideward bendings, turning the trunk, and rotations.

Abdominal Muscles, anterior, lateral and obliques, can pull in opposite directions through fibers that cross the abdominal wall, enabling the trunk to bend forward, sideways, rotate, and twist. The abdominals play important roles in many sport skills, therefore weak muscles can restrict athletes effectiveness in many athletic activities.

All trunk muscles can work as a unit to stabilize, to keep the trunk fixed, during movements of the arms and legs, especially in throwing activities from baseball to track and field.

LAW #4: Before developing the prime movers develop the stabilizers. Prime movers, the muscles primary responsible for performing a technical move, work more efficiently when the stabilizers, or fixator muscles, are stronger. This latter group of muscles contract, especially isometrically, to immobilize a limb so that another part of the body can perform a desired action. Examples: immobilize the shoulders to perform an elbow flexion; contracted abdominals play a fixator role for the arms to throw a ball; or, in rowing when all the trunk muscles are contracted, playing the role of stabilizers, the trunk represents the transmitter of leg power to the arms, which in turn drive the blade through the water. There are several stabilizers at different joints, and although small, they play an important role since a weak stabilizer inhibits the contracting capacity of the prime movers.

As already mentioned, strength training for beginners should be seen as an addition to other sports and activities, but a very important addition. From the total amount of time per week, some 20-30% should be dedicated to physical training; from strength to flexibility. However, such a program should be performed in an attractive environment, in which the instructor tries to make the program an enjoyable, creative and worthwhile experience.

Chapter Eight

Program Design

The Volume of Training

As an important component of strength training, volume refers to the quantity of work performed, incorporating the following integral parts:

1. the time or the duration of training in hours;
2. the number of kg, lbs, or tonnes/ short tons, lifted per training session or phase of training;
3. the number of exercises per training lesson; and
4. the number of sets and repetitions per exercise or training session.

In order to correctly monitor the total volume of work performed, instructors, coaches or athletes, should keep records of the sum of kg/lbs lifted per session or training phase. In this way they can plan more effectively the total volume of training per weeks/ months in the future.

Variations of volume of training exists not only between athletes' classification, strength training background, but also between the type of strength training performed. For instance: high volume of training is planned for athletes attempting to develop muscular endurance or maximum strength. In the first case because there are many repetitions performed, in the second because the load is very high. Medium load, on the other hand, is typical for training different elements of power, since:

1. the load is low—medium; and
2. the rest interval is relatively long.

As an athlete approaches the stage of high performance, the overall volume of training becomes more important. In reaching high performance, there are no shortcuts to high volume of training, including strength training. Athletes' performance improves only as a result of good and constant physiological adaptation, which is directly dependant on the increments of the volume of training.

As the athlete adapts to higher volumes of training, one of the direct benefits is a better recovery between sets, and training sessions. As a direct result of that is more work per training session/ week, and once again the ability to further increase the volume of training.

Increments in the volume of strength training are a function of the athlete's individual characteristics, biological make-up, specifics of the selected sport, and certainly, the importance of strength in that sport. Under these conditions, a mature athlete with a strong strength training background can tolerate higher volumes of strength training. For example, a football player can accomplish a higher volume of work as compared to a tennis player.

Irrespective of the type of sport or the level of the athletes involved, a dramatic or an abrupt increase of volume of strength can be detrimental, resulting in high levels of fatigue, uneconomical muscular work, and even increased danger of injuries. This is why a well and progressively made plan, with an appropriate monitoring method of loads increments, will avoid any detriments.

THE TOTAL VOLUME of strength undertaken by athletes, as said above, depends on several factors, of which the importance of strength to that sport is determinant. For instance international class weight lifters often plan 30 tonnes (33 short tons) per training sessions, and approximately 40,000 tonnes (44,000 short tons) per year. For other sports, as illustrated by Table 3, the volume differs quite drastically. Certainly power/ speed dominated sports require a much higher volume as opposed to boxing. At the same time, for sports where muscular-endurance is dominant, such as in rowing or canoeing, the volume of strength per year can be 3–6 times higher than indicated in Table 3.

THE INTENSITY (LOAD) OF TRAINING

In strength training, intensity as expressed in percentage of load of one repetition maximum (1RM), is a very important component of training. Intensity is a function of the power of the nervous stimuli employed in training. The strength of a stimulus depends on the load, speed of performing a movement, and the variation of rest intervals between repetitions. The last , but not least, important element of intensity is the psychological strain which accompanies an exercise. Thus, the intensity is determined not only by the muscular effort but also by the CNS energy spent during strength training.

TABLE 3. A suggested guideline for the volume (in tonnes) of strength training per year (Bompa, 1990).

No.	Sport/Event	Volume/Microcycle in Training Phases			Volume/Year	
		Preparatory	Competitive	Transition	Minimum	Maximum
1	Shot Put	24–40	8–12	4–6	900	1450
2	Downhill Skiing	18–36	6–10	2–4	700	1250
3	High Jump	16–28	8–10	2–4	620	1000
4	Ice Hockey	15–25	6–8	2–4	600	950
5	Speed Skating	14–26	4–6	2–4	500	930
6	Basketball	12–24	4–6	2	450	850
7	Javelin	12–24	4	2	450	800
8	Volleyball	12–20	4	2	450	700
9	Sprinting	10–18	4	2	400	600
10	Gymnastics	10–16	4	4	380	600
11	Boxing	8–14	3	1	380	500

Intensity Value	Load	% of 1RM	Type of Contraction
1	Supermaximum	>105	Eccentric/ Isometric
2	Maximum	90–100	Concentric
3	Heavy	80–90	- " -
4	Medium	50–80	- " -
5	Low	30–50	- " -

Figure 19. The intensity values and the load utilized in strength training.

The load in training, as an expression of intensity, refers to the mass, or weight that is lifted in training. In isokinetic training the load is expressed in the force performed by the athlete against the resistance provided by the machine. As suggested by Figure 19, the following loads are employed in strength training:

SUPERMAXIMUM or a load which exceeds one's maximum strength. In most cases loads between 100–125% should be used by applying the eccentric, or yielding to the force of gravity method. Elite class weight lifters often employ 105–110% of maximum strength two to three times per week by employing the concentric method. When supermaximum loads are utilized it is advisable to have two individual spotters, one at each end of the barbell, to assist or guard the performer so that accidents are prevented (i.e., in bench press, by employing the eccentric method a barbell may fall on the performer's chest if not spotted).

Supermaximum loads are to be utilized during maximum strength development by only those athletes with a strong background in strength training. Most other athletes should be restricted to a load of up to 100%.

MAXIMUM load, refers to a load of 90–100% of one's maximum.

HEAVY load is utilized when one employs a load between 80—90% of one's maximum.

MEDIUM load refers to a percentage between 50–80% of one's maximum.

LOW is considered tp be any load between 30–50% of 1RM.

The load, however, should also be related to the type of strength that is developed, but more importantly to the sport-specific combination resulted from the mixture of strength with speed, and strength with endurance (as per Figure 5). Although specific references with regard to how these sport-specific combinations have to be trained will be made in the section on power training, Figure 20 gives the reader a general guideline concerning the load to be used to develop each of these combinations. However, the load will not be the same throughout all the phases of training. On the contrary, the application of the concept of periodization will alter the load according to the goals of each training phase. Please note that the load starts from 20% of 1RM to over 105%, having underneath the corresponding intensities. Below that, all the sport-specific combinations, and the suggested load for each is mentioned.

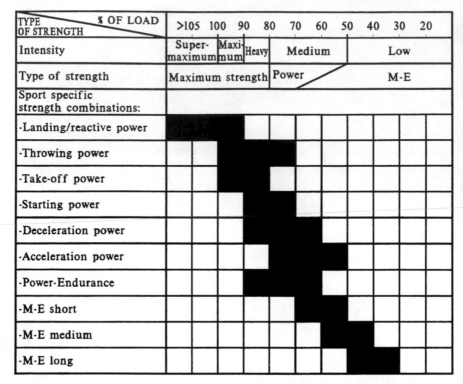

Figure 20. The relationship between the load and different types, and combinations of strength.

THE NUMBER OF EXERCISES

The key to an effective program is an adequate selection of exercises. The establishment of an optimum number of exercises is often overlooked by some coaches. In their desire to develop most muscle groups coaches select too many exercises. Obviously the outcome is an overloaded and fatiguing training program with a questionable effect.

The selection of exercises has to be done in light of the aspects explained below:

AGE AND LEVEL OF PERFORMANCE. One of the main objectives of a training program designed for juniors or beginners is the development of a solid anatomical and physiological foundation. Without such an approach consistent improvement will certainly be less likely. Therefore, as far as strength training is concerned, the coach should select many exercises (9–12) which are addressed to the main muscle groups of the body. The duration of such a program may be up to 2–3 years, depending on the age of the athlete and the expected age of high

64

performance. Considering the above circumstances one of the coach's high attributes should be patience.

Training programs designed for advanced or elite class athletes should follow a completely different approach. For such athletes the main objective of training is to increase performance to the highest possible level. Strength training has its own role in accomplishing such an objective. Therefore a strength program for elite class athletes, especially during the competitive phase, has to be very specific, directed precisely to the prime movers, and containing only a few exercises (3–6).

NEEDS OF THE SPORT. Exercises selected for strength training, especially for elite class athletes, ought to be selected to meet the specific needs of the sport. Thus, an elite class high jumper may perform only 3–4 exercises, while a wrestler has to elevate the number up to 5–8 so that all prime movers are adequately strengthened.

PHASE OF TRAINING. During the commencement of the preparatory phase a general strength training program is desirable. Following the transition phase the coach starts a new annual plan the beginning of which ought to be designed to build the foundation of training to come. Since such a program has to involve most muscle groups, the number of exercises for strength training during the early preparatory phase has to be high (9–12) regardless of the specifics of the sport. As the program progresses, the number of exercises is reduced, culminating with the competitive phase when only the very specific, essential exercises are performed.

THE ORDER OF EXERCISES

Exercises should be planned in such a way that the performer constantly alternates between limbs/ muscle groups for a better recovery. If all parts of the body are utilized, the following order is suggested: legs, arms, abdomen, legs, arms, back, etc. When the number of exercises are selected the coach should consider the proportion of their involvement in performing the skills of the sport. As such, it may happen that out of nine exercises, four exercises would be for legs, 2 for the arms and the other three for the abdominals, shoulders, and back. However, the alternation suggested above could be followed in the same sequence, especially the alternation between agonistic and antagonistic muscles.

Books and articles on the subject of strength training propose another order: work the large muscle groups first, followed by the small muscle groups. It is argued that if one involves the small muscle groups first, they fatigue and the athlete will not be able to train the large muscles. This is the typical influence of bodybuilding and weight lifting on the strength training for other sports. The proponents of such a method certainly have little understanding of the needs and specifics of sports.

Strength training exercises for sports are selected to mimic as much as possible the skills of the sport. In this way the strengthening of prime movers is maximized, and in some cases, there is also a "motor memory", or a consolidation of the technique of the skills involved. That means that by performing strength exercises similar to the technical pattern one repeats similar motions, and as such the exercise has a learning component.

On the other hand the imitation of technical skills has another advantage: the involvement of the chain of muscles in a similar pattern to their involvement in the sport. For instance for a volleyball player it makes sense to perform half squats and toe raises together since spiking and blocking requires exactly the same move, and the chain of muscles involved are acting in the same sequence. Therefore a volleyball player is not concerned whether the small, or large muscle groups are involved first. The player's interest is to mimic the motion and involve the chain of muscles in the same way as in spiking. Therefore the theory of working on large muscle groups first is completely irrelevant for strength training for sports.

Another concept which some strength coaches promote in strength training for athletics is the so-called pre-exhaustion method. The proponents of this method borrowed from weight lifting suggests that in order to better train the large muscle groups the small muscles should be pre-exhausted, and the whole load will be taken over by the large muscles. Once again this concept is not applicable for most sports for the reasons suggested above. Furthermore, in athletics the skills are performed by prime movers together with the synergistic muscles, or the muscles which assist directly for the performance of a skill. They must act in perfect synchronization if a good performance is expected. Therefore the selection of strength training exercises must consider this determinant factor in athletics.

When the training program is established by the coach, as far as the order of exercises are concerned, an athlete has two options:

1. to follow the order of exercises in the sequence they are placed on the sheet for the daily program: from the top down (the "vertical" sequence). As explained above, the advantage of this method is a better recovery for the muscle groups involved. By the time exercise No. 1 is performed again, it takes quite a bit of time, during which the muscles can better recover, and

2. to perform all the sets for exercise No. 1, and then move to the next exercise (the "horizontal" sequence). The disadvantage of this sequence is that by the time all the sets are performed for one exercise, local fatigue may be so high that instead of ower or maximum strength the outcome may be hypertrophy.

Often the rest interval is not as high as necessary to facilitate the development of power or maximum strength. In addition, athletes have the tendency of not watching the clock and respecting the prescribed rest interval. If, on top of this, one follows the "horizontal" sequence then local muscular fatigue is so high that the development of power or maximum strength is hampered by fatigue. Therefore, if for the first 2–3 sets one develops power/ maximum strength, because of inadequate recovery between the sets, the last number of sets of the daily program are performed under a state of exhaustion, and as such the outcome is hypertrophy and not power training.

Therefore, for athletics the most beneficial order of exercises is the "vertical" sequence, which allows a longer rest interval between sets and as such a better regeneration before another set has to be performed by the same muscle groups.

THE NUMBER OF REPETITIONS AND THE RHYTHM OF LIFTING

Both the number of repetitions and rhythm, or speed of execution, are a function of load; the higher the load the lower the number of repetitions and rhythm of execution. As illustrated by Figure 21, for the development of maximum strength (85–105%) the number of repetitions is very low (1–7). For exercises aimed at developing power (50–80% of maximum) the number of repetitions is moderate (5–10) and performed dynamically. For M-E of short duration, one can have a desired effect with 10–30 repetitions; for M-E of medium duration, around 30–60 repetitions are required non stop: while for M-E of long duration, a high number of repetitions are required, sometimes up to one's limits, or over 100–150.

Figure 21 illustrates a graphical representation between load and the number of repetitions. For the disciplined instructor who throughout his/ her athletic life has been exposed to information where 20 repetitions was regarded as M-E, the suggestions made in this book regarding the number of repetitions will be a shock! For sports where M-E of medium or long duration is the dominant combination of biomotor abilities, such as rowing, kayak-canoeing, long distance swimming, long distance speed skating, and cross-country skiing, 20 repetitions has an insignificant contribution to the overall performance.

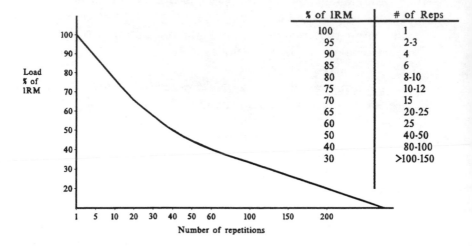

% of 1RM	# of Reps
100	1
95	2-3
90	4
85	6
80	8-10
75	10-12
70	15
65	20-25
60	25
50	40-50
40	80-100
30	>100-150

Figure 21. A graphical illustration between load and number of repetitions.

There are still many coaches who fail to understand that strength training should address the **physiological needs of the sport**. A complete change in the philosophy of strength training is necessary if one is expected to be successful. The sooner a coach implements periodization of strength, with its novel ideas, the faster his/ her athletes will improve (please refer to planning-periodization and training methods).

The rhythm of performing the work is critical for the success in strength training. For best training effects the execution of some type of work has to be fast, explosive, while others slow to medium. The key to this is the way in which the athlete applies force against the resistance. For instance, in lifting a heavy load of 90% of 1RM, the motion performed by the athlete may look slow. However, the force applied against resistance has to be as fast as possible. Only under this condition will an athlete be capable of synchronizing and recruiting all the motor units necessary to defeat resistance. The FT muscle fibers are trained and recruited for the action only when the application of force is fast and vigorous.

Figure 22 illustrates several types of strength training, referring to each type how the athlete thinks, or intends to perform the motion, and how it really looks to onlookers.

Strength training for:	The athlete intends to perform it:	How the athlete performs it:
Hypertrophy	Medium	Slow ———> Medium
Maximum strength	Fast	Slow
Power	Fast	Fast
M-E	Medium ———> Slow	Medium ———> Slow

Figure 22. Types of strength vs. speed of motion.

THE NUMBER OF SETS

A set represents the number of repetitions per exercise followed by a rest interval. The number of sets depend on the number of exercises performed in a training session, and the strength combination one trains. As the number of exercises increases the number of sets decreases, since one does not have the energy and work potential to perform many exercises and repetitions with very high number of sets. Similarly, the strength combination being worked on influences the number of sets as well. For instance, if one is attempting to develop M-E of long duration the key element is not the number of sets but rather the number of repetitions. Since the number of repetitions is high, one would have a hard time performing more than 3, maximum 4 sets.

Furthermore, the number of sets also depends on the following factors: the athlete's abilities and training potential, the number of muscle groups that must be trained, and the phase of training. For instance, a high jumper who is in a very specialized training program may use only 3–5 exercises and employs 6–10 sets per lesson. If the same athlete is using a higher number of exercises the number of sets has to decrease. Under these circumstances the disadvantage is quite obvious. Let us consider that our hypothetical high jumper is using 8 exercises and involves several muscle groups from legs, upper body, and arms. Also consider that for each exercise, or muscle group, the athlete performs a work of 400 kg (880 lbs). Since the athlete can perform just 4 sets the total amount of work per muscle group is 1600 kg (3520 lbs). Now take the example that the same athlete reduces the number of exercises to 4. In such a situation he/ she can perform, say, 8 sets. Thus 8 X 400 kg (880 lbs) is 3200 kg (7040 lbs). Therefore, with a decreased number of exercises and an increased number of sets per muscle group an athlete can double, or even triple the total work per muscle group.

As already mentioned above, the training phase also dictates the number of sets to be performed in a training session. During the preparatory (pre-season) phase, when most muscle groups are used, the number of exercises are high, and conversely, the number of sets are lower (please refer to the planning section). As the competitive phase approaches, training becomes more specific, thus the number of exercises decreases and the number of sets increases. And finally, during the competitive phase (season), when the objective of training is to maintain a certain level of strength, or a given strength combination, everything is reduced, including the number of sets, so that the athlete's energy is spent mostly for technical/tactical work.

In conclusion, the number of sets varies according to the above mentioned factors. In any instance a well trained athlete is capable of performing anywhere between 3 and 8–10, or even 12 number of sets. Certainly, as demonstrated above, it makes sense to perform a higher number of sets. The more sets per muscle group, the more work one can perform, which ultimately leads to higher strength gains and improved performance.

THE REST INTERVAL

Energy represents a necessary prerequisite for strength training. During training an athlete is using the fuel of a given energy system in accordance to the load employed and the duration of activity. During high intensity strength training the energy stores can be taxed to a certain degree, sometimes being even completely exhausted. In order to be able to complete the work, say 4–6 sets, the athlete has to take a rest interval (RI) so that the depleted fuel is restored before another set is performed.

Any coach/ athlete has to be convinced that the RI and the restoration of energy between sets, or training sessions, are as important as training itself. The amount of time allowed between sets determines to a high degree to what extent an energy source is recovered prior to the following set. Careful planning of RI is critical to avoid needless physiological and psychological stress during training.

The duration of the RI depends on several factors, among them being: the combination of strength one is attempted to develop, the magnitude of the load employed, the rhythm of performance, the number of muscles involved, and certainly, the level of conditioning. In calculating the RI one should also consider the total weight of the athlete. Since their muscles are larger, heavy athletes tend to regenerate at a slower rate than lighter ones.

The RI should consider the rest taken between sets and between days of strength training.

REST INTERVAL BETWEEN SETS is a function of the load employed in training, the type of strength being developed, and the rate, or explosiveness of performing the task. Figure 23 attempts to condense all the information into chart form for easier use.

LOAD %	Rhythm of Performance	RI (minutes	Applicability
>105 (eccentric)	Slow	4–5/7	Improve maximum-strength and muscle tone
80–100	Slow to Medium	3–5/7	Improve maximum-strength and muscle tone
60–80	Slow to Medium	2	Improve muscle hypertrophy
50–80	Fast	4–5	Improve power
30–50	Slow to Medium	1–2	Improve M-E

FIGURE 23. A suggested guideline for RI between sets for different loads and their applicable circumstances.

During a RI the ATP/CP is replenished proportionally to its duration and then again used as a source of energy. Properly calculated, the RI will not allow the accumulation of lactic acid (LA) as rapidly, and as such enabling the athlete to maintain the planned training program. When the RI is shorter than one minute, LA concentration is very high. If the RI is shorter than 30 seconds lactate levels are so high that it is difficult to be tolerated even by the well trained athletes. A proper RI on the other hand, will facilitate, at least partially, the removal of LA from the body. However, for sports where the athletes have to tolerate LA, such as short distance events in running, swimming, rowing, canoeing, boxing, and wrestling, coaches are encouraged to plan days of strength training which would result in LA buildup. At the same time one should also consider that:

- a 30 second complete rest restores approximately 50% of ATP/CP that was depleted.
- a 1 minute RI for several sets of 15–20 reps is not sufficient for the restoration of the muscle's energy to be able to perform high muscular tension.
- a RI of 3–5 minutes or longer, allows an almost entire restoration of ATP/CP.
- after working to exhaustion, a 4 minute RI is not sufficient to eliminate LA from the working muscles, or the replenishment of all the energy requirements, such as glycogen.

It is, therefore, fair to say that the shorter the RI the less ATP/CP will be restored, and as such, there will be less energy for the next set. Under these conditions the energy necessary for the following sets will be contributed by the LA system with the undesirable outcome of increased LA accumulation. This in turn will impair one's ability to perform the planned work.

In order to overcome the effects of LA accumulation, a longer RI is required. During the RI, and not during work, the heart pumps higher amounts of blood to the working muscle. A short RI will diminish the volume of blood reaching the muscle, and as a result will supply less of the needed fuel and oxygen. Without fuel and oxygen an athlete will not have the energy to complete his/ her planned training program.

Strength training is also inhibited by local (muscular), and CNS fatigue. Most research findings point to the following possible causes and **sites of fatigue**:

1. The **motor nerve** innervating the muscle fiber. The nervous system transmits nerve impulses to the muscle fiber via the motor nerve. A nerve impulse has a certain degree of force, speed, and frequency. The higher the force impulse the stronger the muscle contraction, and as such the ability of the athlete to lift heavier loads. The force of the nerve impulse which stimulates the muscle to contract is greatly affected by fatigue. If the level of fatigue is increasing, the force of contraction is decreasing. This is why longer RI are necessary for CNS recovery, often longer than 4–5 minutes, up to 7 minutes.

2. The fatigue at the **neuro-muscular junction** (the nerve attachment on the muscle fiber, which relays the nerve impulses to the working muscle). This type of fatigue is most likely due to increased release of chemical transmitters from the nerve endings (Tesch, 1980). Following a set, a 2–3 minute RI facilitates the electrical parameters of the nerve to return to normal. However for work of powerful contractions, such as maximum strength, a longer time is necessary for recovery (even longer than 5 minutes).

3. Fatigue within **contractile mechanism** (actin and myosin), facilitated by the following factors:

*   LA accumulation results in decreasing the peak tension, or the power of the muscle to contract maximally. The higher the LA accumulation, the higher the acidic concentration in the muscle, which in turn affects muscle reactivity to the nerve impulse (Sahlin, 1986; Fox et al, 1989).
*   Depletion of muscle glycogen stores, which during prolonged work, over 30 minutes, are nearly completely depleted, causes the fatigue of the contracting muscle (Karlson and Saltin, 1971; Sahlin, 1986; Conlee, 1987).

Other energy sources available to the muscle, including glycogen from the liver, cannot fully cover the energy demands of the working muscle.

4. The **Central Nervous System** (CNS) and local muscular fatigue. During training, inside the muscle, chemical disturbances occur which affects the muscle's potential to perform work (Bigland-Ritchie, et al, 1983; Hennig and Lomo, 1987). The effect of the chemical disturbance are consequently signalled back to the CNS. The brain in turn sends back weaker nerve impulses to the working muscle, declining its working capacity. During an adequate RI (4–5 minutes) the muscle recovers to a high degree from fatigue, the brain noticing that, being now able to send more powerful nerve impulses, which in turn results in better muscular performance. Failing to allow longer RI results in incomplete restoration and as such the inability of recovering from fatigue. As a consequence the ability to perform quality

work is impaired.

REST INTERVAL BETWEEN STRENGTH TRAINING SESSIONS, depends on the conditioning level and recovery ability of the individual, training phase, and the energy source used in training. Well conditioned athletes always recover faster, especially as training progresses towards the competitive phase, when the athlete is suppose to reach the best level of physical potential.

The energy source taxed in training is probably the main guideline to consider, not only when considering the RI between strength training sessions, but also their frequency. Normally, strength training is planned following technical and/ or tactical training. If during technical and strength training one is taxing the same energy system and fuel, say glycogen, then the next such type of training has to be planned two days later, since it takes 48 hours for the full restoration of glycogen (Piehl, 1973; Fox et al., 1989). Even with a carbohydrate enriched diet the glycogen level will not return to normal levels faster than two days.

If one performs just strength training, as some athletes do in certain days during the preparatory phase, the restoration of glycogen occurs faster: 55% in five hours, and almost 100% in 24 hours. As such strength training can be planned more frequently.

THE ACTIVITY DURING REST

In order to facilitate a quicker recovery between sets, the coach should advise the athlete as to the type of activity to be performed during the rest interval. Relaxation exercises (i.e., shaking the legs, arms and shoulders) and light massage seem to be effective means of facilitating a faster recovery between sets. Relaxation exercises are indicated especially since heavy load exercises increase the quantity of myostromin (a protein occurring within the framework of a muscle tissue) in muscles which causes muscle rigidity (Baroga, 1978).

The mental control of muscle relaxation is of paramount importance. Relaxation means economy of energy and facilitation of the quickness of contraction so that the antagonistic muscles are relaxed and do not oppose the contraction of the agonistic muscles.

During the RI it is also important to perform "diverting activities", to involve the non-fatigued muscles into some light contractions (Asmussen and Mazin, 1978). It was reported that such physical activities can facilitate a faster recovery of the prime movers. Local muscular fatigue is signalled to the CNS via sensory nerves. As a result the brain sends inhibitory signals to the fatigued muscle, declining its work output during the RI. As such the muscle relaxes better, facilitating the restoration of the energy stores.

STEPS FOR TRAINING DESIGN

In order to design a strength training program the coach/ instructor may consider the following steps:

1. *SELECT THE EXERCISES* to be used in training. This is done in accordance to the specifics of the sport, the athlete's needs, and the phase of training. Each athletic skill is performed by prime movers which, reflecting the specifics of the sport, can differ from sport to sport. As such, the instructor should identify the prime movers first and then select the strength exercises which can best involve such muscles.

At the same time, the athletes' needs should also be considered. These needs may depend on the athletes' background, and individual strengths and weaknesses. Since the weakest link in a chain always breaks first, compensation exercises should be selected to strengthen the weakest muscles.

The selection of exercises are also phase-specific, as illustrated in the chapter referring to periodization. Normally, during the "anatomical adaptation" phase, most muscle groups are employed in order to build a better and more multilateral foundation. As the competitive phase approaches, training becomes more specific, and exercises are selected to specifically involve the prime movers.

2. *TEST MAXIMUM STRENGTH*, or the highest load one can lift in one attempt. In this way one will know his/ her athlete's 100%, or 1RM. The coach should know each individual athlete's maximum strength in at least the dominant exercises composing a training program. Often it happens that the load and number of repetitions are chosen randomly, or by following other athletes' programs instead of utilizing the objective data from each individual athlete. This data is valid only for a certain cycle of training (usually a macro-cycle) since the athletes' degree of training and their potential alter continuously.

3. *SELECT THE TYPE OF STRENGTH SOUGHT.* The type, or sport-specific combination of strength, is selected as per the concept of periodization and is phase-specific. Based on that the instructor/coach will decide the percentage of 1RM to be used, the number of reps, and sets. Details on training methods and progression is provided in the chapters on planning and training methods.

4. ***DEVELOP THE ACTUAL TRAINING PROGRAM.*** By now the instructor/ coach knows the exercises to be performed, the athlete's 1RM, and the type of strength to be developed. Based on that, the coach will select the number of exercises, the percentage of 1RM to be used, and the number of reps, and decide the number of sets depending on the athlete's ability to tolerate work. All this information will be used to actually make the training program for a macro-cycle.

But this program cannot be the same for each macro-cycle. The training demand has to be progressively increased so that the athletes will adjust to an increased work load which will be translated into an increase in strength. The training demand may be increased by any of the following means: increase the load, decrease the rest interval, increase the number of repetitions, or increase the number of sets.

Before suggesting the headings of a simple chart to be used for a training program, it is necessary to advice the reader regarding the notation used to express the load, number of reps, and number of sets. Many books and articles on the subject go so far as to actually suggesting the load in lbs/kg an athlete should use! Without being cynical, one may have to question: on what basis can someone actually suggest the poundage the reader should take without knowing anything about him/ her? This is why the **load has to be suggested in percentage of 1RM**. This is the reason the athletes have to be **tested**, especially during the preparatory phase, at the beginning of each new macro-cycle. Knowing 1RM one can select the percentage to be used in training according to the training goals of each training phase.

Among some coaches/ instructors there is held this unfounded belief that testing for 1RM is dangerous! It can result in some sort of injury because the athlete has to lift 100%! For a decently trained athlete, lifting 100% once in every four weeks, or at the beginning of a macro-cycle can not be dangerous. Most injuries do not occur during testing but instead during training and competitions. Avoiding challenging the muscles to their 100% means that they would hardly adapt in order to apply their maximum potential in competition, and this could be one of the reasons injuries occur.

However, a test for 1RM has to be performed following a very thorough and progressive warm-up. In addition, if still reluctant to test 100%, other possibilities are suggested in the index, where using a test for 3RM or 5RM can estimate the 100%.

The **notation** of load, number of reps, and number of sets can be expressed as follows:

$$\frac{80\%}{10}4 \;\Rightarrow\; \frac{load}{no.\ of\ reps}\ (sets)$$

where the numerator (80%) refers to the load to be used, the denominator (10) represents the number of repetitions, and the multiplier (4) suggests the number of sets.

The advantage of suggesting the load in % of 1RM is that in working with a larger group of athletes, such as a football team, the coach does not have to calculate the poundage for each player. By just suggesting the load in percentage, the program is valid for each individual. Individualization is therefore built-in in this method. Each individual athlete, based on his/ her 1RM will calculate their own poundage, which may vary from player to player.

EX. NO.	Exercise	Load, # Reps, # sets	RI (in min.)
1	Leg press	$\dfrac{80}{6}\,4$	3
2	Bench press	$\dfrac{75}{8}\,4$	3
3	Leg curls	$\dfrac{60}{10}\,3$	2
4	Half squat	$\dfrac{80}{8}\,4$	3
5	Abd. curls	15 x 4	2
6	Dead lift	$\dfrac{60}{8}\,3$	2

FIGURE 24. The chart used to design a strength training program. The chart can be listed in the gym for the athlete to see.

Any strength training program has to be written on a sheet of paper, or even better, in the training journal. An example of a format to express a strength training program is illustrated by Figure 24.

In the first vertical column the number of exercises to be performed in a given strength training session is specified, from 1 to X. Exercises are written in the next column, followed by the column where the load, number of reps, and sets are specified. The last column refers to the RI to be taken following each set.

5. *TEST TO RECALCULATE 1RM.* This new test is required prior to beginning a new macro-cycle to ensure that the progress in maximum strength is acknowledged, and as such, the new load is related to the new gains made in strength.

PART 2

PLANNING — PERIODIZATION

In training nothing happens by accident, but rather by design.

Do you want to be successful?

Plan for it!

CHAPTER NINE

SHORT TERM PLANS

A strength training program is successful only if it is related to and part of a longer plan. An athlete should never do strength training just for the sake of it, or only because it helps to improve performance. Although this is true, **a strength program should be viewed as a training component required to be developed if performance is expected to improve**. At the same time, such a program must have a purpose, which normally should be **phase specific**. Since each training phase has certain objectives, strength training must be part of these goals, it must coincide with the overall planning.

A training plan represents a methodical and scientific concept which the coach can put together. Consequently, planning is the most important tool utilized by the coach in attempting to conduct a well organized training program. A coach is only as efficient as he or she is organized. A training program is successful only if it is well designed, it is based on the scientific knowledge available in this field, and if it considers the **periodization of strength** as the key guideline in planing strength and power training throughout the year.

The compilation of a plan, both short and long-term, also reflects the coach's knowledge of methodology, and takes appropriate account of the athlete's background and physical potential. A training plan has to be simple, objective, and above all flexible, as it may have to be modified to match the athlete's rate of adaptation to the physiological challenges and improvements in performance.

In Part 2, the reader will be exposed to several types of plans, from the simple training session to the long-term. Since planning theory is very complex and this book only refers to planning as it pertains to strength training, further information on this topic can be obtained from the book *Theory and Methodology of Training* (Bompa, 1994).

Of all possible plans that can be used, reference will be made in Part 2 only to: the training session plan, the micro-cycle, the annual plan and long-term plan for junior athletes. For other specific information, the reader is suggested to refer to the section on periodization.

THE TRAINING SESSION PLAN

The training session can be described as the main tool used to organize the daily program. For better management and organization, the training session can be structured into four main segments.

1. *THE INTRODUCTION* represents the organizational component of a training session, when the coach/ instructor shares with the athletes the training objectives of the day, and how they are going to be achieved. This is also the time when the coach organizes the athletes into groups and gives them the necessary advice regarding the daily program.

2. *THE WARM-UP* has the specific role of preparing the athletes for the program to follow. During the warm-up, body temperature is raised, which appears to be one of the main factors facilitating performance. Moreover, the warm-up stimulates the activity of the CNS which coordinates all the systems of the body, speeds up motor reactions through faster transmission of nerve impulses, and improves coordination. Also, by elevating the body temperature, muscles, tendons, ligaments and other tissues are warmed-up and stretched, thereby preventing and/ or reducing ligament sprains, and tendon and muscle strains.

For the purpose of strength training the warm-up has two parts: *GENERAL WARM-UP* (10–12 minutes). Through light jogging, cycling or step-ups, followed by calisthenics, and stretching exercises, the athletes increase the blood flow and as a result, body temperature, thus preparing the muscles and tendons for the planned program.

During the warm-up the athlete should also mentally prepare for the main part of the training session by trying to visualize the exercises to be performed and to motivate themselves for the eventual strain of training.

SPECIFIC WARM-UP represents a short transition of some 3–5 minutes to the work to be done during training. By performing a few repetitions on the equipment to be used during training, with much lighter loads than the ones planned for the day, the athlete will be better prepared for a successful workout.

3. *THE MAIN PART* of the training session is dedicated to the actual training program, including strength training. Since in most sports technical and tactical work represents the main objectives of training, strength development is performed after them, often being a secondary priority. As such, first priority activities are performed immediately after the warm-up, followed by strength training.

The succession of the type of training to be performed in a given day depends on the phase of training as well as its own objectives. In Figure 25 the following options are suggested, where T stand for technical training,

TA for tactical, MxS for maximum strength, P for power, SP for speed, END for endurance, and M-E for muscular endurance:

Training Options:	#1	#2	#3	#4	#5
Sequence of types of training	warm-up	warm-up	warm-up	warm-up	warm-up
	T/TA	T/TA	MxS/P	T/TA	END
	MxS/P	SP	END	M-E	M-E
	M-E	MxS/P			

FIGURE 25. Suggested training options for training sessions.

In the first example (#1) of Figure 25, one should assume that a given sport requires all the above elements (i.e. boxing, wrestling, and martial arts) and as such following T/TA work the coach has to plan MxS/P and M-E at the end, since the most fatiguing component has to be performed last, otherwise it will impair gains in other abilities. In the second example, speed and power are dominant (i.e. football, baseball), but a workout for MxS/P is also necessary to be trained. In this case a short speed workout can be performed since gains in MxS/P were found to be more effective when they followed a few short but maximum velocity sprints (Ozolin, 1971; Baroga, 1978).

Apparently powerful stimuli, such as short sprints prior to strength training, stimulates strength development, a method often used by weight lifters from Eastern Europe. Fox et al. (1989) also suggest that changes in the CNS act as stimuli for gains in strength. Display of the muscles's maximum potential is often limited by the inhibiting influence of proprioceptors such as the Golgi tendon organs. The CNS itself also seems to inhibit the activation of all the motor units available in a muscle or muscle groups. In order to partially overcome that, in some workouts the coach should plan work of maximum intensity which would have stimulating effects on the muscles trained (please refer to the section on micrco-cycles).

The third example considers an endurance-dominant sport during the preparatory phase, where both MxS/P and END are trained in the same day. The justification of the above sequence is based on the fact that the most fatiguing ability has to be trained last. If reversed, one would certainly have difficulty in working effectively on the development of MxS/P following an exhausting program of endurance. As competitions approach the sequence can be reversed. In such a case, strength, as a secondary priority, is performed in addition to other elements of training.

The last two examples consider sports requiring M-E, from speed skating, and cross-country skiing, to rowing and swimming. As a very fatiguing element, M-E is logically performed following T/TA work (example #4). In the last case (#5) M-E is placed following END since it is an addition to the main focus of that day of training.

The above options do not exhaust all the possibilities, however, it would hardly be advisable to perform power training such as plyometrics, following END or M-E. An exhausted body will not be able to perform quick and powerful muscle contractions. This is why the types of strength training (MxS and P) requiring a high recruitment of FT muscle fibers are performed before endurance.

The **duration** of a strength training session depends on the importance of strength in that sport, as well as the phase of training. During the preparatory phase, a strength training session can last 1–2 hours, whereas in the competitive phase it is much shorter, 30–45 minutes. Such work is dedicated mostly for the maintenance of strength gained during the preparatory phase. Exceptions to this basic rule are made for throwers in track and field, linemen in football, and the heavy weight category in wrestling, where more time for strength training is needed (1–1.5 hours).

4. *COOL-DOWN*. As the warm-up is considered a transition from the normal biological state of daily activities to high intensity training, a cool-down has the opposite effect — progressively to bring the body back to its normal functions.

During a cool-down of 10–20 minutes, the athlete can perform certain activities which would facilitate a **faster recovery and regeneration** from the strains of training. Having this purpose in mind it would be inappropriate for the athlete to leave for the showers immediately following the last exercise.

As a result of training, especially following intensive work, the athlete builds high amounts of lactic acid. In addition the muscles are exhausted, tensed and rigid. To overcome that, and to speed-up the process of recovery, relaxation exercises should be performed (please refer to the chapter on fatigue and recovery).

The removal of lactic acid from blood and muscles would also be necessary if the effect of fatigue is to be eliminated soon. This is best achieved by performing 15–20 minutes of light continuous, aerobic type of activity. By doing so the body continues to perspire, thus removing about half of the lactic acid from the system, assisting the athlete to recover faster before the next training session.

THE MICROCYCLE

A microcycle refers to a weekly training program, and is probably the most important tool in planning. Throughout the annual plan the nature and dynamics of microcycles alter according to the phase of training, the training objectives, and the physiological and psychological demands of training.

A discussion regarding the planning of a microcycle should refer to: 1) how to plan a microcycle for a longer training phase (a macrocycle, or 4–6 weeks of training), and 2) how to plan the load of training per microcycle.

1. *LOAD INCREMENTS PER MACROCYCLE*, follows a **step-type progression**, the standard approach being exemplified by Figure 26. From the intensity point of view, microcycles follow the principle of progressive increase of training load.

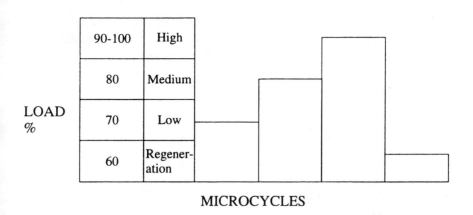

MICROCYCLES

Figure 26. The dynamics of increasing the training load over four microcycles.

As illustrated in Figure 26, during the first three cycles the load is progressively increased, followed by a regeneration cycle where the load is decreased, in order to facilitate recuperation and replenishment of energy before another macrocycle begins.

Based on the above model (Figure 26) a practical example can be produced (Figure 27) in which increments in load will be suggested using the notation proposed in chapter 8 (Program Design).

Training Load	$\frac{70}{10}2$ $\frac{80}{8}2$ $\frac{85}{7}1$	$\frac{80}{9}2$ $\frac{85}{7}2$ $\frac{90}{2}2$	$\frac{85}{7}2$ $\frac{90}{5}3$ $\frac{95}{2}2$	$\frac{70}{10}4$
Step #	1	2	3	4

FIGURE 27. A practical exemplification of load increments in training (a macrocycle).

By examining Figure 27 the reader will observe that the work, or the total load in training is increased in steps, the highest being in step #3. To increase the work from step to step the instructor/ coach has two options:
- to increase the load — the highest one being in step #3; and
- to increase the number of sets: from five in step #1, as per our example above, to seven in step #3.

In the above example (Figure 27) both options were used at the same time. However, this approach can be changed to suit the needs of different classifications of athletes. For athletes with a good background in strength training the above approach can be used, whereas younger athletes will have a harder time tolerating a high number of sets. For young athletes it is more important to have a high number of exercises to develop the whole muscular system, as well as to adapt the muscle attachments on the bones (tendons) to strength training. Therefore, a high number of sets and exercises at the same time is quite difficult to tolerate. As a consequence it is advisable to choose a high number of exercises at the expense of the number of sets.

Step #4 represents a regeneration cycle, where both the load and the number of sets are lower to facilitate the removal of fatigue acquired during the first three steps, to replenish the energy stores, and to psychologically relax.

It is essential to mention that the load suggested in each microcycle refers to the work per day, which can be repeated 2–4 times per week, depending on the training goals.

2. *LOAD INCREMENTS PER MICROCYCLE.* The work, or the total load per microcycle, is increased mainly by increasing the number of days of strength training per week. However, one should not forget that in athletics strength training is subordinated to technical/tactical training. Consequently, the load of strength training per week should be calculated by keeping in mind the overall volume and intensity of training.

Before discussing options of strength training per microcycle, it is important to mention that the total work per week is also planned following the principle of progressive increase of load in training. The following Figures (28–30), illustrate three microcyles, each of them being suggested for each of the conventional steps which was refered to above.

Certainly, in most cases, strength training is planned on the same days as other activities such as technical and/ or tactical work. Similarly, in a training session a coach may plan to work on the development of certain physical qualities such as speed, strength or endurance. Then what is the best approach to be considered in planning strength training per microcycle?

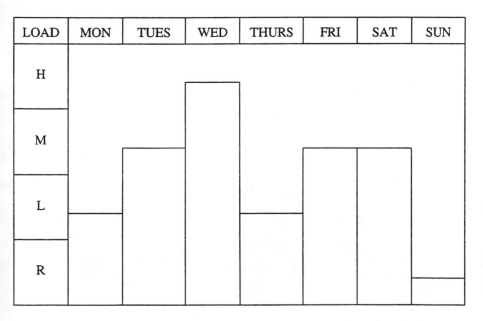

FIGURE 28. A low intensity microcycle (first level as per figure 17) where there is one high intensity training day (H), and several medium (M) and low (L) intensity days. Sundays is a rest day (R).

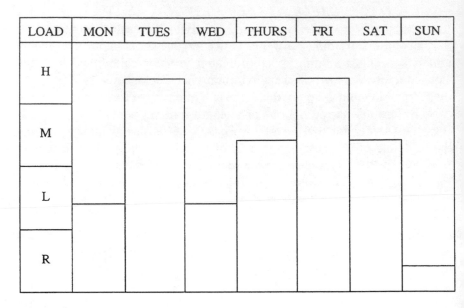

LOAD	MON	TUES	WED	THURS	FRI	SAT	SUN
H							
M							
L							
R							

FIGURE 29. An example of a medium intensity microcycle (second level as per figure 17).

LOAD	MON	TUES	WED	THURS	FRI	SAT	SUN
H							
M							
L							
R							

FIGURE 30. A high intensity microcycle (third level as per figure 17) where three high intensity training days are planned.

There are some proponents, authors and coaches alike, who suggest that strength training should be planned on "easy days." To a certain extent, this makes sense. However, from a physiological point of view, this issue demands a more complex analysis.

Most sports need to train, to a greater or lesser extent, most, if not all, the motor abilities (speed, strength, endurance). Each ability is dependent on and utilizes a certain energy system. But the recovery, and restoration of the fuel utilized by each energy system has a different rate.

The restoration of glycogen, which is the main fuel for strength training, is between 24–48 hours. Glycogen restoration from continuous, intensive work, is achieved in approximately 48 hours, whereas from intermittent activity, such as strength training, requires about 24 hours (Brooks et al. 1973; Fox et al., 1989). However, following maximum intensity training when the CNS is also taxed, it often takes up to 48 hours before regeneration is experienced.

The rate of regeneration from aerobic activities is much faster, approximately 8 hours. A quick restoration of energy stores occurs also as a result of the so called "technical work", which often is of a lower intensity. These types of training days can be considered as being "easy".

Now let us assume that on Monday, Wednesday, and Friday the coach plans intensive training sessions, and "easy days" for Tuesday and Thursday. Since between the intensive days there are 48 hours, and especially since there is an "easy day" between, glycogen can reach full restoration before another intensive day is planned. However, this can be drastically changed if in the "easy days" the coach schedules intensive strength training sessions. As a result the athletes are taxing the anaerobic energy system not only on the days mentioned above but also on the "easy days". In doing so the **glycogen is taxed every single day** and strength training represents an **obstacle** to the **restoration**. This complicates not only the energy expenditure-restoration ratio, but it can also bring the athlete to a state of fatigue, and even exhaustion. **From exhaustion to overtraining is just a short step.**

Consequently, **strength training has to be planned in the same days when technical/ tactical training, or speed/ power, are trained, namely in the days when the glycogen stores are taxed**. As such, the athletes deplete all the glycogen stores, and the overall training program **does not interfere with its restoration** by the time the next high intensity training is scheduled 48 hours later.

The number of strength training sessions per microcycle depends on:

1. **Athlete's classification.** Young athletes should be progressively introduced to strength training. At first they could be exposed to two shorter strength training sessions following technical/ tactical work. Progressively, and over a longer period of time, 2–4 years, they could be increased to 3–4 sessions. For higher level athletes, competing at national/ international competitions, they could take part in 3–4 strength training sessions (mostly during the preparatory phase).

2. **Importance of strength in the chosen sport.** According to the type of skills, energy requirement, and the dominant abilities in a given sport, strength training can have a lower or higher importance. For a sport where aerobic endurance is clearly dominant, such as a marathon, strength is less important. On the other hand, sports where power is dominant, such as in football, and throwing events, strength plays a predominant role. In the first example 1–2 sessions per week of specific strength training may suffice, whereas in the second, training must occur at least four times per microcycle, especially during the preparatory/ pre-season phase.

3. **Phase of training.** As illustrated in the next chapter (the periodization of strength), the number of strength training sessions depends on the phase of training: 3–5 during preparatory, and 2–3 during the competitive phase.

Since some sports may have four strength training sessions per week, some are performed on consecutive days. In such circumstances, some coaches influenced by weightlifting or bodybuilding concepts, apply the so called "split routine", or to train different body parts in each day separately in order to recover faster. It has to be stated once again that such influences are not acceptable in athletics. The reason weight-lifters and bodybuilders use the split routine is because they train daily, and international class lifters often train 2–3 times per day. They do not do anything else but "pump iron". As such it would be very difficult for them to train the same muscle groups in each training session, often 6–12 times per microcycle. Under these circumstances it would be very hard for the muscles involved, to recover between training sessions, therefore the split routine is incorporated.

The same is not true for sports, where the use of strength training is just one of many elements, being performed in addition to technical/tactical training. For maximum effectiveness, and for the best economical use of the athletes' energy, strength training exercises have to be selectively chosen, stressing mostly the prime movers.

In order to increase its effectiveness, strength training exercises for sports have to be reduced to the lowest level possible. The main benefit of this is that the **number of sets can be increased**, and as such, the **prime movers can contract many times**. The outcome will be **more power development for the needed muscles**.

For a better demonstration of the above proposition an example is necessary. A coach designs a strength training program to make a ball player faster. The coach selects three exercises for leg power (knee extensor and flexors, and toe raises), one each for abdominals and back, and two for arms and shoulders. In total seven exercises. As anybody knows, one will never be a fast runner without having strong knee extensors and flexors.

Let us also assume that this is the preparatory phase and that the coach decides to have four strength training sessions per week, four sets, eight repetitions, with a load of 100 kg (224 lbs) for 1:15 hours. If the coach considers the split routine then the knee extensors and flexors will be trained:

- 2 sessions per week x 4 sets x 8 repetitions x 100kg (224lbs) = 6,400kg/14,336lbs.

If, on the other hand, the coach considers that the split routine is not applicable to his/ her needs then the result will be:

- 4 sessions per week x 4 sets x 8 repetitions x 100kg/224lbs = 12,800kg/28,572lbs.

The difference between the two training options is: 6,400kg/14,336lbs vs. 12,800kg/ 28,572lbs!!

Which option would you choose?

The above example is far from being exaggerated, any decently trained athlete is capable of doing it. However, as demonstrated above, the work performed in the two options is drastically different.

The conclusion from the above example should be obvious: **the split routine is impractical and inapplicable in strength training for sports**.

CHAPTER TEN

THE ANNUAL PLAN-PERIODIZATION

If the microcycle can be considered as the most important tool for a short term plan, the annual plan has the same significance over a longer period of time. Such a plan is based on the **concept of periodization** and employs the training principles as its guiding concepts. A training program organized and planned over a year represents a necessary requirement for anyone who intends to maximize his/ her strength improvements.

One of the main objectives of training is to reach a high level of performance at a given time which usually is the main competition of the year. In order to achieve such a performance, the entire training program has to be properly periodized and planned, so that the development of skills, and motor abilities proceeds in a logical and methodical manner.

PERIODIZATION

As one of the most important concepts in training, periodization refers to two basic components:

1. the periodization of the annual plan, or how a year is divided in various training phases; and

2. the periodization of strength, or how to structure strength training in order to be most effective according to the needs of the chosen sport.

PERIODIZATION OF ANNUAL PLAN

The first component of periodization considers the division, the partition of the annual plan into shorter and easier to manage training phases. Such a division enhances appropriate organization of training, allowing the coach to conduct the program in a systematic manner.

The annual training cycle, in most sports, is conventionally divided into three main phases of training: preparatory, or pre-season, competitive, or season, and transition, or off-season.

Each training phase is further subdivided into cycles, the microcycle being the most important. The duration of each training phase depends heavily on the competition schedule, as well as the time needed to improve skills and to develop the dominant biomotor abilities. During the preparatory phase, the coach usually attempts to develop the physiological foundations of the athlete's systems, whereas throughout the competitive phase the coach strives for perfection in accordance with the specific demands of the competition.

Figure 31 illustrates the periodization of the annual plan into phases and cycles of training. Since this type of plan has only one competitive phase the athletes have to peak only once during the year. Such a plan is called a **mono-cycle**, one, or **single peak** annual plan.

THE ANNUAL PLAN			
Main phases	Preparatory	Competitive	Trans.
Macro-cycles			
Micro-cycles			

FIGURE 31. A graphical illustration of the periodization of the annual plan (mono-cycle).

Not all sports have only one competitive phase. Some of them, such as track and field, swimming (in some countries), and other sports have either indoor and outdoors seasons, or two major competitions to peak for. Such a plan is usually called a **bi-cycle**, or **double peak** (Figure 32).

THE ANNUAL PLAN					
Prep. I	Compet. I	T	Prep. II	Compet. II	Trans.

FIGURE 32. The periodization of a bi-cycle is made up of two preparatory (Prep. I and II), two competitive and two transitions (T and Trans) phases.

PERIODIZATION OF STRENGTH

In planning, one should not be concerned with what kind of drills, or skills to do in a given training session or phase, but rather one should ask himself/ herself what kind of **physiological reaction** or **training adaptation** is desired in order to lead to best improvements. After making such a decision the coach will then have an easy time in selecting the appropriate type of work which will result in the desired development. Only in this way, will the coach work correctly from the physiological point of view. This approach alone will result in the best training adaptation, which will then lead to improvement in the athletes physiological capacity, and as such, to the betterment of athletic performance.

Such an innovating approach in training is in fact facilitated by periodization. In the case of strength, sports do not require strength development for the sake of strength. Each sport, as explained in the second chapter, needs to perfect either P, M-E, or both. The periodization of strength, with its specific sequence of training phases, leads to the development of P/ M-E according to the specifics of each. This section of the book intends to demonstrate the above assertion.

As illustrated by Figure 33, the periodization of strength has certain phases, each having specific strength training objectives. Following a general description of each phase, variations of periodization and periodization of strength for several sports will be presented.

Preparatory			Competitive		Transition
AA	MxS	Conver-sion to: P/M-E	Maintenance of: • P • M-E	C	Compensation training

FIGURE 33. Periodization of strength for a mono-cycle (C = cessation of strength).

ANATOMICAL ADAPTATION PHASE

Following a transition phase, when in most cases athletes do not particularly do much strength training, it is scientifically and methodically sound to commence a strength program aimed at adapting the anatomy of the athlete for the future strength program. Thus, the **main objective** of this phase is to **involve the most numbers of muscle groups, to prepare**

the muscles, ligaments, tendons, and joints, to endure the following long and strenuous phases of training.

The title of this phase was purposefully selected to clearly imply the scope of the first phase of the periodization of strength. Strength training programs should not revolve only around the legs or arms extensors, but should focus particularly on strengthening the "core" muscles: the abdominals, the lowerback, and spinal column musculature. These sets of muscles work together to insure that:

1. the trunk represents a support, so that the legs and arms have a strong pillar to rely on for all the movements they perform; and,

2. to represent a shock absorbing devise for many skills and exercises, especially for landing and falling. Consequently, when preparing athletes, especially young ones, for the strength training phases to follow, the coach should start from the core section of the body and work towards the extremities. In other words, before strengthening the legs and arms, concentrate on developing the link between them, the support, which is the spinal column, and the trunk in general.

Other additional objectives for anatomical adaptation (AA) are:
- work on strength balance between flexors and extensors surrounding each joint;
- balance the two sides of the body, especially the shoulders and arms;
- perform compensation work for the antagonistic muscles;
- strengthen the stabilizer muscles (please refer to the chapter on Exercise Prescription).

Throughout the AA phase, the scope of the program is to involve most, if not all, muscle groups in a multilateral type of program. Such a program should have a high number of exercises, 9–12, performed **comfortably**, without "pushing" the athletes. Remember, vigorous strength training always develops the strength of the muscles faster than the strength of the muscle attachments (tendons), and joints (ligaments) to withstand the strain of heavy loads. Consequently such programs often result in injuries of tendons and ligaments.

Many injuries also occur when large muscle groups are weak and as a result the small muscles take over the strain of the work. As a result, small muscle groups may injure faster. Other injuries also occur not because of lack in landing skills, but rather the force to control it, to absorb the shock, to balance the body quickly and be ready to perform another athletic action.

The duration of the AA phase is a function of several elements: the length of the preparatory phase, the athlete's background in strength training, and the importance of strength in that sport. A long preparatory phase always allows more time to work on the anatomy of the athlete. Similarly, athletes with a weak strength training background logically require a much longer AA so that they will progressively adapt to training loads, improving at the same time the ability of the muscle tissue and muscle attachments to withstand the heavier loads of the following phases. And finally, as compared to sports where strength training is less important (such as marathon running), a well planned and longer AA will influence the final performance and will hopefully produce an **injury free athlete**.

For young, **inexperienced athletes, 8–10 weeks** of AA is necessary. On the other hand, a **mature athlete**, with 4–6 years of strength training background does not require more than **3–5 weeks** of the AA phase. Anything longer than that might not have any significant training effect, and therefore can be a loss of time.

MAXIMUM STRENGTH PHASE

The **main objectives** of this phase is to **develop the highest level of force** possible as well as muscle tone.

Most sports require either power (i.e., long jumper), muscular endurance (i.e., 800–1500 m swimming), or both (i.e., rowing, canoeing, wrestling, and team sports). Each of these two types of strengths are affected by the level of MxS. Without a high level of MxS, P cannot reach high standards. Therefore, since P is the product of speed and MxS, it is logical to first develop MxS and then convert it into P. During this phase the objective is to develop MxS to the highest level of the athlete's capacity.

The **duration** of this phase **(1–3 months)** is a function of the sport/event, and the athlete's needs. For a shot putter or football player it may be quite long (3 months) as opposed to an ice hockey player who may allocate only a month for the development of this type of strength.

Since the load is increased in steps, normally three, the **duration of the maximum strength phase has to be a multiple of three**. As such, and considering the above examples, a shot putter, or a linemen, may have either 9, 12, or even 15 weeks of maximum strength. On the other hand a hockey or soccer player may need only 6, or a maximum 9 weeks of maximum strength.

The duration of this phase also depends on whether an athlete has to follow a mono, or a bi-cycle annual plan. For obvious reasons, young athletes may have a shorter maximum strength phase, with loads below maximum.

CONVERSION PHASE

The **main purpose** of this phase is to convert or to **transform gains in MxS into competitive, sport specific combinations of strength**. As such, depending on the characteristics of the sport/ event, MxS has to be **converted** into either a type(s) of P, M-E, or both.

By applying the adequate training method for the type of strength sought, and through the application of training methods specific to the selected sport (i.e., speed training), MxS is gradually converted. Throughout the duration of this phase, depending on the needs of the sport and the athlete, a certain level of MxS still has to be maintained, otherwise towards the end of the competitive phase P may slightly decline (detraining). This is certainly the case for professional football and baseball players who have such a long season.

For sports where P or M-E is the dominant strength ingredient, the appropriate method has to be dominant in training. When both P and M-E are required, an adequate training time and method(s) should reflect the optimal ratio between these two abilities. For instance, for a wrestler the ratio has to be almost equal. In a canoer's (500 m) program, P should dominate, while for a rower M-E should prevail.

For team sports, martial arts, wrestling, boxing, and most other power-dominant sports, during the conversion phase, often even prior to that, the coach must plan exercises leading to the development of agility, reaction time, and movement time. Only such an approach would prepare the athletes for the sport-specific requirements of competitions.

The duration of the conversion phase depends on the ability to be developed. For the **conversion to P, 4–5 weeks** of specific power training is sufficient. On the other hand, **conversion to M-E** takes a much longer time, **6–8 weeks**, since the physiological and anatomical adaptation to such demanding work takes much longer.

MAINTENANCE PHASE

In many sports the tradition is that as the competitions/ games start, strength training is eliminated from the athletes' overall program. If strength training is not maintained during the competitive phase the athlete will be exposed to a **detraining effect**, with all its negative elements:

1. muscle fibers decrease to their pre-training size (Thorstenson, 1977; Staron et al., 1981);

2. some elements of detraining can be observed in 5–6 days of no training. In **two weeks time detraining can become evident:** skills requiring strength are not performed as proficiently as before (Bompa, 1990);

3. decrease of motor recruitment pattern, and the **loss of power** becomes more visible. The body fails to recruit the same number of motor units that it once could. Thus there is a **net decrease in the amount of force** that can be generated (Edgerton, 1976; Hainaut and Duchatteau, 1989; Hammard, 1991);

4. decrease in speed followed by **decrease of power,** since muscle tension depends on the force and speed of stimuli and firing rate.

As the term suggests the **main objective** of strength training for this phase is to **maintain the standards achieved during the previous phases.** Once again the program followed during this phase is a function of the specific requirements of the sport. The ratio between MxS, P, and M-E has to reflect such requirements. For instance, a shot putter may plan two sessions for MxS and two for P while a jumper may consider one and three respectively. Similarly, a 100 m swimmer may plan one session for MxS, two for P and one for M-E, while a 1500 m swimmer may dedicate the entire strength program to perfecting M-E.

For team sports the ratio should also be calculated according to the role of strength in that sport as well as being position-specific. For instance a pitcher should perform equally: MxS, P, and power-endurance. Similarly, compensation work should also be considered in order to avoid injuries of the rotator cuff.

Distinctions should also be made between linemen and wide receivers in football, and swippers and midfielders and forwards in soccer. The former have to spend equal time for MxS and P, the receivers just P, whereas the latter group of soccer players have to maintain both power and power-endurance.

The **number of sessions** dedicated to the maintenance of the required strength has to be **between 2–4**, depending on the athlete's level of performance, and the role played by strength in the skill and performance. Considering the objectives of the competitive phase, the time allocated to the maintenance of strength is secondary. Therefore, the coach has to develop a very efficient and specific program. Two to a maximum of four exercises involving the prime movers may suffice the needs of maintaining previously reached strength levels. At the same time the duration of each strength **training session** has to be **short: 30–60 minutes.**

THE CESSATION (C) PHASE. **Prior (5–7 days)** to the **main competition** of the year the strength training program is ended, so that all energies are saved for the accomplishment of a good performance.

TRANSITION PHASE

Traditionally the last phase of the annual plan is inappropriately called "off-season", but in reality it represents a transition from one annual plan to another. **The main goal** of this phase is (through a decreased volume, and especially intensity) to **remove the fatigue** acquired during the annual plan, and to **replenish the exhausted energy stores**. Furthermore, during many months of training and competitions, the athletes were exposed to many psychological and social stressors which drains the mental energies of most athletes. Consequently, during the transition phase the athletes have time to **relax psychologically** by being involved in varied physical and social activities which are enjoyable, and fun.

For the serious athlete, **the duration** of this phase should not be longer than **4–6 weeks**, otherwise many **fitness benefits will fade away**. An athlete works hard to make gains in skills, general fitness, and strength. If a real "off-season", for longer time is considered, then **detraining**, or the loss of most training gains, will be experienced, deteriorating most of the strength gains. Therefore the athlete and coach should not forget that strength "is hard to gain but easy to lose".

If during the transition phase athletes do not perform any strength training at all, and especially if they have a real "off-season", **muscles may decrease in size** together with a considerable **loss in power** (Wilmore and Costill, 1988). And since power and speed are interdependent, loss of speed will be experienced as well. Some authors claim that the disuse of muscles also reduces the frequency of neuromuscular stimulation and the pattern of muscle fiber recruitment. Therefore, **strength loss may be the result of not activating some muscle fibers**.

Although, during transition, physical activity is reduced by 60–70%, one still should find the time to work on **antagonistic**, **stabilizers**, and other muscles which eventually might not be involved in the performance of a skill. Similarly, **compensation exercises** should be planned for sports where there is an imbalance between parts, or size of the body, such as in pitching, throwing events, archery, soccer (work upperbody), cycling, etc.

DETRAINING

The improvement, or maintenance of a desired level of strength is possible only if an adequate load, or training intensity is constantly administered. When strength training is decreased or ceased, such as often is the case during the competitive or a long transition phase, there is a disturbance in the biological state of the muscle cell and bodily organs. As a result, there is a **marked decrease in the athlete's physiological well-being and work output** (Kuipers and Keizer, 1988; Fry et al., 1991).

The state of decreased or diminished training, can leave the athlete vulnerable to the "detraining syndrome" (Israel, 1972) or "exercise-dependency syndrome" (Kuipers and Keizer, 1988). The severity of strength loss depends on the time elapsed between the last and the next training session. Many organic and cellular adaptation benefits, including the increments of the protein content of myosin, may be degraded.

When training proceeds as planned, the body uses protein to build and repair damaged tissues. However, when in a state of disuse, the body increases the process of **protein degradation**. Thus, it starts to breakdown some of the gains that were made during training. At this point, the body starts to catabolize protein, meaning that there is an **increase in the degradation of protein** (Edgerton, 1976; Appell, 1990).

Testosterone levels, whose presence in the body is so important for gains in strength, have also been shown to **decrease as a result of detraining**, which consequently may have a diminished effect on the amount of protein synthesis (Houmard, 1991).

The rise of psychic disturbances such as headaches, insomnia, the feeling of exhaustion, increased tension, increased mood disturbances, lack of appetite and psychological depression are among the usual symptoms associated with total abstinence from training. Each athlete may develop anyone of these symptoms or a combination of them. Whatever the case may be, all these symptoms have something in common with the lowered levels of testosterone and beta-endorphine, a neuro-endocrine compound, the main forerunner to euphoric post-exercise feelings (Houmard, 1991).

The symptoms are not pathological and can be reversed, if training resumes shortly. However, if the cessation of training continues for a prolonged period of time, the athlete may in fact display these symptoms for sometime, indicating the inability of the human body and its systems to adapt to the state of inactivity. The length of time needed for these symptoms to incubate will vary from athlete to athlete, but in general, they can appear after 2–3 weeks of inactivity and vary in severity.

The **decrease in the muscle fiber cross-sectional area** is quite apparent after several weeks of inactivity. These changes are the result of protein breakdown, as well as a reduction in the recruitment pattern of the working muscle. The increased levels of some chemicals ($Na+$ and $Cl-$) in the muscle, plays a role in the **breakdown of muscle fiber** (Appell, 1990).

The general trend of the degeneration of the muscle fiber is partly due to the **degeneration of the motor units, where ST fibers are usually the first to lose their ability to produce force**. FT fibers, on the other-hand, are generally least affected by the state of inactivity. This is not to say that their atrophy does not occur— they just take a little longer than ST muscle fibers. For an inactive athlete, the rate of **strength loss per day can be roughly 3-4%** for the first week (Appell, 1990). For some athletes, especially in power-speed dominant sports, this can be a substantial loss.

The **reduction in speed** tends to be the first to be affected by detraining since the breakdown of protein and the degeneration of motor units decreases the power capabilities of muscle contraction. Another reason for speed loss is perhaps due to the sensitivity of the nervous system to detraining. Since the motor unit itself is the first thing that deteriorates, the muscle fiber has a reduction in the nerve impulses to make it contract and relax at very rapid rates. The strength and frequency of these impulses can also be affected by lowering the total number of motor units recruited during a series of repeated contractions (Edgerton, 1976; Hainaut and Duchateau, 1989; Houmard, 1991).

As a result of diminished motor recruitment patterns, the loss in power becomes more prominent. The **body fails to recruit the same number of motor units** that it once could, resulting in a **net decrease in the amount of force** that can be generated.

VARIATIONS OF PERIODIZATION OF STRENGTH

In the early part of this chapter, as well as through Figure 33, the basic concept of periodization of strength was presented. However, it is known that a basic concept cannot be a model for every situation or sport. Athletes' strength training background, specific characteristics of sports/ events, as well as gender differentiations, requires specific treatment of each group. This is why it was necessary to develop this section on variations of periodization with its follow-up illustrations of specific periodization models for sports/ events.

In athletics there are sports, or specific positions in team sports, which require not only strength or power, but also a heavy mass. As such, for linemen in football, some throwing events in track and field, and heavyweight categories in wrestling and boxing, it is an advantage to be both heavy and display a great deal of power. Therefore these types of athletes would follow a different model of periodization, where a phase of training to develop hypertrophy is planned (please also refer to the chapter on training methods; specifically hypertrophy training).

The development of hypertrophy first, seems to faster increase one's strength potential, especially if it is followed by MxS and P development phases. The latter are recognized to stimulate motor units activation and to increase the recruitment of FT muscle fibers.

Preparatory				Competitive	Trans.
AA	Hyp.	MxS	Con. to P	Maintenance: - Power - MxS	Compen.

FIGURE 34. A periodization model for athletes requiring hypertrophy.

Figure 34 suggests a periodization model for heavy and powerful athletes, such as throwers and linemen in football. After the traditional anatomical adaptation (AA) there is a phase of hypertrophy (Hyp) of at least 6 weeks, followed by MxS and conversion to power (Con. to P). Considering the needs of the above athletes, during the maintenance phase the time should be equally dedicated to preserve P and MxS. The yearly plan concludes with compensation training, specific for the transition phase.

For the same types of sports, there can also be the situation where the preparatory phase is very long (i.e. US/ Canadian college football) and the coach decides to build even more muscle mass. For such a situation another model can be followed (Figure 35), where phases of hypertrophy alternate with phases of MxS. Please note that in the top corner there are digits to indicate the duration in weeks for each phase.

Preparatory								Competitive	Trans.
3 AA	7 Hyp.	6 MxS	3 H	3 MxS	3 H	3 MxS	3 Con. to P	Maintenance: P/MxS	Compen.

FIGURE 35. A variation of periodization for development of hypertrophy and MxS.

Although, strength training for female athletes follows a similar pattern as their male counterparts, during long phases of MxS they need more individual variations, more frequent changes, and shorter phases. Figure 36 illustrates such a periodization in which the preparatory phase is longer, assuming either a summer sport (track) or a sport played during winter and early spring (volleyball), therefore the long preparatory phase.

Preparatory							Competitive		Trans.
7	6	3	3	3	3	4		16	6
AA	MxS	P	MxS	P	MxS	Con. P	Maintenance:	P	Compen.

FIGURE 36. A hypothetical periodization for female athletes who might require more frequent alternations of training phases.

For sports where power is dominant, similar variations of P and MxS phases are necessary since **gains in power are faster if muscles are trained at various speeds of contractions**, as opposed to being trained at the same load (Buhrle and Schmidtbleicher, 1981; Buhrle, 1985). In addition, both **P and MxS trains the FT fibers,** resulting in more **effective recruitment** of these fibers, which are determinant in the production and display of MxS and P.

As compared to the traditional work to exhaustion proposed by coaches influenced by bodybuilding, where lots of pain does not result in power gain, this type of periodization is superior because it **trains the nervous system to improve synchronization and quick recruitment of FT fibers**. The outcome is great increments in MxS and P.

The alternation of MxS and P phases also change the **pattern of motor recruitment, resulting in higher CNS stimulation**, especially during the **P phase**, or when the load for **MxS is over 85%**. Maximum loads for the development of MxS, using eccentric contraction and explosive power exercises, such as high impact plyometrics, results in the recruitment of more FT fibers for the maximum benefit of the athletes involved.

Long phases of MxS represent a CNS stimulus in its early stages only. If the same methods and loading pattern are maintained for a period longer than two months, especially for athletes with a strong background in strength training, the **pattern of fiber recruitment becomes standard, resulting in an eventual plateau**. No drastic improvements from such an approach is to be expected. As far as applying bodybuilding methods is concerned, the employment of submaximum loading will definitely not stimulate the FT muscle fibers nor result in the development of MxS and P. **For sports where speed and power are the dominant abilities bodybuilding methods defeat their purpose**. That explains why Figure 35, 45, 48–53, and others, propose alternations of MxS and P phases. Also, one should not underestimate the importance of MxS phases, since any of its deterioration would affect the ability to maintain power at the desired level throughout the competitive phase.

103

There are, however, sports where a bi-cycle annual plan is followed, where the athletes have to peak twice per year, such as in swimming, track and field and others. Figure 37 illustrates the periodization of strength for a double-peak annual plan.

OCT	NOV	DEC	JAN	FEB	MAR	APR	MAY	JUN	JUL	AUG	SEP
Prep. I			Compet. I		T	Prep. II		Compet. II			Trans.
AA	MxS		Con. P	Maint.		AA	MxS	Con. P	Maint.		Comp.

FIGURE 37. Periodization of Strength for a bi-cycle.

For sports with a long preparatory phase, such as in softball, football, and track cycling, another option of periodization is possible. In fact such a periodization was tested by this author with both a football team and a sprinter in cycling. It should be stated that the experiment was very successful, all the athletes increased their MxS and P to the highest level ever. The coach of the football team requested the assistance to improve MxS and P of his players. Previous programs did not meet his expectation of increasing muscle mass, MxS and P. The proposal made to the coach was to follow a double-peak periodization (Figure 38), where the first peak was an **"artificial peak"**, whereas the second was the real one, the peak for the football season. This new approach for a typical mono-cycle sport, was based on the fact that:

1. a very long preparatory phase, with training methods using heavy loading was considered too stressful, with low variety, and therefore with doubtful physiological incentives, and;

2. a **double-peak** periodization had the advantage of planning **two phases of MxS and two for P**. The benefits were what the coach had expected: increase in overall muscle mass, increase in maximum strength, and the highest level of power ever achieved by his players (Linemen had followed a slight different approach, where hypertrophy training was incorporated in the MxS phase).

DEC	JAN	FEB	MAR	APR	MAY	JUN	JUL	AUG	SEP	OCT	NOV
Preparatory									Compet.		Trans.
AA	MxS		Conv. P.	T	AA	MxS		Conv. P.	Maint. P/MxS		Comp.

FIGURE 38. A double-peak periodization, where peak performance was achieved at the end of April ("artificial peak") and in the fall.

PERIODIZATION MODELS FOR SPORTS

In order to make this book more practical, and this chapter more applicable, several periodization models for strength are presented. For a better understanding of the physiological implications of each sport, before a periodization model is suggested, three factors are mentioned:

1. **the dominant energy system(s)** for that sport;
2. **limiting factor(s) for performance** from the strength training point of view; and,
3. **objective(s) for strength training.**

For training purposes, the reader should **link the energy systems with the limiting factors for strength.** In doing so it will be relatively easy to decide the strength training objectives. For instance, sports where the anaerobic alactic system is dominant, the limiting factor for performance is power. If, on the other hand, the lactic acid or aerobic system is dominant, such a sport always requires a certain component of M-E. In this way the coach will be able to better train the athlete physiologically, and as a result, to improve performance (e.g. one should never expect increments in power if bodybuilding methods are applied). The terms **"limiting factors for performance" should mean that if one fails to develop them at the highest level possible, the desired performance will not be achieved.** A low level of development of the sport-specific combination of strength will limit, or will hinder the achievement of a good performance.

The examples provided below cannot consider all the variations possible for each sport. In order to develop such a model it is necessary to know the exact competition schedule a coach has selected. Therefore, for some sports, such as track and field (athletics) and swimming, periodization models are made around the main competition for winter and summer. Some examples will also be given for some specific positions in team sports (e.g. football and soccer) without exhausting all the possibilities.

1. ATHLETICS (Track and Field)

a) Sprinting
- the dominant energy system: anaerobic alactic and lactic
- limiting factors for performance: reactive, starting, andm acceleration power; power-endurance
- training objectives: maximum strength; reactive, starting, acceleration power, and power-endurance

OCT	NOV	DEC	JAN	FEB	MAR	APR	MAY	JUN	JUL	AUG	SEP
Prep. I				Comp. I		T	Prep. II		Comp. II		Trans.
5 AA	6 MxS		4 Conv. P	10 Maint. -improve P/ specific P		2 AA	5 MxS	4 Conv. P	9 Maint. -improve P/ specific P		6 Comp.

FIGURE 39. A suggested periodization model for strength for a sprinter (specific P = those listed above under "limiting factors").

b) **SHOT PUT**
- the dominant energy system: anaerobic alactic
- limiting factors for performance: throwing power; reactive power
- training objectives: maximum strength; throwing power; reactive power

OCT	NOV	DEC	JAN	FEB	MAR	APR	MAY	JUN	JUL	AUG	SEP
Prep. I				Comp. I		T	Prep. II		Comp. II		Trans.
3 AA	5 Hyp	6 MxS Hyp	3 Con.	8 Maint. -MxS -Hyp -Improve P		2 A A	3 Hyp	4 MxS Hyp	2 Con.	10 Maint. -MxS -Improve P	6 Comp.

FIGURE 40. A suggested periodization model for shot-put. Please note that hypertrophy training follows AA and has to be maintained in some places, but at a ratio of 3 MxS and 1 hypertrophy.

2. **BASEBALL** (professional team)

- the dominant energy system: anaerobic alactic
- limiting factors for performance: throwing and acceleration power
- training objectives: maximum strength; throwing power, acceleration power

DEC	JAN	FEB	MAR	APR	MAY	JUN	JUL	AUG	SEP	OCT	NOV
Prep.			Pre-comp.	Competitive							Trans.
4 AA	6 MxS		4 Conv. P	Maintenance: P, P-E							Comp.

FIGURE 41. A suggested periodization model for baseball. Since the competition phase is very long, detraining of strength may occur, therefore players have to maintain not only P but as much as possible MxS as well.

106

3. BASKETBALL (professional and college team)

- the dominant energy system: anaerobic lactic; aerobic
- limiting factors for performance: take-off power, acceleration power, and power-endurance
- training objectives: maximum strength, take-off power; acceleration power, power-endurance

AUG	SEP	OCT	NOV	DEC	JAN	FEB	MAR	APR	MAY	JUN	JUL
Prep.			Competitive							Trans.	
3 AA	MxS	6 3 Con. P	Maintenance: P, P-E							Comp.	

FIGURE 42. A suggested periodization model for a professional team.

JUL	AUG	SEP	OCT	NOV	DEC	JAN	FEB	MAR	APR	MAY	JUN
Preparatory			Competitive							Trans.	
AA	6 MxS	6 4 Conv. P	Maintenance: P, P-E							Compens.	

FIGURE 43. A periodization model for a college team.

4. BOXING

- dominant energy system: anaerobic lactic; aerobic
- limiting factor for performance: power-endurance, reactive power, M-E medium, M-E long (especially for professional boxers)
- training objectives: power-endurance, reactive power, M-E medium and long

SEP	OCT	NOV	DEC	JAN	FEB	MAR	APR	MAY	JUN	JUL	AUG
Prep.		Spec. Prep.	M T	Prep.	Spec. Prep.	M T	Prep.		Spec. Prep.	M	Trans.
3 AA	3 3 MxS Con	Maint. P/M-E	6 2 AA MxS	3 Con. P	3 Maint.	7 2 AA MxS	3 3 Con. P	Maint.		8	Comp.

FIGURE 44. A hypothetical periodization model for boxing (Spec. Prep. = specific preparatory for a match; M = match) Note: MxS at 60-80% of 1RM.

5. FIGURE SKATING

- dominant energy system: anaerobic lactic; aerobic
- limiting factor for performance: take-off power, landing power, power-endurance
- training objectives: specific power, MxS

MAY	JUN	JUL	AUG	SEP	OCT	NOV	DEC	JAN	FEB	MAR	APR
Preparatory						Competitive					Trans.
AA	11	3 MxS	3 P	3 MxS	4 P/P-E	3 MxS	6 Conv. P/P-E		Maint.	10	7 Comp.

FIGURE 45. A suggested periodization model for figure skating. Please note the alternation of phases for MxS with P/P-E.

6. FOOTBALL (professional and college team)

a) LINEMAN
- dominant energy system: anaerobic alactic and lactic
- limiting factors for performance: starting power, reactive power
- training objectives: MxS, hypertrophy, starting power, reactive power

APR	MAY	JUN	JUL	AUG	SEP	OCT	NOV	DEC	JAN	FEB	MAR
Preparatory					Competitive						Trans.
AA 4	Hyp. 6	MxS 6		Conv. P. 4	Maintenance: MxS, P						Comp. 6

FIGURE 46. A suggested periodization model for a linemen for a professional football team.

MAR	APR	MAY	JUN	JUL	AUG	SEP	OCT	NOV	DEC	JAN	FEB
Preparatory						Competitive					Trans.
AA 4	Hyp. 6	MxS		9	Conv. P. 4	Maintenance: MxS, P					Comp. 7

FIGURE 47. A suggested periodization model for a linemen for a college football team.

108

b) WIDE RECEIVERS, DEFENSIVE BACKERS, TAIL BACKS

- dominant energy system: anaerobic alactic and lactic
- limiting factors for performance: acceleration, reactive, and starting power
- training objectives: acceleration, reactive, and starting power, MxS

APR	MAY	JUN	JUL	AUG	SEP	OCT	NOV	DEC	JAN	FEB	MAR
Preparatory					Competitive						Trans.
AA	MxS 3	P 2	MxS 3	P 2	MxS 3	Conv. P 4	Maintenance: P					Comp. 6

FIGURE 48. A suggested periodization model for a professional team (the above listed players).

MAR	APR	MAY	JUN	JUL	AUG	SEP	OCT	NOV	DEC	JAN	FEB
Preparatory						Competitive					Trans.
AA	MxS 3	P 3	MxS 3	P 3	MxS 3	Conv. P 4	Maintenance: P				Comp. 7

FIGURE 49. A suggested periodization model for strength for a college team (for the above listed players).

7. ICE HOCKEY

- dominant energy system: anaerobic lactic, aerobic
- limiting factors for performance: acceleration, deceleration power, power-endurance
- training objectives: MxS, acceleration, deceleration power, power-endurance

JUN	JUL	AUG	SEP	OCT	NOV	DEC	JAN	FEB	MAR	APR	MAY
Preparatory				Competitive							Trans.
AA 4	MxS 6	P 3	MxS 3	Conv. P/P-E 6	Maintenance: P, P-E, MxS				23		Comp. 8

FIGURE 50. A suggested periodization model for ice hockey.

8. MARTIAL ARTS

- dominant energy system: anaerobic alactic and lactic, aerobic
- limiting factors for performance: starting power, power-endurance, reactive power, M-E medium
- training objectives: starting, reactive, power-endurance, M-E

JUN	JUL	AUG	SEP	OCT	NOV	DEC	JAN	FEB	MAR	APR	MAY
Preparatory							Competitive				Trans.
4	3	2	3	3	3	3	3	6			7
AA	MxS	P	MxS	P	MxS	P	MxS	Conv. P	Maintenance: P		Comp.

FIGURE 51. A periodization model for martial arts.

9. ROWING

- dominant energy system: aerobic
- limiting factors for performance: M-E medium and long, starting power, MxS
- training objectives: M-E, P, MxS

SEP	OCT	NOV	DEC	JAN	FEB	MAR	APR	MAY	JUN	JUL	AUG
Preparatory							Competitive				Trans.
	6	9	3	3	3	3		8		10	7
AA		MxS	P	MxS	P	MxS	Conv. to M-E		Maint. M-E/P		Comp.

FIGURE 52. A periodization model for rowing where the major regatta is in July.

10. SWIMMING

a) SPRINTING

- dominant energy system: anaerobic alactic and lactic; aerobic (for 100m)
- limiting factor for performance: P, power-endurance, M-E short
- training objectives: P, M-E shorts, MxS

110

SEP	OCT	NOV	DEC	JAN	FEB	MAR	APR	MAY	JUN	JUL	AUG
Preparatory				Comp. I		T	Prep. II	Comp. II			Trans.
AA [4]	MxS [6]	P [3] MxS [3]	Conv. P/P-E [4]	Maint. P, P-E M-E [7]		[2] AA [3]	MxS [6]	Conv. P/P-E M-E [4]	Maint. P, P-E M-E [7]		Comp. [7]

FIGURE 53. A suggested periodization model for a national class sprinter in swimming (bi-cycle).

b) LONG DISTANCE

- dominant energy system: aerobic
- limiting factors for performance: M-E long
- training objectives: M-E long, power-endurance

SEP	OCT	NOV	DEC	JAN	FEB	MAR	APR	MAY	JUN	JUL	AUG
Prep. I				Comp. I		T	Prep. II		Comp. II		Trans.
AA [5]	MxS [3]	M-E [3]	MxS [3]	Conv. M-EL [6]	Maint. M-E [6]	AA [4]	MxS [3]	Conv. M-EL [6]	Maint. M-E [7]		Comp. [6]

FIGURE 54. A periodization model for national class long distance swimmer.

c) MASTER ATHLETE (short distances)

- dominant energy systems: anaerobic lactic, aerobic
- limiting factors for performance: power-endurance
- training objectives: P

OCT	NOV	DEC	JAN	FEB	MAR	APR	MAY	JUN	JUL	AUG	SEP
Preparatory							Competitive				Trans.
AA [13]		MxS [3]	P [3]	MxS [3]	P [3]	MxS [3]	Conv. P/P-E [6]	Maint. P/P-E [10]			Comp. [8]

FIGURE 55. A periodization model for strength for volleyball.

11. VOLLEYBALL

- dominant energy systems: anaerobic alactic and lactic (aerobic)

111

- limiting factors for performance: reactive power, power endurance, M-E medium
- training objectives: P, M-E, MxS

JUN	JUL	AUG	SEP	OCT	NOV	DEC	JAN	FEB	MAR	APR	MAY
Preparatory					Competitive						Trans.
AA	MxS 6	P 3	MxS 3	Conv. P, P-E M-E 7	Maintenance: P, P-E						Comp.

FIGURE 56. A periodization model for strength for volleyball.

CHAPTER ELEVEN

LONG-TERM PERIODIZATION OF STRENGTH FOR JUNIOR ATLETES

It is widely recognized that a good background of several years of strength training will assist in advancing faster through the progression of strength and power exercises. This experience is also an important factor in preventing injuries.

A long term strength training program, with a specific progression, is an important requirement, for avoiding the negative effects of using heavy loads at an early age, such as depressing normal skeletal growth. At the same time it is critical to teach children the correct lifting techniques, and to **prevent the development of muscular imbalance**. By planning several years of anatomical adaptation, the young athletes will progressively develop for future stress the tendons, ligaments, and connective cartilages. In this way the coach will categorically improve his/her chances of training an injury-free athlete.

Figure 57 recommends a long-term progression for strength training in which forms of training, training methods, volume, intensity, and means of training are suggested for athletes over the stages of development. Please note that pre-puberty is regarded as the "initiation phase" in sports and training in general. This means that pre-pubescent children, approximately between 6–11(12) years old, where some individual variations of growth and development exists, should start to be initiated in sports and training in general.

Although this section of the book will focus mainly on puberty and post-puberty as related to strength training, a few remarks should be made for pre-pubescence.

The early age of a child's involvement in sport is crucial for his/ her future in an athletic lifestyle. A positive experience, with a great deal of fun and enjoyment, means a child dedicated to sports for the rest of his/ her life. This is why coaches working with pre-pubescent athletes should be very careful with regard to the type of program they organize, its difficulty, and the overall physical and psychological stress.

Strength training, as part of an overall training program, should be carefully selected and organized, where the main goal should be AA. Exercises selected for the general strength development of this age should mostly use medicine balls (MB), and own body weight. Such exercises can be organized following a circuit training (CT) method, very informal, and without any regimentation. The work performed should not cause any **discomfort** or **pain**. On the contrary, it should be fun, and often performed in a playful way. Relays using light MB (2kg/ 5lbs) are both exciting and stimulating. They can be carried, rolled, or thrown, and used as well in a play environment.

During puberty, or the athletic formation stage, the aim of the athletic program is to create the basis for the future stages, leading to high performance. Post-puberty, on the other hand, represents the stage of specialization, when the athletes specializes in a given sport or event.

In the case of children starting a strength training program at puberty, or slightly later, the following long-term progression is suggested:

- the first 2 years: AA.
- next 2 years: AA and muscle hypertrophy.
- the following 2–3 years: AA, hypertrophy, P.
- the remaining years in athletics: follow the periodization of strength as suggested in chapter 10.

The application of the suggested long-term periodization of strength (Figure 57) is visible in the following two sections: strength training for puberty and for post-puberty.

STRENGTH TRAINING FOR PUBERTY

A training program for pubescence should be viewed as a continuation from pre-puberty, building the foundation of training necessary to specialize an athlete in a given sport. Such a base is paramount for the success aspired by many athletes during the high performance phase. Therefore, puberty should be viewed as an important element in the equation of producing high quality athletes.

Although pubescent children grow rapidly during this stage of development, sometimes 10–12 cm (4–5 inches) per year, adequate strength training is essential for the young athletes. However, the intensity, the loads used for training should be low since hard training during pubescence may affect normal growth, being liable for injuries as well.

From puberty on, strength training for boys and girls will have different dynamics of gains since, as compared to girls, boy's development of sexual organs results in much higher levels of growth hormones (some 10 times higher levels of testosterone). Therefore, boys start looking bigger and stronger, and adequate muscle development may play a stabilizing roll for the fast growing skeleton.

Stages Of Development	Pre-Puberty (Initiation)	Puberty (Athletic Formation)	Post-Puberty (Specialization)	High Performance
Forms of Training	•simple exercises •games/play	•AA •relays •games	•AA •specific strength	•specific
Training Methods	•informal •CT	•CT	•CT •power training	•hypertrophy •MxS •power •M-E
Volume	•low	•low to medium	•medium	•medium •high
Intensity	•very low	•low	•low •medium	•medium •high •maximum
Means of Training	•own body weight •partners •light medicine balls (MB)	•MB •light free weight •tubing	•MB •machines (light) •tubing	•free weights •others

FIGURE 57. A suggested long-term periodization for strength training. (CT = circuit training; MB = medicine balls; tubing = surgical tubing, or rubber cords).

Strength training for puberty should be viewed as part and parcel of overall development. Multilateral training, the development of a high variety of skills and basic motor abilities, such as flexibility, general endurance and speed, is still a very important training goal.

As for strength training the aim of the program is a proportional and harmonious body and musculature development. Except for a very few sports, where high performance is achieved during late puberty and early adolescence, one should resist falling into the trap of specificity. Stressing specificity at this early stage of development of an athlete, means rapid adjustment (adaptation) to it, and as such reaching very good performance at an unnecessary early age. The probability of continuously improving the performance from mid teens to late twenties is rather questionable. Therefore, strength training for pubescence should be viewed as having the goal to further the base of strength for the phase of high performance. And as it was demonstrated during the 1992 Olympic games in Barcelona, most of the medallists were in their late twenties and even early thirties. **Consequently, avoid specificity, work for multilateral development, build a solid base for the future, and equally important, create an environment of fun, enjoyment, and positive physical experience.**

PROGRAM DESIGN

A strength training program designed for pubescence should not only continue but even further apply the four basic laws of strength training. Further work on developing joint flexibility, strengthening the muscle attachments on bones (tendons), continue developing and improving the core area of the body, and work on the stabilizers.

ANATOMICAL ADAPTATION. The development of a **good strength base**, with **harmonious muscles**, to prepare the athlete anatomically for the training stress to be encountered during post-pubescence and especially maturation, is one of the major goals of strength training for this stage. As a direct benefit of such long term progression is the **creation of an injury-free athlete**.

A TRAINING PROGRAM for pubescence represents a more advanced link with the specifics of training for high performance. Although, as compared to pre-pubescence, a coach may employ similar means of training, using approximately the same types of equipment, such as exercises with own body weight, MB and a partner as well as others, the number of repetitions and resistance is slightly more challenging. Exercises with MB have to be continuous, doing mostly throws and relays. In throws the foundation of power is sought, whereas relays will focus on

116

developing speed in an exciting and fun environment. The weight of the balls can be slightly increased: between 2–4 kg (5–9 lbs).

Exercises with dumbbells, and wall pullies can be widely used to develop the base of strength and to further adapt and strengthen the tendons and ligaments.

Since the total amount of work is slightly increased, children will experience some fatigue, especially if they perform in the same day skills of a given sport and some 30 minutes of circuit training for strength development. However, the level of **discomfort should be stopped before pain might be experienced.** Therefore, the instructor should constantly observe his/ her young athletes and learn how much the children can tolerate before high discomfort will be felt.

As a sign of comfortable physical exertion, the moves should look effortless. They should be performed in a relaxed manner, to understand that while the agonistic muscles contract, the antagonistics should be relaxed.

At this stage of training, children can also be exposed to free weights, mostly light barbells available in most gyms. This, however, does not necessarily mean weight lifting, but rather to understand and learn what kind of exercises can be performed with a barbell. The main reason for suggesting barbells and not any sophisticated machines, is because with barbells one can perform a high variety of movements in different positions and planes. Using a barbell one can move easily mimic a skill pattern, which will be sought to be performed during post-pubescence and maturation. However, before attempting to even think about training, one should receive a thorough instruction on **correct lifting techniques.** This is crucial for the avoidance of eventual injuries. As for exercises using gym machines, most of them are not designed for the length of childrens' limbs anyways.

Among the key elements to be considered for basic technical instruction are:

1. teach basic stance, with feet parallel, at shoulder width. This position will guarantee a good base of support, and as such have a good and controlled balance (which means that as an athlete performs, say vertical rowing, he/ she will not lose their balance).
2. lead the lift with head and shoulders. E.g. if the barbell is being lifted from the floor to the chest/ shoulders (in weightlifting this is called "clean") one should concentrate on starting and **leading the move with the head and shoulders.** Do not focus on the barbell: it will nicely follow the upperbody's lead, and flex the arms in the second half of the action. This technical concern will eliminate the fault of "shooting" the legs, leading with the

hips and as such leaving the upper body behind. Such faults can result in low back strains.

Most concerns should relate to multi-joint movements, such as the one above, or performing a half squat. Since half or deep squats are very popular exercises, the progression of teaching is suggested as follows:

1. learn the correct technique without any weights (free squats);
2. place a stick/ broom on the shoulders, hands towards the ends of the stick, in order to learn to balance the barbell to be used in the future;
3. go through the motion by using dumbbells;
4. use just a barbell, with no additional weights attached;
5. use slightly increased loads, while concentrating on a correct technique;

If an instructor is not aware of correct technique, he/ she should learn that from specialists. In any instance, one should understand that the above suggested progression is a long-term proposition. Usually taking a couple of years before a heavier load is used. Normally that refers to late post-puberty. An important note of caution: **improper progression** or the **employment of heavy loads much too soon**, normally **results in improper technical acquisition**, or **causes some anatomical discomforts and strains.**

As children develop a better training background, they have to progressively be exposed to slightly more challenging training loads. In this way their adaptation will reach higher ceilings, illustrated by their increasing capacity to tolerate more work, and progressively increasing their physical potential (superior testing results). In order to achieve that, the load in training has to progressively be increased, following a certain methodology, such as the one suggested below:

1. increase the duration of a training session. Assume that an athlete is training twice a week for one hour. In order to slightly increase the training capacity, the coach will add an additional 15 minutes for each session. Now the children will train 75 minutes, twice a week, or a total gain of 30 minutes per week. Over time, such progressive increments can go up to 90 minutes.

2. increase the number of training sessions per week. Considering that a 90 minute session is long enough for a training session, the new height in training challenge will come from increasing the number of training sessions from 2 to 3 per week.

3. increase the number of repetitions per training session. If for a certain period of time the coach feels that 3 x 90 minutes per week is what his/ her children can tolerate, the next training increment will come from performing more work in 90 minutes training time. This means more technical drills or exercises for physical development. As such the rest interval between drills is slightly decreased and children are challenged to adapt to higher training demands.

4. increase the number of repetitions per set. After exhausting the above three elements of progression, higher training strains will come from increasing the number of repetitions performed per set. In this way the new training task is to progressively adapt a child to perform these increased number of repetitions per set non-stop, without a rest interval between them.

The above proposed methodical progression has to be applied carefully, over longer time. It can take even 2–3 years to increase the load in training from a 2 X 60 minutes to 3 X 90 minutes training sessions per week. The intelligence and experience of a coach will certainly make this a smooth and careful transition.

For **strength training**, the **increment can be from 20 to 30**, and even **40 minutes per session towards the end of pubescence.**

Circuit training methods can satisfy the needs of strength development, with the number of exercises being increased progressively from 6–9 to 10–12 with 8–15 repetitions per exercise.

Individualization has to be strictly adhered to, so that training programs match individual potentials. Similarly, the **rhythm of performing an exercise must be a child's own natural choice**, without additional pressure coming from the instructor. As such the child will find his/ her own way according to individual rhythm of growth and development, which at this age can be drastically different between two individuals of the same age (sometimes at the same chronological age there can be a **difference of 2–4 years in terms of biological age, or biological potential**).

The instructor can use **rewards as a motivational tool.** However, any rewards (e.g. praise for achieving a task) should not be made to the best athlete in the group, and use him/ her as an example, but rather **use it for each individual's self improvement.**

Strength Training for Post-Puberty

The strength training program proposed for pre-pubescence and pubescence were seen as preparatory, as the building of the foundation for the specifics of training to be developed during post-pubescence and maturation. As compared to the training program for pre-puberty, and puberty, when the major scope of training was multilateral, from post-pubescence on it slightly changes. **Progressively, training becomes more**

specific to the needs of the selected sport. With the foundation created during pre-pubescence and pubescence, training for post-pubescence can become sport-specific. With such a background, strength training can diversify to **include power**, and to progressively **use a periodization model** for each competition year.

As a result of increasing the content of growth hormones, mostly for boys, muscle size and strength will be noticeably increased during post-pubescence. From this stage of development on, up to maturation, boys will increase the proportion of their muscles from approximately 27% to about 40% of their total body mass. Certainly, under such circumstances strength will improve drastically. Although the above proportion will be slightly different for girls, they will also improve their strength to much higher standards.

Since post-pubescence is a phase of children's development which incorporates young athletes with a difference in chronological age of 2–3 years, the introduction of specificity of training according to the needs of the selected sport has to be carefully and progressively monitored. Even for children who follow a long-term model, one should not exaggerate specificity of training for this stage.

Multilateral training development has to be maintained during post-pubescence, although the proportions between it and sport-specific training will be progressively altered in favour of specificity. In this way, the tendons and ligaments will constantly be strengthened. Of equal importance is to maintain work for strength improvement and functionality of the core area of the body.

Specificity of strength training has to be viewed as incorporating exercises which should mimic the pattern of the motion performed by the prime movers, motion which has to be angle and plane specific to the technical skills prevailing in the selected sport. However, specificity should be implemented in such a way that it should not disturb the harmonious development of other muscles (antagonists) and organs' functions. As such, the instructor should be constantly concerned to correct the eventual imbalance between body parts, limbs, and muscle groups (agonistic vs. antagonistic muscles).

As the prime movers will progressively be stressed in training, one should constantly pay attention to the strengthening of stabilizers, the limb fixator muscles.

Since strength training diversifies to address to the specific needs of a given sport, different components of strength ought to be developed, such as power and muscular endurance. Specific training methods have to be employed to address such needs. As a direct result, periodization of strength per competitive year has to also be comprehended and implemented.

PROGRAM DESIGN

Following the first 1–2 years of post-pubescence, when pubescent-specific training is still applicable, training becomes more complex. Additional training methods are incorporated using, at the same time, more complex training machines.

As training becomes more intricate, one should be very careful monitoring the stress in training in general, where strength plays an important role. As more power and higher loads are added, intensity of training starts to take a higher toll in the total level of fatigue one is exposed to. Therefore, the instructor must be familiar with the methodology of **how to increase the load in strength training**, according to the following suggestion:

1. **Increase the training load.** According to the principle of progressive increase of load in training, the load is increased in steps, usually three, followed by a regeneration week. In order to adapt to the new load, a training program of similar intensity has to be maintained for approximately a week, followed by a new load increment.

2. **Decrease the rest interval between sets**, say, from 3 to 2:30 minutes.

3. **Increase the number of sets per training session**, especially for the higher percentage of 1RM.

Certainly, the above suggested methodology of increasing the load in training is applied over a longer period of time. In doing so, it is normal to expect that a high percentage, close to 1RM, will be used at the end of post-pubescence and during maturation. Similarly, the number of sets can be increased to 4–6.

As more sport-specific exercises and methods are progressively employed, specificity in strength training becomes dominant as the athlete approaches the stage of high performance. As such, the instructor has to select the type of equipment which best suits the needs of the selected sport. Although some of the machines can be used in certain training phases (e.g. "maximum strength phase"), free weights seem to be more practical since they allow for a greater mechanical similarity with most athletic skills, and provide coordination between different muscle groups. While a proper technique for free weights is more difficult to learn, they allow one to perform moves in various directions and planes, and more importantly, one can duplicate the ballistic nature of sport actions to create a sport-specific acceleration throughout the range of motion. In fact this is one of the most important advantages of free weights.

Since free weights are very popular, in addition to teaching the technique, the instructor should also insure that a **spotter is constantly assisting**, or spotting the performer. In fact the **main objective of spotting is safety**, the **prevention of injuries**.

As the athlete approaches maturation, the methodology of developing strength changes, becomes more complex since the athlete seeks now not just to develop general strength, but rather to train for maximum strength or one of its components: power or muscular endurance.

Figures 58 and 59 refers to training models for post-pubescence (the specialization stage in a selected sport). These suggested models assume a summer competitive phase, which is preceded by a preparatory phase during fall, winter and the months of spring.

It is assumed that strength training follows technical or tactical training. Therefore, it is a complimentary activity, which can have a duration of 30–60 minutes. This is especially the case for the competitive phase. Changes to such a trend can be operated during some segments of the preparatory phase, when a strength training session can be organized outside of technical or tactical training. In either case, the instructor should make sure that the athletes have a comprehensive warm-up.

DATES	OCT	NOV	DEC	JAN	FEB	MAR	APR	MAY	JUN	JUL	AUG
Training Phase		PREPARATORY						COMPETITIVE			
Type of Strength		AA				Power with light implements		Maintenance			
Muscle Groups		All				All/Prime movers		⟶			
Load (% of 1RM)		30–50				30–40		⟶			
# of Reps		8–15				3–6		⟶			
# of Sets		2–3				2		⟶			
Rhythm of Execution		slow-medium				medium-fast		⟶			
Rest Interval		2–5 minutes				3–5		⟶			
Frequency/Week		2–3				⟶				2	

FIGURE 58. A suggested periodization model for strength for an annual plan for the first two years of post-pubescence (early specialization). The horizontal arrows indicate that the program suggested in a given box will be continued in the box from the left.

DATES	OCT	NOV	DEC	JAN	FEB	MAR	APR	MAY	JUN	JUL	AUG
Training Phase	PREPARATORY							COMPETITIVE			
Type of Strength	AA				MxS		Conv. to P	Maintenance			
Muscle Groups	All				prime movers		→	→			
Load (% of 1RM)	40-60				70-80		40-50	→			
# of Reps	6-12				4-6		3-5	→			
# of Sets	3-4				3-5		3-4	2-3			
Rhythm of Execution	slow-medium				slow		fast	→			
Rest Interval	3-4 minutes				3-5		→	→			
Frequency/Week	2-3				→			2			

FIGURE 59. A suggested periodization model for strength for the late post-pubescence (late specialization).

PART 3

TRAINING METHODS AS APPLIED TO PERIODIZATION OF STRENGTH

One who knows training methods can produce successful programs.

Do you want to be successful?

You must know the methods!

CHAPTER TWELVE

TRAINING METHODS FOR ANATOMICAL ADAPTATION AND HYPERTROPHY PHASE

Strength training represents an important element in a coach's quest in producing good athletes. All the athletes involved in competitive sports follow a program which, hopefully, results in peak performance at the time of the main competition(s) of the year. As such, strength training, along with other abilities, has the role of representing the physiological foundation for achieving peak performance.

In order to achieve peak performance the coach has to plan and periodize training in such a way that it ensures improvement of performance from phase to phase, leading to highest levels during the competitive season. The same approach ought to be followed with strength training as well. Consequently, coaches should not see the development of strength as a scope in itself, but rather as modeling it through various phases to **create a final product: the sport-specific strength combination** (Figure 5). And this final product should represent the physiological base for the achievement of peak performance.

As illustrated by Figure 33, strength alters throughout the annual plan according to the concept of periodization of strength. As explained earlier, each sport requires a given type, or sport-specific combination of strength, which should represent the physiological base for performance. The transformation of strength into a sport-specific quality is made possible by applying periodization of strength and by using specific training methods according to the needs of a given strength training phase. Therefore, as training phases change, so do training methods.

The intent of chapters 12–15 is not just to list all the training methods available to the coach, but rather to discuss them as they relate to the periodization of strength. Consequently, each training phase will be taken separately and shown which method best suits that phase as well as the needs of the athlete. An attempt will also be made to explain the positive and negative parts of most methods, how to apply them, as well as to suggest training programs using a given method.

TRAINING METHODS FOR ANATOMICAL ADAPTATION

The scope of the AA phase is to progressively adapt the muscles, and especially muscle attachments to the bone, to easier cope with heavier loads during the following training phases. As such, the overall load in training has to be increased but without experiencing much discomfort. The easiest method to consider for AA is **circuit training (CT)**, mainly because it is a good organizational method, and it alternates muscle groups.

CIRCUIT TRAINING

Although CT can be used to develop both cardio-respiratory endurance, as well as combinations of strength, for the purpose of the AA phase it will be adjusted to serve the development of strength. Other variants will be proposed in the section referring to the development of M-E.

The first variant of CT was proposed by Morgan and Adamson (1959) from Leeds University, and used as a method to develop general fitness. The initial CT considered several stations, arranged in a circle (therefore "circuit training"), in which muscle groups were supposed to constantly alternate from station to station. As CT became more popular other authors provided additional information, probably the best book on the market being written by Scholich, 1992, and edited and published by P. Klavora.

In developing a CT a high variety of exercises can be used, such as: own body weight, surgical tubing, medicine balls, light implements, dumbbells, barbells, and any strength training machines. A circuit may be short (6–9 exercises), medium (9–12 exercises), or long (12–15 exercises). A circuit may be repeated several times, depending on the number of exercises involved. Obviously, the number of circuits, number of repetitions per station, and the load, has to consider the individual's work tolerance and fitness level since during AA the total work should not be so high as to push the athlete to the level of pain or discomfort; individual athletes can have an input in suggesting how much work can be performed.

CT exercises must be selected to **alternate muscle groups**, favouring therefore a better and faster recovery. The rest interval **(RI) between stations** can be anywhere, between **60–90 seconds**, and **1–3 minutes between circuits**. Since in a normal gym there are different apparatuses, workstations, and strength training machines, a high variety of circuits can be created thus constantly challenging athletes' skills, and at the same time keeping the athletes interested.

Considering the general purpose of the preparatory phase, and particularly the scope of AA, exercises should be selected to **develop the core area of the body**, as well as prime movers (please refer to the chapter 18: Exercise Prescription).

CT should not be used as a testing devise or used to make comparisons between the athletes involved mainly because of differing body weights and limb lengths. Therefore competition between athletes is unfair to say the least, since the speed of performance, and degree of flexion/ extension can be so different. On the contrary, achievements could be compared only with the individual athlete's past performance.

PROGRAM DESIGN

Since CT may be used from the first week of AA, the coach should **test for 1RM** in order to **calculate the load** for at least the **prime movers**. The stations of a CT should be selected according to the equipment available in a gym. Depending on one's knowledge and inventivity, a high variety of circuits can be created. In doing so, the coach should follow a certain progression, depending on the level of the athletes' classification and training background. For younger athletes with no strength training background, one can start with exercises using own bodyweight, and overtime progress to exercises using light implements/ weights and then barbells, Universal Gym, and other strength machines. Certainly, for the AA phase exercises have to be selected to involve most muscle groups, irrespective of the needs of the selected sport. Far from exhausting the knowledge in the area, below are exemplified four circuits using various pieces of equipment:

Circuit "A"
(own body weight)

1. Half squat
2. Push-ups
3. Bent-knee sit-ups
4. Two-legs, low hops on spot
5. Back extensions
6. Pull-ups
7. Burpees

Circuit "B"
(using stall bars and gym benches)

1. Step-ups
2. Incline push-ups (palms on bench)
3. Incline, bent-knee sit-ups (toe behind third rung)
4. Chin-ups (gripping the highest rung)
5. Zig-zag jumps over benches (long side)
6. Trunk lifts (hips on a bench, feet under a low rung)
7. Jumping on and off a bench

Circuit "C"
(dumbbells and MB)

1. Half wquats
2. MB chest throws
3. Military press
4. Bent-knee sit-ups (MB held at chet level)
5. MB forward throws (between legs)
6. Lunges
7. Back arches, ball behind the neck
8. Upright rowing
9. Toe raise
10. Trunk rotationns
11. Overhead, backward MB throws
12. Jump squats, and MB throws

Circuit "D"
(barbells/strength machines)
1. Leg press
2. Bench press
3. Incline sit-ups
4. "Good-morning"(hip extension with light load)
5. Upright rowing
6. Leg curls
7. Lats pull-down
8. Sitting bench press
9. Toe raises

The duration of AA, frequency of training sessions per week and other parameters for CT are suggested below for both younger and experienced athletes:

Nr.	Training Parameters	Novice Athletes	Experienced Athletes
1	Duration of AA	8–10 weeks	3–5 weeks
2	Load (if weights are used)	30–40%	40–60%
3	Nr. of stations/circuit	9–12(15)	6–9
4	Nr. of circuits/session	2–3	3–5
5	Total time of CT/session	20–25 min.	30–40 min.
6	Rest interval between exercises	90 sec.	60 sec.
7	Rest interval between circuits	2–3 min.	1–2 min.
8	Frequency/week	2–3	3–4

FIGURE 60. Suggested training parameters for circuit training.

As illustrated by Figure 60 training parameters for experienced athletes are quite different than those for novice. A longer AA phase makes good sense for novice athletes, since they need a longer time for adaptation, and for creating a good base for the future. On the contrary, a much longer AA phase than 3–5 weeks does not result in visible gains for the experienced athletes.

Similar observations can be made for the number of stations per circuit. Since novice athletes have to address as many muscle groups as possible the circuits are longer. Experienced athletes would reduce the number of stations to focus on, mostly exercises for the prime movers, compensation and exercises involving the stabilizers.

The total physical demand per circuit has to be progressively but individually increased. As evidenced in the above example, the load and its pattern of increasing it has to differ between novice and experienced athletes (Figure 61). Novice athletes need better adaptation, therefore the load remains the same for two weeks, for experienced athletes it changes from cycle to cycle.

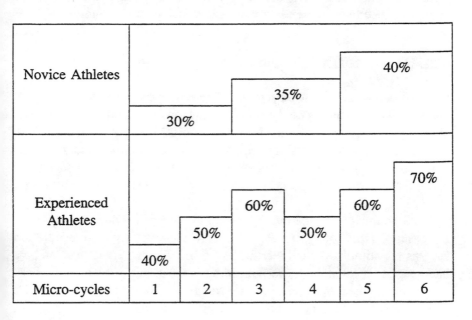

FIGURE 61. A suggested pattern of load increments for CT for novice and experienced athletes.

In order to better monitor improvements in training as well as to constantly calculate the load every three weeks, testing for 1RM is suggested to take place in weeks: 1, 4, and at the end of week 6.

As illustrated by Figure 61, towards the end of the AA phase, the load reaches percentage which allows the athlete to immediately make the transition to the MxS phase. This can be the normal approach for most athletes except for those requiring to increase muscle mass, such as throwers and linemen in football. For such athletes, a hypertrophy phase has to be planned between AA and MxS (please refer to figures 34, 40, 46 and 47).

TRAINING METHODS FOR MUSCLE HYPERTROPHY

The popular view that the larger the body size, the stronger the person is not always a valid statement. For example, a weight lifter may have a smaller body size but is stronger or capable of lifting more heavier loads than a larger, bulky looking bodybuilder. What is necessary in athletics is not exactly a large body size but rather to have a large active body mass, or fat-free body mass. The greater the active body mass, the greater the strength, since **force depends on muscle density and diameter**.

THE HYPERTROPHY (BODYBUILDING) METHOD

The enlargement of muscle size (hypertrophy) is best achieved by applying the methodology of bodybuilding. However, unlike bodybuilders, hypertrophy training for the needs of most sports/ events is focusing mostly on enlarging not the overall musculature but rather on increasing the size of the specific prime movers. The only exception could be the shot-putters, and linemen, where—especially for the latter athletes—total body weight is an asset in the position they play.

Although the application of bodybuilding does produce an important increase of hypertrophy, it does not result in nervous system adaptation such as the stimulation and recruitment of FT fibers. Since this can be a handicap for most athletes, bodybuilding is used only for a certain phase in the development of some athletes' strength (e.g. figures 34, 40, 46–47). However, bodybuilding, without working to exhaustion in each set, can be utilized for novice athletes because it is relatively safe since it employs moderately heavy loads. It can also be applied in sports when one wants to move up a weight class (boxing, wrestling).

The main objective of bodybuilding is to provoke high chemical changes in the muscles, thereby developing muscle mass, which very often is the result of the rise of fluid/ plasma and not necessarily the contracting elements of muscle fibers (the myosin filaments). This is why a bodybuilders' strength is not proportional to their size.

Since bodybuilders do not employ maximum loads this method does not provoke maximum tension in the muscles. And since with the typical submaximum load the athletes contract the muscles to exhaustion, the recruitment of muscle fibers varies: when some begin to fatigue, others start to function.

It is very important in bodybuilding training to reach a maximum number of repetitions within a given set. The number of repetitions can vary between six and twelve. If one uses a lower number of repetitions, one should increase the load and vice-versa.

During exercise, the resistance of a constant weight varies depending on the number of repetitions. Weight which at the beginning of an exercise is felt to be relatively light, with increasing number of repetitions, becomes submaximum and is maximum with the last repetition. With increased fatigue the recruitment and synchronization of motor units is much greater and the physiological benefits are often similar to those observed during lifting heavy weights.

PROGRAM DESIGN

As in any other new training phase, hypertrophy training should **start with a test for 1RM**. The athlete then takes a 70–80% load, or a load which allows him/ her to perform 6 repetitions. As the athlete adapts to the load he/ she will progressively be able to perform more repetitions. When one can perform 12 repetitions, the load is increased again to enable one to perform 6 repetitions.

For maximum training benefits it is important for the athlete to reach the highest number of repetitions he/ she can perform in each set. Therefore, an athlete should always reach a degree of exhaustion which prevents him/ her from doing the last repetition even if the athlete applies maximum contraction. If the individual set is not performed to exhaustion, muscle hypertrophy will not reach the expected level since the first repetitions do not produce the stimulus necessary to increase muscle mass. Therefore, the **key element in hypertrophy training is not just exhaustion per set but rather the cumulative effect of exhaustion in the total number of sets.** This cumulative exhaustion **stimulates the chemical reactions and protein metabolism in the body so that optimal muscle hypertrophy will be achieved.**

The rhythm of performing the exercise is low to moderate. However, athletes from sports where speed-power is dominant, they are strongly advised against slow rhythm of execution, especially if the hypertrophy phase is longer than 4–6 weeks. The main reason being that the neuro-muscular system will adapt to a slow execution and as a result will not represent a stimulation for the recruitment of FT muscle fibers, so crucial for the sports belonging to this group.

Unlike bodybuilding, hypertrophy training for athletics involves a lower number of exercises. This is critical since the scope of training is not to involve all the muscle groups, but mostly the prime movers. Such an approach has the benefit of performing more **sets** per exercise, **4–6**, or even higher (8), and as a result, **stimulating a better muscle hypertrophy for the prime movers**.

No.	Training Parameters	Work
1	Duration of hypertrophy phase	4–6 weeks
2	Load	70–80%
3	# of exercises	6–9
4	# of reps/ set	6–12
5	# of sets/session	4–6 (8)
6	Rest interval	3–5 minutes
7	Rhythm/ speed of execution	slow-medium
8	Frequency/ week	2–4

FIGURE 62. Training parameters for the hypertrophy training phase.

During the **RI**, which is longer than in bodybuilding, **3–5 minutes**, and at the end of the training session, the athletes should **stretch the muscles** they worked on. As a result of many repetitions of contractions, the muscles shorten, which in turn produces premature inhibition of contraction of the antagonistic muscles. As a result, the muscles reduce their range of motion, decrease their quickness of contraction, affecting the overall performance ability of the muscles involved. To overcome that, the athletes should constantly stretch their muscles, to **artificially lengthen them to their biological length**. In addition, **a muscle which is shortened has a slower rate of regeneration**. Only the normal biological length facilitates **active biochemical exchanges**, such as providing nutrients to the muscle and removing the metabolic wastes, and as a result facilitating a better recovery between sets and following training sessions.

VARIATIONS OF BODYBUILDING METHODS. Since repetitions to exhaustion represents the main element of success in bodybuilding several variations from the original method were developed. All of them have the same scope: when exhaustion is reached 2–3 more repetitions have to be obtained through sweat and tears. The expected result is a higher muscle growth, increased hypertrophy.

Of the total number of variations, more than 20(!!) the following are considered to be the most representative:

Split Routine. Since in bodybuilding the athletes perform 2–3 exercises per muscle group and since they address every muscle of the body, one may have to be in the gymnasium for at least half a day if he/she expects to finish the entire program. And even if the athlete may have the energy to do it, time constraints represents an important limitation. Hence, the solution is to divide the total volume of work into parts, addressing each day to one part of the body, therefore the "split routine". Under these conditions, even if an athlete trains 5–6 times per week, an actual muscle group is worked-out only 1–2 times per week.

Assisted Repetitions. As an athlete performs a set to temporary exhaustion of the neuro-muscular system, a partner assists the performer with sufficient support to be able to perform 2–3 more repetitions.

Resistive Repetitions. The athlete performs a set to temporary exhaustion. The partner assists the athlete to perform another 2–3 repetitions concentrically but provides some resistance for the eccentric segment of contraction for each of the additional repetition (therefore "resisted repetitions"). As such, the eccentric part of the contraction is performed twice as long as the concentric one, overloading the muscles involved beyond the standard level.

Athletes performing "resistive repetitions" should know and be cautioned that the longer the active muscle fibers are held in tension, the higher the nervous tension and energy expenditure. If a normal contraction time is 2–4 seconds, a repetition performed against resistance can be 6–8 seconds long, consuming 20–40% more energy (Hartman and Tünnemann, 1989). As the muscles are in longer tension the muscles' metabolism is stronger activated, stimulating the muscle growth beyond the standard norms.

Because of higher demands in training both the "resisted repetitions" and "superset" have to be applied only to athletes with a good and long training background.

Superset represents a method in which the athlete performs a set for the agonistic muscles of a given joint, followed without a rest period by a set for the antagonistic muscles (e.g. elbow flexion followed immediately by elbow extension).

Variation: perform a set to exhaustion, followed after 20–30 seconds by another set for the same muscle group. Of course, due to exhaustion, in the second set the athlete may not be able to perform the same number of repetitions as in the first one.

Cheated Repetitions, normally used for the lack of a partner, refers to performing an exercise to exhaustion. When unable to perform another repetition through the whole range of motion, the athlete tries to compliment the action by jerking another segment of the body towards the performing limb. Example: perform elbow flexions to exhaustion and then jerk the trunk towards the forearm, in this way being able to preform additional tension in an exhausted muscle. Considering the jerking action, one has to "cheat" the muscles in order to maintain a longer contraction time, this method is limited only to certain limbs and exercises.

Pre-exhaustion suggests that: 1)before large muscle groups are contracted the small muscles have to be pre-exhausted so that during the actual work the whole load will be taken only by the large muscle groups, and 2) before performing a set involving 2–3 joints (e.g. half squats), the muscles of a given joint have to be pre-fatigued and then further exhausted in the complete motion of all the other joints.

This method was assumed to evolve from weight lifting, and then used in bodybuilding. However, as with superset, this method is not proven yet, being therefore at the stage of speculation. Bodybuilding books, and especially some magazines, often refer to many other methods, some of them doing . . . miracles for athletes! Therefore, the reader has to be cautious in distinguishing the fine borderline, separating reality from fantasy.

Even if the "split routine" method is employed bodybuilding workouts are very exhausting, often in a training session some 75–160 repetitions are performed. Such a high muscle loading requires a long recovery following a training session. Considering the type of work specific for bodybuilding, most, if not all the ATP/CP and glycogen stores are exhausted following a demanding training session. Although the restoration of ATP/CP occurs very quickly, the exhausted liver glycogen requires some 46–48 hours to replenish. Therefore one logically may assume that heavy workouts to complete exhaustion, ought to be performed not more than 3 times per micro-cycle (please refer to planning the micro-cycles for variations of intensities).

With the employment of "split routine" one may argue that a given group of muscles are trained every second day, and as such there are 48 hours between two training sessions, therefore sufficient time for restoration of energy fuels. Although this may be true for local muscle stores, it disregards the fact that when glucose is exhausted, the body starts tapping the glycogen stored in the liver. And if the same source is tapped everyday, namely the liver, there may not be sufficient time to restore glycogen in 24 hours. As a result, the overtraining phenomena may occur if the recovery phase is too short.

Constant, repetitive training will not only exhaust the energy stores but it also wears and tears the contractile myosins, exceeding their anabolism (the myosins' protein building rate). The undesirable outcome from such overloading can be that the muscles involved no longer increase their size, therefore no gains in hypertrophy. Consequently, one should re-examine the application of the overloading principle and start using the "step-type" method as suggested by the principle of progressive increase of load in training. In addition, the alternation of intensities per micro-cycle should be highly regarded. The alternation of intensities in training, the concern to constantly alter work with regeneration, is equally important as training itself.

As already specified the duration of the hypertrophy phase can be between 4–6 weeks, depending on the needs of the sport/ event and the athlete. Important in this decision is also the total length of the preparatory phase. The longer the preparatory phase, the more time there is to work on hypertrophy as well as on MxS.

Of equal importance is to understand that as the hypertrophy phase is over, it does not mean that an athlete who needs to build muscle mass has to stop it. As illustrated by Figure 63, during the MxS phase hypertrophy training can be maintained and even further developed. As such, depending on the needs of the athlete, the proportion between MxS and hypertrophy can be 3:1, 2:1 or even 1:1.

Preparatory				Competitive
3	4	6		5
AA	Hyp. 3/4 (sessions)	MxS MxS: 2/3 (sessions) Hyp: 1/2 "	Conv. P: 2 (sessions) MxS: 1 " Hyp: 1 "	Maintenance: P, MxS, Hyp (?)

FIGURE 63. A suggested proportion between hypertrophy, MxS, and P for a linemen. Hypertrophy training during the maintenance phase may be used by very few athletes, such as shot-putters and linemen, and only during its first half. As the most important competitions are approaching P and MxS should prevail in training.

CHAPTER THIRTEEN

TRAINING METHODS FOR MAXIMUM STRENGTH PHASE

Almost every single sport requires a certain degree of strength, but, as explained in chapter 2, Figure 5, what sports actually need is a sport-specific combination of strength. Irrespective of the needs of a given sport, in the menu put together to create that sport-specific strength, MxS plays a very important, if not the determinant role. Although variation between sports regarding the role of MxS does exist, most of it refers to the length of the phase. The more important the role of MxS, the longer the phase (e.g. linemen in football). The contrary is true if the final performance does not depend too much on the MxS contribution (e.g. table tennis).

An athlete's ability to generate MxS depends to a high degree on the following factors:

1. **the diameter**, or the cross-sectional area of the muscle involved, more specifically the **diameter of myosin filaments**, including their cross bridges;
2. the **capacity to recruit FT muscle fibers**, and;
3. the ability to successfully **synchronize together all the muscles involved in the action**.

In the first case, the size of a muscle depends to a high degree on the duration of the hypertrophy phase, but the diameter of myosin, and more specifically the **increase in the protein** content in the form of **cross bridges**, specifically **depends on the volume and duration of the MxS phase**.

In the second case, **the capacity to recruit FT fibers**, it particularly depends on training content, in which **maximum loads**, and **explosive power** ought to be dominant. **Only this type of strength training results in the involvement in action of the powerful FT motor units**.

As for the improved **synchronization of the muscles** involved in a strength exercise, it has a **learning component**, which is based on many repetitions of the same exercise, but performed with **heavy loads**.

In practice, especially in North America, most gains in MxS, some two thirds of the total, is based on increased muscle diameter, since most strength specialists and coaches are still too much influenced by bodybuilding methods. What is still quite neglected is the type of training which stimulates the recruitment of FT muscle fibers.

In many cases strength training is based on a high number of repetitions, 12–15, performed to exhaustion. Such a program develops mostly the size of the muscle and to a low degree its quick contraction. However, as illustrated by Figure 64, the **application of force in sports is performed very quickly,** between **100–200 ms** (milliseconds). The **only type of strengths which stimulates** such a **quick application of force is MxS and P**. The curve of force application of such strength components are below 200 ms, approaching 100 ms.

The opposite is true if a variant of bodybuilding is employed. The total amount of strength may be higher than MxS and P, but the force application is longer, over 250 ms, therefore not specific for the needs of the vast majority of sports.

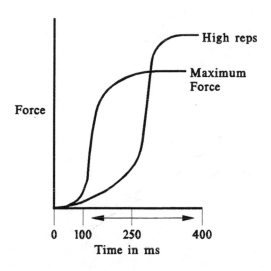

FIGURE 64. The force-time curve of two different weight training program (from Schmidtbleicher, 1984).

Since the application of force in training is very fast, the **main purpose of training is to shift the force-time curve to the left,** or in other words, as close as possible **to the time of the force application (below 200 ms).** Figure 65 illustrates the intent of training, namely that through the **utilization of MxS and P**, the force-time curve can be shifted to the left.

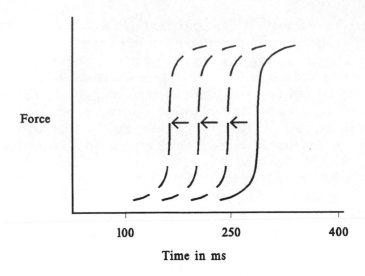

Force

100   250   400

Time in ms

FIGURE 65. The purpose of strength training is to shift the force-time curve to the left.

However, the realization of this shift towards the time of the sport-specific application of force is not achieved quickly. In fact the whole **scope of the periodization of strength** is exactly that: as a result of the **phase-specific strength** training, the **force-time curve is to be shifted to the left** (i.e., decrease execution time) **prior to the commencement of the main games/ competitions. This is the time when the quick application of strength is needed.** This is the time when the athletes will benefit from gains in power. And that is the entire reason why the periodization of strength was created.

As already explained, each training phase of the periodization of strength, has certain objectives. By plotting the force-time curve against each training phase the reader will be able to see from an other angle how training influences the force-time curve. Figure 66 exemplifies the periodization of strength, where a hypertrophy phase is also included. Certainly, there will be only some sports which may use this model, many others will exclude hypertrophy from the annual plan.

Preparatory				Competitive
AA	Hyp.	MxS	Conv. P	Maintenance
100 250 400	100 250 400	100 250 400	100 250	100 250
Remains unchanged	Shifts to the right	Shifts to the left	Shifts to the left	Remains shifted to the left

FIGURE 66. An illustration of how the specifics of training for each training phases influences the force-time curve.

As illustrated by Figure 66, the type of program performed during the AA phase does not influence the force-time curve too much. At worst it may shift it slightly to the right (i.e., increase execution time). However, training methods typical for hypertrophy training increases the total amount of strength training performed, as illustrated by the height of the curve. But because the load is submaximum and each set is performed to exhaustion, therefore not explosive, the curve will shift to the right. As such, gains in muscle size do not translate into gains into the fast application of strength.

From the MxS phase on, due to the utilization of heavy loads, and explosiveness during the conversion of MxS into P, the curve shifts to the left. As the same type of strength training is preserved during the maintenance phase, the curve should remain shifted to the left.

Strength improves as a result of creating high tension in the muscle, and is directly related to the training method employed. Thus **MxS increases as a result of recruiting a great number of FT motor units into the action.** Unlike the popular belief, to become significantly stronger an athlete does not necessarily have to develop large muscles and bodyweight. What is particularly important for an athlete to gain in MxS and P is, through training, to **learn to better synchronize the muscles involved in a movement,** as well as to **utilize loads which result in higher FT muscle fiber recruitment (loads over 80–85%).**

Therefore, as a result of using the methods suggested for the MxS phase, especially the **maximum load method**, the athletes will improve MxS but with insignificant gains in muscle mass.

As discussed in this section of the chapter, the type of contraction employed is critical for the muscle's ability to produce tension. Of the types of contraction that will be refered to, the highest tension is obtained by applying eccentric contraction, followed by isometric, and concentric. However, concentric strength has to be developed at the highest levels since the vast majority of sport actions are performed concentrically. Furthermore, by applying some other types of contraction, especially the eccentric one, it will directly result in improvements of the concentric force for the benefit of athletic performance.

Exercises used for the development of MxS are not carried out under the conditions of exhaustion as in bodybuilding. On the contrary, because of the maximum activation of the CNS, including factors such as maximum concentration and motivation, MxS training improves links with the CNS, which leads to improved muscles coordination and synchronization.

High activation of the CNS (e.g. muscle synchronization) also results into an adequate inhibition of the antagonistic muscles, so that when one applies maximum force these muscles are coordinated in such a way that they do not contract to oppose the movement.

Most **changes in strength** are said to **occur at the level of muscle tissue**. Not much is said, however, about the **involvement into MxS by the nervous system**. In fact very little research has been conducted on the subject. However, there seems to be an increased interest in the implication of the nervous system in strength training, suggesting that the **CNS acts as a stimulus for gains in strength**. The CNS normally inhibits, acts as a restrainer to activate all the motor units available for contraction. Under extreme circumstances, such as fear, or life and death situations, the inhibition is removed and as a result all the motor units are activated (Fox et al., 1989). **One of the main objectives of MxS training is to learn to eliminate CNS inhibition.** Therefore, a reduction in the inhibition of the CNS, duplicated by an increase of strength would result into the highest improvement of one's strength potential.

THE MAXIMUM LOAD METHOD (ISOTONIC)

In the entire concept of the periodization of strength, MxS improved through the **maximum load method (MLM)**, represents one of the, if not the most **determinant factor in the development of other types of strengths** used in the production of sport-specific strength.

The improvement of **MxS** using maximum loads has certain advantages, such as:

1. **increases motor units activation** resulting in **high recruitment of FT muscle fibers.**

2. represents the **determinant factor in increasing P.** As such, it has a high **neural output** for sports where **speed/ power are dominant.**

3. it is a **critical element in improving M-E**, especially M-E of short and medium duration.

4. since it results in minimal increase in hypertrophy, it is **very important** in sports where **relative strength** is crucial, such as in martial arts, boxing, wrestling, jumping events, and in most team sports (relative strength represents the relationship between one's body weight and MxS. The higher the relative strength, the better the performance).

5. **improves** the **coordination and synchronization of muscle groups** during performance. Since in physical actions the muscles are involved in a certain sequence, the MLM has a **learning, neural, component.** The better the coordination and synchronization of the muscles involved in contraction, and the more they learn to recruit FT muscles, the better the performance.

One of the most positive outcomes of the **MLM on speed/ power** dominant sports is an **increase in the number and the diameter of the contracting elements** of the muscle, the **myosins of the FT fibers**, and the **recruitment in greater number of FT fibers.**

MLM can result in gains in MxS far more striking, up to 3 times, than the proportional gain in muscle hypertrophy. More gains in muscle size are possible mostly for athletes who just start experiencing MLM. For athletes with a better background this is less visible, and most gains in MxS occur as a result of better synchronization and increased recruitment of the FT muscles.

The main factors responsible for hypertrophy are not fully understood, although it is increasingly believed that growth in muscle size is stimulated mainly by a disturbance in the equilibrium between consumption and re-manufacturing of ATP. This is called the **"ATP deficiency theory"** (Hartman and Tünnemann, 1989). During and immediately **following a** MxS training, due to the **depletion of ATP**, the **protein content** in the working muscles **is very low**, if not even exhausted. As the athlete is **recovering** between two training sessions, the **protein level exceeds the initial level**, resulting in an **increase in the size of the muscle fiber**, especially if one follows a protein-rich diet.

What this theory means in practice is that muscle stores of ATP/CP should be constantly taxed, not only for gains in hypertrophy, which after a while will level off, but mostly for constant increases of MxS. **Loads of 80–90 % seem to be the most effective.** But of equal importance, however, is also to allow a **long-enough rest interval so that ATP/ CP can be fully restored** (please refer to the "program design" of this chapter). Higher **loads (85–100 %)**, which allows only **2–4 repetitions**, are of short duration, allowing therefore a **complete restoration of ATP.** As such the ATP deficiency and the **depletion of structural protein** is **too small to activate the protein metabolism which stimulates hypertrophy.** Consequently, **maximum loads with long rest intervals result in an increase of MxS but not in hypertrophy.**

MLM also increases the testosterone level, representing, therefore, another explanation why it **improves MxS.** Certainly, **male athletes** with higher testosterone levels have a **better trainability**, whereas the **female** counterparts, with a **lower level of testosterone have a lower trainability.** During the MxS phase the testosterone level increases only in the first 8 weeks, after that showing a decrease, which is still higher than at the start (Häkkinen, 1991). Apparently, the **level of testosterone** in the blood also depends on the **frequency of MLM per day and week. It increases when the number of MLM per week is not high, and it decreases when it is planned twice a day.**

Such findings substantiates and further justifies the suggestion already made regarding the frequency of high intensity training sessions per micro-cycle.

Program Design

Because of the strain of training and the utilization of maximum loads, MLM has to be performed only after a minimum 2–3 years of general strength, using lighter loads. But strength gains are to be expected even during this phase of long-term AA, mostly because of motor learning, when the athletes learn to better use and coordinate the muscles involved in training.

Highly trained athletes, with a **background in MLM of 3–4 years** are adapted so well to such a training that they are able to **recruit some 85 % of their FT fibers.** The remaining 15% represent a "latent reserve" which is not easily tapped through training (Hartman and Tünnemann, 1989).

Once an athlete has reached such a level he/ she might find it very hard to further increase MxS. However, if MxS is expected to be further developed, to overcome this stage of stagnation, in order to further improve performance, alternative methods have to be utilized. Among the suggested possibilities the reader is invited to consider these new options:

1. start applying the principle of progressive increase of load in training. Every athlete using it in the past has experienced improvements without feeling the pain of exhaustion.

2. immediately commence an annual plan for strength training based on the concept of periodization. By following the phase-specific training the athlete will reach the highest sport-specific strength at the time of the main competitions or league games.

3. if one has used the periodization of training for 2–4 years, and has reached a plateau which can not be overpassed, the coach has to start **alternating different stimulations of the neuro-muscular system.** Following the AA and the first phase of MxS the coach should plan alternations of **3 weeks for MxS with 3 for P.** Power training, with its explosiveness and fast application of force, will represent a desired stimulation for the CNS (figures 36, 48, 49 and 51).

4. for sports where power is the dominant ability, one can use another option for stimulation: **alternate 3 weeks of hypertrophy training followed by 3 weeks of MxS.** The additional hypertrophy phases will result in a slight enlargement of muscle size, in an increase of the "active muscle mass". This additional **gain of hypertrophy** will represent a new **biological base for further improvement of MxS.**

5. **increase the ratio between concentric and eccentric** types of contraction (please refer to chapter 16). The additional eccentric training will represent a **higher stimulation** for the MxS improvement, since **eccentric contraction creates a higher tension** in the muscle.

Among the most important elements of success for MLM are: the load utilized in training, the loading pattern, and the rhythm, or speed of performing the contraction. A brief presentation of these methodical concerns will better clarify the above statement.

THE LOAD. As already mentioned, **MxS is developed only if one creates in the muscle the highest tension possible.** Lower loads engage in action the ST muscle fibers. However, if most muscle fibers, especially FT, are to be recruited in contraction, **loads over 85% are necessary. Maximum loads with low repetitions result in significant nervous system adaptation, in better synchronization of the muscles involved, and in an increased capacity to recruit the FT muscle fibers.** This is why MxS and explosive power is also called **nervous system training** (Schmidtbleicher, 1983).

If, as suggested by Goldberg et al. (1975), the stimulus for protein synthesis is proven to be the tension developed in the myofilaments, then this will be a further proof that training for MxS should be carried out only with maximum load.

LOADING PATTERN. Of all the loading patterns available (e.g. waves, steps, variations of pyramids) reference will be made only to 3 examples. However, before referring to them it is essential to mention that if one employs too many sets at a lower load the outcome will not be MxS but rather hypertrophy training. Furthermore, this may lead to some fatigue symptoms which might impair MxS development. However, according to some loading patterns, even if one starts with 1–2 sets of a submaximum load, it is essential to increase it relatively fast to maximum loads in order to obtain the most favourable conditions for MxS development.

The pyramid, represents one of the most popular loading patterns. Its structure (Figure 67) implies that the load increases progressively to maximum while the number of reps decreases proportionately. The physiological advantage of using the pyramid is that the activation or recruitment of most, if not all of the motor units, is ensured.

In all the pyramid patterns, exemplified below, the program starts from its base towards the peak, or from the bottom up. It should also be mentioned that the suggested load is performed for all the exercises selected for the workout before one moves up to the next load.

The double pyramid represents in fact two pyramids, one on the top of the other, with the number of repetitions decreasing from the bottom up, and increasing again in the second pyramid towards the upside down base (Figure 68).

Although the double pyramid may have its own merits some comments, however, are necessary. Most of the proponents of the double pyramid are suggesting that the last sets with a load of 85 and 80% are meant to improve power. It is assumed that since the load is lower, one can apply the force faster. Yet, by the time these last sets are to be performed both the CNS and the muscles involved may be exhausted, and as such, these last sets will not have the expected benefits. On the contrary, since the fatigue may impair a fast recruitment of the FT fibers, the actual outcome of the last sets of this loading pattern will be the development of muscle hypertrophy, and not power.

If one intends to enhance the FT fibers recruitment, this has to be done in the early part of the session. If, on the other hand, one plans to train both MxS and hypertrophy in the same training session, the double pyramid may be an acceptable solution. But do not expect the enhancement of power at the end of a training day. Fatigue may interfere with your expectations.

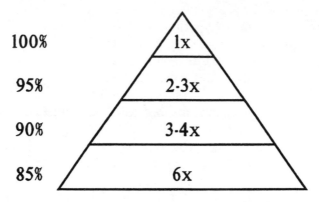

FIGURE 67. An example of the pyramid loading pattern. The number of repetitions (inside of the pyramid), refers to their number per training session

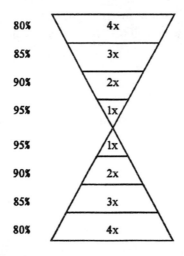

FIGURE 68. An example of the double pyramid loading pattern, as suggested by Grosser and Neumeier, 1986.

The skewed pyramid is proposed as an improved variant of the double pyramid. The load is constantly increased throughout the session, (80%–85%–90%–95%–80%), exception being made for the last set, when the load is lower. The intent of this last set is variation and motivation, since the athletes will be asked to perform the lift as quickly as they can. As is the case for the double pyramid, fatigue may hamper a quick application of force, but this should not stop athletes from trying. However, since there is only one set to be performed, and the number of repetitions is low (4–6), one will not experience exhaustion, and as such this single set will not trigger gains in hypertrophy.

The flat pyramid. For the maximum benefit of MxS I consider the flat pyramid as the best loading pattern. Lets try to make a logical comparison between the traditional pyramids and the flat pyramid I propose in this book.

In the traditional pyramids the load varies too much, often from 70–100%. As per Figure 19, or load variation of such magnitude crosses over three intensity (load) borders: medium, heavy and maximum. And, as already mentioned, the load necessary to produce gains in MxS is anywhere between 85–100%. As such, a traditional pyramid using a load of 70–100%, may result in gains in both P and MxS. Although this may be for the general benefit of the athlete, it does not maximize gains in MxS.

If the intend of training is the **development of MxS only, I strongly suggest the flat pyramid.** This type of loading pattern starts with a warm-up lift of, say, 60%, an intermediary set at 80%, stabilizing the load for the entire workout at 90%. If the instructor intends some variation at the end of training, a set of lower load (80% in the example of Figure 69) may be utilized.

The physilogical advantage of the flat pyramid is that by using the load of only **one intensity level,** it results in the **best neuro-muscular adaptation for MxS,** without "confusing" the body with several intensities. Therefore, if MxS is your goal please consider the flat pyramid.

Certainly, variations of the flat pyramid are possible. For as long as the load stays inside of the required intensity for gains in MxS (85–100%), other variations are possible.

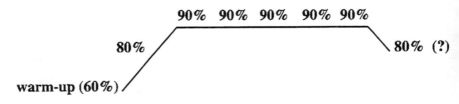

Figure 69. The flat pyramid represents the best loading pattern for the MLM

If **MLM** is to have the **highest benefit** for improving MxS one should **expose the prime movers to the highest amount of work.** In order to achieve that the coach should plan a training session with the **highest number of sets** the athlete can tolerate **(8–12).** However, this is possible only if the number of exercises are low, not higher than 3-5. In doing so the coach has to be very selective, to choose only those exercises which

148

address the prime movers. As such, one should resist the temptation promoted by some strength specialists, who under the influence of bodybuilding, suggest higher number of exercises.

The order of exercises has to be arranged in such a way that allows a better alternation of muscle groups, and as such, to better facilitate local muscle recovery between sets. However, even if the order of exercises follows the above concept, it appears that there are two approaches with regard to the sequence of performing the exercises. Some prefer to perform the exercises **vertically**, meaning from top down. In other instances, exercises are performed **horizontally**, meaning to perform all the sets for the first exercise, and only then move to the next one (see Figure 71 for an example).

As in previous occasions the reader is suggested to use the **vertical** approach, since it results in better recovery between sets, and as such, a lower level of fatigue. And since in most sports strength training is just one of the elements which leads to a better performance, one should be careful about how energy is spent, especially during the competitive phase. Similarly, the coach should also consider the overall fatigue encounter in training.

On the other hand, the **horizontal** approach should be discouraged since it results in a higher local fatigue, exhausting the muscles much faster. And, as the reader may recall, **working the muscles in a state of exhaustion results not in gains in MxS but rather in gains in hypertrophy.** Under these conditions, MxS benefits will occur only for the early sets. As the muscles exhaust, muscle mass will be the beneficiary.

Since **the load for the MLM is maximum, the number of repetitions per set is low: 1–4(6),** and the suggested **number of repetitions** per exercise for a **training session** is **between 15–80.** However, variables of the number of repititions per exercise can exist, depending on the athlete's classification, background in strength training, and the phase of training. Hartman and Tünnemann (1989) proposed the following number of repetitions per exercise per training session for highly classified athletes:

- — 100–95% : 15–25 repetitions
- — 95–90% : 20–40 "
- — 90–80% : 35–85 "
- — 80–75% : 70–110 "

However, the number of exercises dictates which of the two columns of repetitions will be considered. If 4 exercises are selected, the left column is recommended, while for 2 exercises the column on the right is suggested. If the number of repetitions is much lower than the above, MxS benefits will be seriously reduced.

From the above suggestions the reader will certainly realize the benefit of selecting a low number of exercises. The lower the number, the more sets and repetitions will be performed, and as such, the higher the MxS improvement per muscle group.

The **RI between sets** is a function of the athletes' fitness level, and it should be calculated to ensure an adequate recovery of the neuro-muscular system. For **MLM a 3–6 minute RI** is necessary since maximum loads **involve the CNS system**, and thus its recovery takes a longer time than the skeletal muscle system. **If the RI is much lower, the nervous system participation in the form of maximum concentration** for the task at hand, **motivation, and the power of nerve impulses sent to the contracting muscle, could be doubtful.** Similarly, the complete restoration of the required fuel for contraction (ATP/CP) can also be jeopardized.

THE RHYTHM, or speed of execution, plays an important role in MLM. In athletic activities almost everything is performed fast, explosively, or with a high rate. In order to maximize one's ability for high performance, the entire neuro-muscular system has to be adapted to such requirements, to be able to quickly recruit the FT fibers, so determinant in all the sports where speed/ power are dominant. Therefore, even with maximum loads typical **for MLM, athlete's force application against resistance has to be exerted as fast as possible, or even explosively.**

Of great importance in achieving explosive force application, is the athlete's maximum concentration and motivation before each set. Although, considering the magnitude of the load the barbell may travel slowly, the athlete has to concentrate to **activate the muscles as briskly as possible.** Only a **high speed of contraction performed against a maximum load will quickly recruit the FT fibers, resulting in considerably increased MxS.** Furthermore, **for maximum training benefits, the mobilization of all the strength potentials should be performed in the shortest time possible,** and from the early part of the lift.

Considering the high demand placed on the entire neuro-muscular system, the **frequency of MLM per week should be 2–3 times.** Only international class athletes may entertain the idea of training 4 times per week, especially if they are linemen in football, or compete in shot put in track and field. Certainly, during the **competitive phase** the **frequency per week can be reduced to 1–2 MLM** sessions per week, often in combinations with other types of strength components, such as power.

A strength training program for a sprinter for the MxS phase is suggested by Figure 71. This program was successfully used by Ben Johnson in the mid 1980's. To better emphasize the "step-method" for the load increment, the bottom of the chart graphically illustrate the step method/ loading pattern. This addition to the original training program was made only for that particular reason.

No.	Training Parameters	Work
1	Load	85–100%
2	# of exercises	3–5
3	# of repetitions per set	1–4
4	# of repetitions/ set	15–80
5	# of sets/session	6–10(12)
6	Rest interval	3-6 min.
7	Frequency/week	2-3(4)

Figure 70. Suggested training parameters for the MLM.

The program is 9 weeks long and it was repeated twice per year, since sprinters usually follow a bi-cycle annual plan. For an easier comprehension of the program, the weeks are numbered from 1-9. A testing (T) session was planned in each of the low steps, the test itself was performed in the second part of the week, when the athlete was **better recovered** from the strain of a high step. Obviously, the scope of the test was to find out the new 100% (IRM), and as such to use it to calculatethe load for the following cycle of 3 weeks.

One may also notice a discrepancy regarding the number of sets performed, some exercises represent a top priority, and the others a second priority. In this way most of the energy and concern is for the first priority exercises.

The vertical arrows indicate that the same loading pattern was used for the exercise below. For leg curls the load is lower than for most exercises not because it represent a lower priority, but rather because the knee flexors are often more prone to injuries. In addition, the athlete did not reach at that point a balanced development between knee extensors and flexors.

For the low step the reader will notice that the load is always decreased, and the number of sets reduced.

Nr.	Exercise	T	Week 1	Week 2	Week 3	T	Week 4	Week 5	Week 6	T	Week 7	Week 8	Week 9
1	Half Squat	✓	$\frac{70}{8}1$ $\frac{80}{6}2$	$\frac{80}{6}2$ $\frac{85}{5}2$ $\frac{90}{3}1$	$\frac{85}{5}2$ $\frac{90}{3}3$ $\frac{95}{2}1$	✓	$\frac{80}{6}2$ $\frac{85}{4}1$	$\frac{85}{5}2$ $\frac{90}{3}3$ $\frac{95}{2}1$	$\frac{90}{3}2$ $\frac{95}{2}2$ $\frac{100}{1}2$	✓	$\frac{80}{6}3$	$\frac{85}{5}1$ $\frac{90}{3}3$ $\frac{95}{2}2$	$\frac{90}{3}2$ $\frac{95}{2}3$ $\frac{100}{1}2$
2	Arm Pulls	✓	↓	↓	↓	✓	↓	↓	↓	✓	↓	↓	↓
3	Leg Curls	✓	$\frac{60}{12}1$ $\frac{70}{10}2$	$\frac{60}{12}1$ $\frac{70}{10}2$ $\frac{80}{6}2$	$\frac{70}{8}2$ $\frac{80}{6}2$ $\frac{85}{4}2$	✓	$\frac{70}{8}3$	$\frac{70}{8}1$ $\frac{80}{6}2$ $\frac{85}{5}3$	$\frac{80}{6}1$ $\frac{85}{5}3$ $\frac{90}{3}2$	✓	$\frac{80}{5}3$	$\frac{80}{6}1$ $\frac{85}{5}3$ $\frac{90}{3}2$	$\frac{85}{5}2$ $\frac{90}{3}2$ $\frac{95}{2}2$
4	Reverse Leg Press	✓	$\frac{70}{8}2$ $\frac{80}{6}2$	$\frac{80}{6}2$ $\frac{85}{5}2$ $\frac{90}{3}1$	$\frac{85}{5}2$ $\frac{90}{3}3$ $\frac{95}{2}1$	✓	$\frac{80}{6}2$ $\frac{85}{4}1$	$\frac{85}{5}2$ $\frac{90}{3}3$ $\frac{95}{2}1$	$\frac{90}{3}2$ $\frac{95}{2}2$ $\frac{100}{1}2$	✓	$\frac{80}{6}3$	$\frac{85}{5}1$ $\frac{90}{3}3$ $\frac{95}{2}2$	$\frac{90}{3}2$ $\frac{95}{2}3$ $\frac{100}{1}2$
5	Bench Press	✓	↓	↓	↓	✓	↓	↓	↓	✓	↓	↓	↓
6	Power Clean	–	$\frac{60}{10}1$ $\frac{70}{8}2$	$\frac{60}{8}1$ $\frac{70}{6}2$ $\frac{80}{4}1$	$\frac{70}{6}1$ $\frac{80}{4}3$	–	$\frac{70}{6}3$	$\frac{70}{6}1$ $\frac{80}{4}3$	$\frac{80}{4}4$	–	$\frac{70}{6}3$	$\frac{70}{6}1$ $\frac{80}{4}3$	$\frac{80}{4}4$

Loading Pattern:

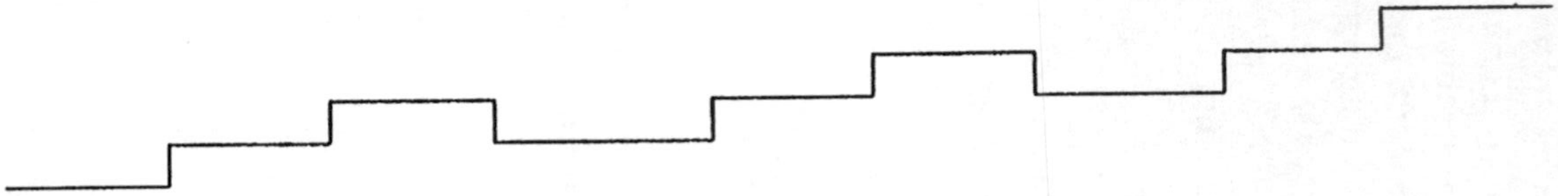

FIGURE 71. An example of MLM program for a sprinter.

The Isometric Method

Although this training method was known and used for some time, Hettinger and Muller (1953) and again Hettinger (1966) scientifically justified the merits of static contractions in the development of maximum strength. This method reached its climax in the sixties and has since faded in popularity. Although static contraction does not have a marked functional effect (i.e., for muscular endurance) it still can assist the development of maximum strength and therefore may be used by weight lifters and throwers in their strength training efforts. Static conditions may be realized through two techniques:

1. by attempting to lift a weight heavier than one's potential.
2. by applying force (push or pull) against an immobile object.

Since during the isometric contraction the **tension** produced in the muscle **is very high**, this method is **useful mostly during the MxS phase**, and with disputed merits, can be applied in the maintenance phase to preserve MxS. Even if true, as some enthusiasts claim, that isometric training can increase MxS by 10–15% more than other methods, it has **clear limitations regarding the development of P and M-E.**

As isometric force is applied against a given resistance, the tension in the muscle builds up progressively, reaching its maximum in about 2–3 seconds, and towards the end decreases in a much shorter time (1–2 seconds). Since **training benefits** are **angle-specific**, one has to train a group of muscles at different angles. If, for instance, the range of motion of a joint is 180°, in order to benefit throughout this range, one has to use angles of 15°, 45°, 75°, 105°, 135°, and 165°. Only now the tension completely covers the whole range of motion. Reservations can also be expressed with regard to transferability of angle-specific strength gains into dynamic or explosive athletic-actions, which often involves the muscles throughout the whole range of motion.

It is, therefore, expected that the isometric method may have some advantages of using it, but also disadvantages, such as:

ADVANTAGES:

1. isometric exercises can be performed with a simple apparatus or equipment.

2. it results in a relatively rapid increase of strength, especially for beginners, although a strength background is necessary.

3. does not require partners, or a close supervision such as free weights.

4. can be used for the rehabilitation of injured muscles. Since no joint motion occurs, "the athlete may continue training even with a joint or bone injury" (Hartman and Tünnemann, 1989). This certainly can reduce the risk of muscular atrophy.

5. for the concerned athletes, isometric training produces negligible increase of muscle hypertrophy. And for some athletes this can be an advantage (sports where relative strength prevails).

6. the duration of a training session is short, 20–30 minutes.

7. well trained athletes may reach the capacity to mobilize in contraction most, if not all of the motor units.

8. fatigue encountered at the end of a training session may not be higher than that for MLM.

DISADVANTAGES:

1. strength development is angle-specific. In order to cover the whole range of motion, one has to use contractions at different angles (20o span).

2. gains in MxS cannot be readily applied to dynamic contractions.

3. does not have a motor memory, meaning that it does not have a learning component of the technical skills involved in the selected sport, exception probably being some skills in male gymnastic (e.g. ironcross). As such, coordination capacity, its enhancement, is at least questionable.

4. since isometric contraction is performed statically, it does not stimulate the development of flexibility. As such, exaggeration of isometric training may affect muscle elasticity.

5. since isometric contraction is performed in a state of apnea (breath holding) an oxygen debt is acquired during work. This has to be compensated during the rest interval through a higher breathing rate.

6. isometric contractions have a very low, if any, effects on the cardio-respiratory systems.

7. during contraction, which can last up to 12 seconds, blood circulation may be restrained, therefore the supply of exercise nutrients is hampered. Therefore, it is advisable that isometric training be performed together with other methods. In any instance, athletes with heart and circulation problems, are strongly discouraged in involving themselves in isometric training.

8. gains in MxS may be lost as quickly as it is gained.

9. **isometric training** may add to the overall gains in MxS but it **does not shift the force-time curve to the left.** And definitely, this is a disadvantage not to be easily disregarded!

Program Design

For maximum gains in isometric training, one has to use specificity, or to select exercises as similar as possible with the technical skill. Of similar importance, and especially in view of its disadvantages, the isometric method has to be used mostly for advanced athletes, and together with other MxS methods.

No.	Training Parameters	Work
1	Load	80–100%
2	# of Exercises	4–6
3	Duration of Contraction/Set	6–12 sec.
4	Duration of Contraction/ Session	60–90 sec.
5	# of Sets/Session	6–9
6	Rest Interval	60–90 sec.
7	Frequency/ Week	2–3

Figure 72. Suggested training parameters for isometric training.

Isometric contraction can be performed with all limbs, using angles from a completely open to fully bent. The user is suggested to consider the following methodical aspects:

1. isometric training is most effective when contraction is near to maximum, therefore from 80–100%.

2. the duration of contraction can be between 6–12 seconds, with a total of 60–90 seconds per muscle per training session.

3. the load in training is intensified by increasing the number of exercises and sets, and not by increasing the duration of contractions per set.

4. during the rest interval (60–90 seconds) relaxation and breathing exercises are recommended. The latter is a compensatory necessity since static contraction is performed in apnea (breath hold). In addition, the intra-thoracic pressure is elevated restricting circulation and thus the oxygen supply.

5. for a more effective program alternate static with isotonic contractions, especially for sports requiring speed and power.

6. a more effective variant of the isometric method is the **functional isometric contraction**, which involves free weights. This variant combines isotonic with isometric exercises, in that the athlete lifts the object to a certain angle, where it is stopped for 6–8 seconds. Throughout the range of motion one may stop 2–4 times, thus combining both isotonic and

isometric methods. This variant has a better physiological benefit, especially for M-E short, therefore the term "functional".

THE ISOKINETIC METHOD

The term isokinetic means equal motion, or same speed of movement throughout the range of motion. By using specially designed equipment the muscles are encountering the **same resistant for both the concentric and eccentric part of the contraction**.

Although the equipment used can provide maximum activation of the muscles involved, training velocity is very important in this mode of contraction since the benefits are proportional to the velocity employed. Slower speeds seem to increase strength only at that speed, and as such the major gains are for muscle hypertrophy. On the other hand, training at a higher speed may increase the strength at all speeds of contraction at or below the training speed, with major benefits for MxS and even some gains in P.

More advanced, motor-driven, computerized equipment can be used to set the desired velocity, as well as to be used as strength measurement devices. Although, isokinetic equipment is yet to fulfill the major requirement in strength training, namely to constantly increase acceleration, as a training method it can be used with its advantages and disadvantages.

ADVANTAGES:

1. it offers an athlete a safe training environment, therefore suggested for novice athletes during their early years in strength development.

2. it is well suited for the AA phase, when overall strength development and muscle attachment adaptation is the main purpose of training.

3. a good training device for rehabilitation of injured athletes.

4. can be used for gains in muscle hypertrophy, if the load and number of repetitions are performed as requested by this training method.

5. with a higher velocity and therefore increased resistance, it can result in gains in MxS.

DISADVANTAGES:

1. the equipment is expensive.

2. since the equipment permits only a constant exercise speed, it runs counter to the manner in which most athletic moves are performed: constantly increased acceleration. In athletics the application of force is progressively increased to reach maximum possible acceleration towards the end of the action, an element which is not possible to duplicate with the isokinetic equipment.

3. because of the constant resistance provided by this type of equipment, and non-explosive actions, the outcome of applying this training method is that **the force-velocity curve cannot be shifted to the left**.

PROGRAM DESIGN

A training program designed for isokinetic contraction for the benefit of MxS, has to follow the same methodology as MLM (explained above). Therefore, the resistance has to be set close to, or at maximum so that the highest strength mobilization will occur. Since the load (resistance of the machine) has to be set to maximum, obviously an athlete will not be able to perform more than 3–4 repetitions.

The isokinetic equipment allows the athlete to pre-set the speed of performance. With the maximum resistance provided by the machine, the movement cannot be performed quickly. However, for MxS benefits, one has to attempt to apply force as dynamically as possible, so that the FT muscle fibers will be recruited in the highest proportion. All the other training parameters have to follow the suggestions made for the MLM, or as per figure 71.

Since the isokinetic method has the disadvantages explained above, one is suggested to use this method together with MLM. This is why some of the training parameters are not as high as for the MLM, and the frequency per week is very low. The balance is assumed to be performed with other methods, mostly with MLM.

No.	Training Parameters	Work
1	Load (resistance)	Maximum
2	# of Exercises	3–5
3	# of Reps/ Set	1–4
4	# of Reps/ Session	40–60
5	# of Sets/Session	3–5
6	Rest Interval	3–6 min.
7	Frequency/ Week	1–2

FIGURE 73. Suggested training parameters for the isokinetic method.

THE ECCENTRIC METHOD

Any strength exercise using free weights, or most of the isokinetic apparatuses, employs both the concentric and eccentric type of contraction. During the concentric phase, force is produced while the muscle shortens, whereas during the eccentric segment the same result is achieved as the muscle lengthens.

Practice has demonstrated that the eccentric phase always seems to be easier than the concentric one. When one performs the bench press, the return of the barbell to the starting point (the eccentric part of the lift) always seems to be easier than the lift itself. Logically, this has led to the conclusion that since an athlete can work with heavier loads during the eccentric contraction, he/ she can certainly improve strength to higher levels by using just the eccentric method alone.

As strength training specialists became more interested in the eccentric method so did some researchers. Both researchers and practitioners arrived at the same conclusion, namely that **eccentric training creates a higher tension in the muscles than the isometric or isotonic contractions.** Furthermore, since higher muscles tension is normally equated with higher strength development and in many cases it induces hypertrophy (Goldberg et al., 1975), **eccentric training** would logically be considered a **superior training method.** Komi and Buskirk (1972) demonstrated the superiority of eccentric over the isokinetic method, but at the same time, other studies could not show much of a difference.

At the same time training specialists from the former East Germany claim that the **eccentric strength method results in a 10–35% higher strength gain as compared to the other methods** (Hartman and Tünnemann, 1989).

As the load in eccentric training is much higher than the maximum concentric contraction, the rhythm/ speed of performance is quite slow. Since such a **slow rate of contraction does not result in higher neural activation** (Komi, 1984), it can represent a **larger stimulus for protein synthesis,** and as such it can normally **result in muscle hypertrophy** but not necessarily greater strength development. However, if the eccentric contraction is performed fast, muscle force improves to higher levels as compared to the concentric method (Astrand and Rodahl, 1985). This can create an important difficulty in training, especially if free weights are employed. Since the load for eccentric training is higher than 1RM, for the concentric phase of the work two spotters are needed to help the athlete lift the barbell. The same spotters are necessary to ensure that as the bar is lowered, as in the bench press, the athlete will not drop it on their chest, resulting in an undesirable injury. Therefore, if a person requires careful

158

assistance as the bar is lowered slowly, how can he/ she perform it fast? Unless one has access to special isokinetic equipment, or he/ she can stop the barbell before it reaches their chest (security pins or keys), fast eccentric contraction is not easy or safe to perform.

During the first few days of using the eccentric method the athletes may experience muscle soreness. However, this can be expected since higher tension provokes some muscle damage. As the athlete adapts to it, muscle soreness disappears within 7–10 days. In any case, even this short-term discomfort can be avoided if the load is increased in steps.

As expected, the **eccentric method influences the force-time curve, by shifting it to the left**. Heavy loads, which generates high tension in the muscle, improves strength since it results in high recruitment of the powerful FT motor units. Such results are even more superior if the movement is exerted faster. Therefore, the outcome of using the eccentric method is positive, very beneficial for the athlete, and results in a shift to the left of the force-time curve.

Program Design

Since the eccentric method employs the **heaviest loads** in strength training **(110–160%)** only athletes with a **good strength training background** should be exposed to it. Therefore, **2–4 years** of background experience is strongly advisable for anyone intending to use the eccentric training method.

The eccentric method can be used alone in a training session, or a short training phase, or in combination with other methods, especially the MLM. Eccentric contractions should not be "abused", or overly used by everyone and every time. Used in this way, it may have its limitations, and therefore reach a plateau, often difficult to break and improve further. In addition, every time one employs maximum or supermaximum loads, there is a great deal of mental concentration and psychological weardown. This is why the eccentric method has to be used with care.

For maximum training benefits an athlete should use the MLM for as long as practically possible. **Where one reaches a plateau**, with little or no improvement anymore, **then the coach should plan the eccentric method**. In this way the **ceiling of adaptation** of that plateau is **broken**, resulting in **new heights in strength improvements**.

Since the coach is concerned with training mainly the agonistic muscles, the prime movers, he/ she should not forget to balance out the antagonistic muscles as well by exposing them to the same methods, but not necessarily the same number of sets. While such training is performed, assistance from **two spotters** is always necessary since most eccentric work is performed with free weights. In this way imminent danger or injury will be prevented. Such assistance is also necessary for the concentric part of the lift, when the athlete alone will not be able to return the barbell to the starting point.

If muscular soreness is experienced by some athletes, active recovery techniques should be used so that the discomfort will be eliminated and the athletes have a chance for a quicker regeneration. For further information please refer to chapter 17.

Training parameters for the eccentric method are presented by Figure 74. The range of the load is presented as the percentage of the maximum strength capacity for the concentric contraction, and suggests a resistance between 110–160%. Certainly, lower loads ought to be used for the less experienced athletes, with the most effective load for athletes of high calibre being around 130–140%. However, such loads are not used in the first few months of training, but rather after at least two seasons of MxS training where the eccentric contraction is employed as well.

The suggested number of sets should be viewed as a guideline for experienced athletes, the others performing a lower number, as per their training potential. The same is true for the number of sets per training session, which depends on the number of exercises.

The RI is an important element in the capacity to perform highly demanding work. If the athlete does not recover between two sets well enough to perform the next set at the same level, the RI has to be slightly increased. The speed of execution is low since the load is supermaximum. However, considering the type of equipment available in the gym, the athlete should try to perform the exercise as fast as realistically possible. Remember that MxS and P are developed only if the application of force against the resistance is high. However, before considering this option safety factors should be ensured.

Since eccentric contraction utilizes such heavy loads, before performing a set the athlete must be highly motivated and have maximum concentration. Only under such mental/ psychological conditions will he/ she be capable of performing eccentric contractions effectively.

The eccentric method is rarely performed in isolation from the other MxS methods. Even during the MxS phase the **eccentric method is used together with MLM**. Therefore, only **one** eccentric training session per week is suggested. The frequency may eventually be increased only for high calibre athletes during the "third step" of the pattern of increasing the load in training.

No.	Training Parameters	Work
1	Load	110–160%
2	# of Exercises	3–5
3	# of Reps/ Set	1–4
4	# of Sets/ Exercise	4–6(8)
5	# of Sets/ Session	20–36
6	Rest Interval	3–6 min.
7	Rhythm/ Speed of Execution	slow
8	Frequency/ Week	1

Figure 74. Suggested training parameters for the eccentric method.

CHAPTER FOURTEEN

TRAINING METHODS FOR THE CONVERSION PHASE: CONVERSION TO POWER

Strength training went a long way to establish itself as an increasingly determinant element in athletic performance. Now it is so popular that almost every athlete does some sort of strength program in the hope of breaking new athletic standards. However, what most strength programs are lacking is the transformation of strength gains into the sport/event-specific strength. Thus the **conversion** phase!

The main scope of the conversion phase is to transform all the gains in strength into a competitive and sport-specific P or M-E. It should be obvious to everyone that the raw (i.e., basic and unspecific) gains in strength does not aid athletic performance, but rather this new, sport-specific product which is the outcome of the conversion phase. Only this new, sport-specific product, represents the physiological foundation for new advancements in athletic performance during the competitive phase. **By the time the conversion phase ends the important competitions start.** And at this time this new strength ingredient should be at the highest levels to assist the athletes to achieve their performance goals.

The determinant elements in the success of the conversion phase are its duration, and the specific methods employed to transform MxS gains into sport-specific strength needs. The duration of the conversion phase was discussed in chapter 10. Further references will be made during this discussion as well as at the end of chapter 16 (planning the training methods). As for the training methods, they will be discussed in this chapter and in chapter 15.

TRAINING METHODS FOR SPORT-SPECIFIC POWER

As already stated, **power refers to the ability of the neuro-muscular system to produce the greatest possible force in the shortest period of time.** Power is simply the product of muscle force (F) and the velocity (V) of movement. Therefore $P = F \times V$. For athletic purposes, any increase in power must be the result of improvements in either strength or speed, or both.

An athlete can be very strong, have large muscle mass, and yet not able to display power for the reason of his/ her inability to contract already strong muscles in a very short period of time. In order to overcome such deficiencies the athlete has to undergo special training, namely power training, which will result in the improvement of the rate of force production.

The advantage of **explosive power, high velocity training** is that it **"trains" the nervous system.** Increases of performance can be based on **neural changes** that help the individual muscle to achieve greater performance capability (Sale, 1986). This is achieved by **shortening the time of motor unit recruitment**, especially **FT fibers**, and by **increasing the tolerance of the motor neurons to increased innervation frequencies** (Häkkinen and Komi, 1983; Häkkinen, 1986).

Power training exercises, therefore, have to be employed in training to activate the motor units more quickly in order to allow for a better nervous system adaptation. As known from training practice and research, the **adaptation of muscles** requires considerable time, and it progresses from year to year. This adaptation, especially in the case of well trained athletes, is shown in the form of a higher and **better synchronization of motor units** and **their firing pattern.** Another physiological adaptation phenomenon, so critical for the display of power, is that **muscles discharge a greater number of muscle fibers in a very short period of time**.

The neuro-muscular adaptation to power training results also in an **improved intramuscular coordination**, or better and improved relations between excitatory and inhibitory reaction of a muscle during the many stimuli an athlete is exposed to during performance. As a result of such an adaptation, the CNS "learns" when to send a nerve impulse, a signal to the muscle to contract and perform a movement, or when to restrain from it.

A further illustration of adaptation to power training results from better **intermuscular coordination**, or the ability of the agonistic and antagonistic muscles to cooperate together to effectively perform a movement. This improved intermuscular coordination, that is to contract some muscles and relax the others, namely the antagonistic muscles, results in **improved speed of contraction** of the prime movers (agonistic muscles).

The human body has the capacity to adapt to any environment, and as such, to any type of training. If an individual, as often is the case, is trained with bodybuilding methods, the neuro-muscular system adapts to them. However, in such a case one should not expect a fast and explosive display of power. The neuro-muscular system was not trained for it.

If, on the other hand, the development of power for a given sport/ event or specific skill is expected, training has to be designed to meet that challenge. Therefore, such a program has to be specific to the sport/ event and use exercises that simulate as closely as possible the dominant skills of the sport. The more specific the muscles are involved in power training, the more effective the intramuscular coordination, the more precise, smooth, and quicker the skill.

During the conversion phase it is necessary to be **energy-conscious**, to spend most energy for technical/ tactical training, and a lower proportion of it to be used for power training. This is why the **lowest possible number of exercises** has to be selected, which, as said, has to be as closely related to the skills as possible. Time and energy should not be wasted on anything else. The program has to be very efficient, 2–3 exercises, dynamically performed, over several sets for maximum return.

The program has to be performed quickly and **explosively**, in order to **recruit the highest number of motor units,** at the **highest rate of contraction** possible. The entire program should have only one **scope: to move the force-time curve as far to the left as possible** (Figure 62, 63, and 64). In this way the muscle will contract explosively for maximum performance benefit.

During the conversion of MxS to P only those training methods which fulfill the requirement of power development ought to be selected: to **enhance quickness, explosive application of force,** and make the muscles **react quickly** to an athletic movement.

The methods presented herewith, can be performed separately or in combination with one another. In such a case the total work per session has to be divided between them. At the end of chapter 16 (see planning the training methods) specific suggestions will be made regarding such possibilities.

THE ISOTONIC METHOD

The attempt to move a weight as rapidly and forcefully as possible through the entire range of motion represents one of the classical methods used for power training. Free weights, or any other piece of equipment which allows one to move it with high acceleration, represents a good means of achieving the goal of power development.

The weight of the equipment used for the isotonic method represents the **external resistance**. The force necessary to defeat the inertia of a barbell, or to move it, is considered the **internal strength. The more the internal strength exceeds the external resistance the faster the acceleration.** If an athlete has to apply 95% of 1RM to lift a barbell he/ she will not be capable of generating any acceleration— the move will be performed slowly.

If, on the other hand, the same athlete works on MxS for 1–2 years, he/ she will increase the strength so much that in order to lift the same weight he/ she will need only 30–40% of 1RM. Under these new conditions the athlete will be capable of moving the barbell quickly, even explosively, generating the acceleration necessary to increase power. This explains why the periodization of strength requires a MxS phase prior to power training. **No visible increments of power are possible without clear gains in MxS.**

A high level of **MxS is necessary** also for the **early part of a lift or a throw.** Any barbell or implement/ ball has a certain inertia (its own mass, or weight). If the barbell/ implement is to be lifted/ thrown explosively, the most difficult part is the early part of the lift/ throw. **In order to overcome the inertia, a high tension has to be built in the muscle to achieve it. The higher the MxS the easier it is to overcome the inertia** and the more explosive the start of the movement.

As the athlete continues to apply force against the barbell/implement he/ she creates an acceleration. As the acceleration is developed, less force is necessary to maintain it. In the case of a throw of an implement, the **highest acceleration has to be reached at the very end. The more force and acceleration one imparts at this time on the implement or ball, the farther it goes.**

However, in order to continuously increase the acceleration, the speed of the movement of the limbs has to be constantly increased. This is only possible if one has the capacity to quickly contract the muscle to create such a speed. This is why any athlete involved in sports where speed and power is dominant, needs to work on power training during the conversion phase. Without the power training one will never be able to jump higher, run faster, throw further, or deliver a quick punch— no matter how strong! For these moves to occur successfully one does not just need MxS. More important than that is to have the capacity to **use MxS at a very high rate.** If this is achieved, performance improvements can be expected. This is possible only by using power training methods.

PROGRAM DESIGN

During the MxS phase the athlete is used to maximum or supermaximum loads. Therefore, to use loads between 30–80% of 1RM for the development of power does not represent a challenge. But to use such a load and also create a high acceleration it does.

For most sports with a **cyclic motion** such as sprinting, team sports, and martial arts, the **load** for the isotonic method can be **30–50, maximum 60%**. For **acyclic sports**, such as throwing events, weight lifting, and linemen in football, the **load** has to be higher **(50–80%)** since such athletes have a much higher MxS to start with, and have to defeat a higher external resistance.

The suggested **number of repetitions** is not high **(4–10)** since the key element for power training is not how many repetitions are performed, but rather how forcefully they are executed. For sports where speed with high frequency is an important attribute, all the number of **repetitions** per set have to be **performed non-stop**, dynamically, and with the highest rate possible. Safety, however, should not be overlooked! As such, when a limb is extended it should not be snapped. Similarly, the exercises should be performed as smoothly as possible, without jerking the barbell/ implement.

For sports where power, explosiveness, such as in throwing, heavyweight categories in boxing, wrestling, or linemen in football, the number of repetitions **do not necessarily have to be performed non-stop**. They could be performed with **some rest between** the repetitions so that the athlete can **concentrate maximally** in order to **achieve the most dynamic move**. As such, an athlete can perform a repetition at the time, but explosively for maximum FT muscle fibers recruitment. **Only maximum concentration and explosive action result in greatest FT fibers recruitment.**

One has to be very selective in choosing the exercises for power training. They have to be very sport-specific, to mimic the skills. Exercises such as bench press, and power cleans should not be taken for granted just because they are part of "tradition"! These two exercises do not have a built-in miracle! Power cleans may be used for a thrower or linebacker but not necessarily for a basketball, soccer, or volleyball player. These athletes are better off using jumping squats, holding heavier dumbbells in their hands (15% in each hand).

It is also very important to select the **lowest number of exercises, 2–4, maximum 5**. By doing so one can perform the **highest number of sets** realistically possible **(3–6)** for maximum benefit of the prime movers. When making the decision on the number of sets and exercises, one should not forget that power training is performed in addition to the technical/ tactical training, with only a certain amount of energy left for it.

No.	Training Parameters	Work
1	Load: -cyclic	30–50%
	-acyclic	50–80%
2	# of Exercises	2–4(5)
3	# of Reps/ Set	4–10
4	# of Sets/Session	3–6
5	Rest Interval	2–6 min.
6	Rhythm/ Speed of Execution	dynamic/ fast
7	Frequency/ Week	2–3

FIGURE 75.　Training parameters for the isotonic method.

A key element in the development of power by means of isotonic method is the rhythm/ speed of execution. For maximum power improvements the **speed of exertion has to be as high as possible**. The **fast application of force** against an implement/ weight, throughout the range of motion, is essential, and it has to start from the early part of the movement. In order to achieve that, the athlete has to maximally concentrate on the task, to be able to displace the barbell/ implement at once, and very dynamically.

THE BALLISTIC METHOD

The energy of the muscles can be applied in different forms and against different resistances. When the resistance is heavier than the internal force of the athlete no motion occurs (isometric). If the resistance is slightly lower than ones' maximum capacity, the barbell, or a strength training equipment, moves slowly (isotonic). However, if the athlete's internal force clearly exceeds the external resistance, a dynamic motion occurs.

For power training purposes the internal, the muscles' force of an athlete, can also be applied against implements, such as shots utilized in shot put in track and field, medicine balls, heavy bells, and rubber cords (or surgical tubbing). Since the force of the athlete exceeds by far the resistance of these instruments, the motion occurs explosively. The method used to enhance power by employing such instruments is called the **ballistic method**.

During a ballistic action the athlete's energy is imparted against the resistance very dynamically, from the beginning to the end of the motion. As a result, the implement is projected at a distance proportional to one's power applied against it. Throughout the motion, the athlete must be able to **develop considerable strength to continuously accelerate** the equipment/ implement, **culminating with the release.** If the implement is to be projected at the maximum possible distance, highest acceleration should be achieved at the instant of release.

The fast, ballistic application of force is possible as a result of a **quick recruitment of the FT muscle fibers,** and an effective **intermuscular coordination** of both the agonistic and antagonistic muscles. As a result of years of practice the agonistic muscles contract forcefully while the antagonistic ones are capable of reaching a high level of relaxation. This high level of intermuscular coordination maximizes the force capabilities of the agonistic, since the antagonistic muscles do not exert any opposition to their quick contraction.

In order to achieve its goal of dynamic contraction, for the ballistic method one can use exercises with medicine balls, shots from track and field, heavy bells, and surgical tubing (for detailed exercises please refer to: T. Bompa, "Power Training for Sport: Plyometric for Maximum Power Development", 1993).

PROGRAM DESIGN

The ballistic exercises can be performed at the end of a training session or immediately following the warm-up, depending on training objectives. If one has planned important technical/ tactical work in a given day, the additional work, such as the development/ improvement of power, becomes a secondary goal. However, for sports where speed-power are dominant, such as sprinting, field events in track and field, martial arts, or any other sports, work on power can often be planned **immediately after the warm-up,** especially in the late preparatory phase.

Under this condition power training of an explosive nature is enhanced since it is performed in a state of **physiological freshness. A rested CNS can send more powerful nervous impulses to the working muscles for quick contractions.** The opposite is true when the CNS and muscles are exhausted: inhibition is dominant, thus preventing an effective involvement of the FT muscle fibers.

Performing intensive work prior to any type of power training of an explosive nature exhausts the athlete's supplies of high energy ATP/CP. If energy is not available, quality work is impossible. In addition, the easily fatiguable FT fibers can hardly be activated, and as a consequence, the movement will be performed without vigor.

168

For the ballistic method the speed of performance represents a paramount concern. Each repetition should start very dynamically, attempting to constantly increase the speed as the release/ end of the motion approaches. By doing so a higher number of FT motor units will be involved, so necessary for the explosive actions to occur.

The load of the ballistic movements is dictated by the standard weight of the implements. Medicine balls have a range of 2–6kg (4.4–13lbs), while heavy bells have a weight between 10–32kg (22–70lbs). The resistance provided by the rubber cords/ surgical tubings depend on how far they are stretched: the greater the stretch the greater the resistance.

As in other power-related methods, the **number of exercises** have to be as **low** as possible so that a **high number of sets are possible** for maximum power benefits. As much as possible, the exercises have to mimic technical skills. If this is not possible, the coach should at least select the exercises which involves the prime movers of the sport/ event.

The number of repetitions and sets are not the critical element. To increase power is not necessary to perform many repetitions! What is **determinant** is the speed of performance which dictates the **speed of muscle contraction.** Therefore, both the number of repetitions and sets have to be performed for as long as quickness is possible. The number of repetitions have to be **discontinued at the moment speed is declining.**

The speed/ explosiveness of an exercise is guaranteed only as long as a high number of FT fibers are involved. When they fatigue speed decreases. To further continue the activity is futile, since from this point on the ST fibers will be called into action, an unwanted situation for an athlete who seeks the development of power.

For any explosive power methods, including ballistics, the **RI** should be **as long as necessary to reach an almost full recovery** so that the same quality of work can be repeated in the following sets. However, since most ballistic exercises are performed with a partner(s) there is a short interval between each repetition which is dictated by the fact that, for instance, a shot has to be fetched, take the position, make few preparatory swings, and only then heave the shot back to the first athlete. By the time all these occur some 15–20 seconds are passing, thus facilitating a better rest than in most other training methods. This is why the number of repetitions are higher than in other power training methods.

The frequency per week of the ballistic method depends on the training phase: less (1–2) in the late preparatory and more (2–4) during the conversion phase. Certainly, one has to take into consideration the characteristics of the sport/ event. For speed-power dominant sports the frequency will be higher than for sports where power is of secondary importance.

No.	Training Parameters	Work
1	Load	standard
2	# of exercises	2–5
3	# of reps/ set	10–20
4	# of sets/session	3–5
5	Rest interval	2–3 min.
6	Rhythm/ speed of execution	explosive
7	Frequency/ week	2–4

FIGURE 76. Suggested training parameters for the ballistic method.

THE POWER-RESISTING METHOD

This proposed method represents a three-way combination between isotonic, isometric and ballistic method. An exemplification of an exercise will easier explain the method. An athlete lays on their back with the intent of performing a sit-up. The athlete's toes are under a rung of a stall bar, or held against the ground by a partner, while the coach is behind him/ her. The athlete begins the sit-up. As he/ she performs approximately a quarter of the hip flexion, reaching some 135–140°, the coach opposes resistance by placing the palms on the chest or shoulders, stopping the athlete's movement. At this point the athlete is in a maximum static contraction, since he/ she wants to defeat the resisting power of the coach by recruiting most/ all the motor units possible. After 3–4 seconds the coach takes their hands off, and the maximum static contraction is converted for the rest of the sit-up into a dynamic, ballistic motion. The athlete returns slowly to the starting position, rests for 10–30 seconds before another repetition is performed.

The **most important moments** of this method is the **maximum isometric contraction and the ensuing ballistic action**. The ballistic type of motion, with its quick muscle contraction, results in power development. The type of actions for this method is similar to a catapult machine. The initial isotonic action has to be performed slowly. Following the stop, the maximum isometric contraction represents a high pre-tension (the loding phase) of the muscles involved. As the coach releases the chest/ shoulders, the trunk is catapulted forward (the ballistic phase).

Similar power-resisting exercises can be performed for other parts of the body, such as:

1. pull-ups: after an early elbow flexion, the coach/ partner stops the action for few seconds, followed by a dynamic action

2. dips
3. jumping squats (no weights)
4. half squats with weight
5. bench press
6. trunk rotations, with a medicine ball held sideways, by the hands. The athlete performs a rotation backward. As he/ she rotates forward, he/ she is stopped for 2–4 seconds, followed by the ballistic action which culminates with the release of the ball.

Any other movements which can duplicate the above phases of actions can be categorized under this method, with similar effect on power development.

Another type of power stimulation can be achieved through isotonic weight training, by **alternating the loads**. At first, the athlete performs **2–4 repetitions with a load of 80–90%, immediately followed** by a similar number of **repetitions performed with a low-resistance (30–50%)**. The heavy load exercises represents a **neuro-muscular stimulation** for the low-resistance repetitions. As such the athlete can perform the last repetition more dynamically.

A high variety of exercises can be performed to best benefit this method: from bench pulls to bench press, etc. However, a note of caution is necessary for any motions involving knee and arm extensions: one should avoid snapping or jerking actions since they can result in some joint damage (forced, snapped extensions).

PROGRAM DESIGN

The load for the power-resisting method is related to the exercise performed. For the isometric phase the contraction is for 3–4 seconds, or the duration necessary to reach maximum tension. For the exercises where the resistance is provided by a barbell, the load is 80–90% for the stimulating phase and 30–50% for the explosive repetitions.

The exercises have to be selected carefully to match the direction of contraction of the prime movers. For maximum power benefit they have to be low (2–4) so that a greater number of sets (3–5) can be performed.

Once again the number of repetitions do not represent a determinant element, but rather the manner in which the exercise is performed should be regarded as the deciding factor for power improvement.

This type of training method can be performed separately, or in combination with other power training methods. The latter case is preferable since other power training methods may be more beneficial for certain sports or athletes.

No.	Training Parameters	Work
1	Load	exercise related
2	# of exercises	2–4
3	# of reps/ set	4–8
4	# of sets/session	3–5
5	Rest interval	2–4 min.
6	Rhythm/ speed of execution	explosive
7	Frequency/ week	1–2

Figure 77. Training parameters suggested for the power-resisting method.

THE PLYOMETRICS METHOD

Since ancient times athletes have explored a multitude of methods designed to enable them to run faster, jump higher, and throw an object further. In order to achieve such goals, power is essential. Gains in strength can only be transformed into power by applying specific power training methods. It is probable that one of the most successful of these methods is training employing plyometric exercises.

Also known as the **stretching-shortening cycle**, or **myotatic stretch reflex**, the exercises popularly known as plyometrics are those in which the muscle is loaded in an eccentric (lengthening) contraction, immediately followed by a concentric (shortening) contraction. In physiological terms, it has been demonstrated that **a muscle that is stretched before a contraction, will contract more forcefully and rapidly** (Bosco and Komi, 1980; Schmidtbleicher, 1984). For example by lowering the centre of gravity to perform the take-off (in any sports activity) or swinging the golf club before the ball is hit, the athlete stretches the muscle which results in a more forceful contraction.

The action involved in a plyometric type of exercise relies mechanically on the **stretch reflex** which is found in the belly of the individual muscle. The main purpose of the stretch reflex is to monitor the degree of muscle stretch and to thereby prevent overstretching of any muscle fibers which can otherwise be torn. When an athlete jumps off the ground, a large amount of force is required to propel the entire body mass off the ground. The body must be able to flex and extend body limbs very quickly, in order to leave the ground. A plyometric type of exercise relies on this quick body action in order to attain the power which is required for the movement.

172

Plyometric movement is based on the **reflex contraction** of the muscle fibers **resulting from the rapid loading** (and thus stretching) of these same muscle fibers. Physiologically, when excessive stretching and tearing become a possibility, the stretch receptors cause proprioceptive nerve impulses that are sent to the spinal cord and then through a rebounding action they are received back at the stretch receptors. By this rebounding action, a braking effect is applied, further stretching of the muscle fibers is prevented, and most importantly, in terms of plyometrics, a powerful muscle contraction is released.

Plyometrics work within the complex neural mechanisms. As a result of any plyometric training, changes occur at both the muscular and the neural levels that facilitate and enhance the performance of more rapid and powerful movement skills.

The contractile elements of the muscles are the muscle fibers. Certain parts of the muscles are non-contractile, and thus result in what is known as the "**series elastic component**". The stretching of the series elastic component during muscle contraction produces an elastic potential energy similar to that of a loaded spring. When this energy is released, it augments to some degree the energy of contraction generated by the muscle fibers. This action is seen in plyometric movements. When the muscle is being stretched rapidly, the series elastic component is also stretched, thus storing a portion of the load force in the form of elastic potential energy. The recovery of the stored elastic energy occurs during the concentric or overcoming phase of muscle contraction, which is triggered by the myotatic reflex.

Summary of plyometric training:
1. a muscle will contract more forcefully and quickly from a **prestretched** position;
2. the more rapid the prestretch, the more forceful the concentric contraction;
3. it is essential to learn correct techniques for performing plyometric exercises;
4. it is important to ensure the athlete lands in a pre-stretched, or bent legs (arms) position;
5. the shortening contraction should occur immediately after the completion of the pre-stretch phase;
6. the transition from the pre-stretch phase should be smooth, continuous and as swift as possible;
7. plyometric training results in:
   • the quick mobilization of **greater innervation** activities;
   • the **recruitment** of most, if not all, **motor units** and their corresponding muscle fibers;

- an **increase in firing rate** of the motor neurons;
- the transformation of muscle strength into **explosive power**;
- plyometrics develop the nervous system so that it will **react with maximum speed** to the lengthening of the muscle; in turn, it will develop the ability to shorten (contract) rapidly and with maximum force;
- repeated reactive training induces fatigue which affects both the eccentric, but more noticeably, the concentric work capacity; fatigue is characterized by increases in the duration of the contact time (Gollhofer et al., 1987).

It is widely recognized that a good background of several years of strength training will assist in advancing faster through the progression of plyometric exercises. This experience is also an important factor in preventing injury.

As far as establishing a good base of strength and developing shock-absorbing qualities are concerned, the benefits of introducing children to plyometric exercises should not be dismissed, providing these exercises are performed over a period of several years, and the principle of progression is respected (Figure 78). The key element of this approach is **PATIENCE**. A healthy training progression would be to expose children to low impact plyometrics first, during a period of several years, say between the ages of 14 and 16 years, and only after that introduce the young athlete to the more demanding reactive jumps.

Throughout these years of a long term progression, teachers in the school system and coaches in sports clubs should teach young athletes the correct plyometric techniques, in which the "hop" and "step" from the triple jump are the ABC's of plyometric training.

In addition to the amount of strength which should be developed before doing plyometrics (some authors consider the ability to perform half squats with a load of twice the body weight a safe guide), the type of training surface, the equipment to wear, and whether to carry additional weights when performing plyometric exercises (heavy vests, ankle and waist belts) are also controversial topics.

For the person concerned about injury, the surface of the floor should be soft. That means that outdoors these exercises should be performed on grass or soft ground, and indoors on a padded floor. Although this precaution may be appropriate for beginners, it should be remembered that a soft surface can dampen the stretch reflex. Only a hard surface can enhance the reactivity of the neuro-muscular system. Therefore, for athletes with a better background in sports and/ or strength training, a hard surface is recommended. The training surface is not the only important element to consider in order to avoid injuries, but rather to follow a very methodical progression over several years of training.

Finally, weighted ankle and waist belts should not be used during plyometric drills, simply because (as in the case of a soft surface) they help to decrease the reactive ability of the nerve-muscle coupling and obstruct the reactivity of the neuro-muscular system.

Furthermore, while such overloading may result in increased strength, it certainly slows down the speed of reaction and rebounding effect.

PROGRAM DESIGN

In order to properly design a plyometrics program one has to realize that there are several levels of intensity, which for a better progression are classified in different groups.

The level of intensity is directly proportional to the height and/ or length of an exercise. High intensity plyometric exercises, such as reactive or drop jumps, result in higher tension in the muscle, recruiting more neuro-muscular units to perform the action or to resist the pull of gravitational force.

Plyometric exercises can be divided into two major groups, reflecting the degree of impact the exercises have on the neuro-muscular system:

1. **LOW IMPACT EXERCISES:**
   - skipping
   - rope jumps
   - jumps: low and short steps, hops and jumps
   - jumps over low benches/ rope: 10–15" (25–35cm)
   - medicine ball throws: 2–4kg (5–9 lbs.)
   - tubing
   - throwing of light implements (i.e. baseball)
2. **HIGH IMPACT EXERCISES:**
   - standing long, and triple jump
   - jumps: higher and longer steps, hops and jumps
   - jumps over higher benches/ rope: >15" (35cm)
   - jumps on, over, and off boxes of >15" (35cm)
   - heavy medicine ball throws: 5–6 kg (11–13lbs.)
   - throwing heavy implements
   - drop jumps/reactive jumps
   - "shock" muscle tension induced by machines

From a more practical perspective, plyometric exercises can be divided into five groups of intensity (see Figure 78). This classification can be utilized to facilitate better alternation of training demand throughout the week.

Any plan to incorporate plyometric exercises into a training program should consider the following factors:

- the age and physical development of the athlete
- the skills and techniques involved in plyometric exercises
- the principle performance factors of the sport
- the energy requirements of the sport
- the particular training phase of the annual plan
- the need to respect a methodical progression over a longer period of time (2–4 years): to progress from low impact (#5 and #4) to simple bounding (#3), and then to high impact exercises (#2 and #1).

Plyometric exercises are fun to perform but because they demand a high level of concentration, they are deceptively vigorous and taxing. The lack of patience and discipline to wait for the right moment for each exercise can result in incorporating high impact exercises into the training program of athletes who are still not ready. Often, the resultant **injuries** or physiological **discomfort is not the fault of the plyometric exercises themselves,** but rather the **lack of knowledge** and **application** of the coach or instructor.

This is why knowledge of the five levels of intensity will help in the selection of appropriate exercises which follow the same steady and orderly progression, and with the suggested rest interval. However, the suggested number of repetitions and sets are for advanced athletes. The coach should resist the temptation to apply the same number of repetitions and sets to beginners, or athletes with insufficient foundations in sports and/ or strength training.

Progress through the five values of intensity is a **long term proposition**. The incorporation of low impact exercises into the training program of young athletes, for 2–4 years, represents the time needed for a progressive adaptation of ligaments, tendons, and the bony structure of the limbs involved. It also allows for the **gradual preparation of the shock-absorbing sections of the body, such as the hips and spine.**

Figure 79 illustrates a long-term, comprehensive progression of strength and power training, including plyometric training. It is important to observe the age at which it is suggested that low-impact plyometrics be introduced, and the fact that high-impact plyometrics are only introduced after four years. This implies that this is the length of time required to

INTENSITY VALUES	TYPE OF EXERCISE	INTENSITY OF EXERCISE	NR OF REPS AND SETS	NR OF REPS/ TRAINING SESSION	REST INTERVAL BETWEEN SETS
1	Shock Tension, High Reactive Jumps >24" (>60cm)	Maximum	8–5 x 10–20	120–150 (200)	8–10 Min.
2	Drop Jumps >32–48" (80–120cm)	Very High	5–15 x 5–15	75–150	5–7 Min.
3	Bounding Exercises – 2 legs – 1 leg	Submaximum	3–25 x 5–15	50–250	3–5 Min.
4	Low Reactive Jumps 8–20" (20–50cm)	Moderate	10–25 x 10–25	150–250	3–5 Min.
5	Low Impact Jumps/ Throws – On Spot – Implements	Low	10–30 x 10–15	50–300	2–3 Min.

FIGURE 78.   The five levels of intensity of plyometric exercises.

AGE GROUPS	FORMS OF TRAINING	METHODS	VOLUME	INTENSITY	MEANS OF TRAINING
PRE-PUBERTY: 12–13	– general exercises only – games	- Muscular endurance	– low – medium	very low	– light resistance exercises – light implements – balls/med.ball
BEGINNERS: 13–15	– general strength – event oriented exercises	- M-E (CT)	– low – medium	low	– dumbbells – tubing – balls – univ. gym.
INTER-MEDIATE: 15–17	– general strength – event oriented	– body building – M-E (C.T.) – power	– low – medium – high	– low – medium	– all the above – free weights
ADVANCED: >17	– event oriented – specific strength	– body building – M-E – power – MxS – low imp.plyo.	– medium – high – maximum	– medium – high	– free weights – special strength equipment

HIGH PERFORM-ANCE:	– specific	– all the above
		– eccentric
		– plyometrics
		  – low impact
		  – high impact
			as above	– medium
				– high
				– super max.
					as above

FIGURE 79. A long-term strength development and the progression of plyometric training.

learn proper technique and to allow for a progressive anatomical adaptation. From this point on in the athlete's training, high impact plyometrics can be part of the normal diet of training.

The intensity in plyometric exercises— the amount of tension created in the muscle— depends on the height of the exercise performed. Although the height is determined strictly by the individual qualities of the athlete, the following general principle applies: **the stronger the muscular system the greater the energy required to stretch it to obtain an elastic effect in the shortening phase.** This is why optimal height for one athlete may not generate the greatest stimulation for another. Therefore, the following information should be treated only as a guideline.

According to Verkhoshanski (1969) the optimal height for depth (reactive) jumps for speed training is between 75cm (30 inches) and 110cm (43 inches), in order to make gains in dynamic strength (power). Similar findings were reported by Bosco and Komi (1980). Above 110cm (43 inches), the latter authors concluded, the mechanics of the action are changed, so that the time and energy it takes to cushion the force of the drop on the ground defeats the purpose of plyometric training. Exceptional heights were tried by other authors: Zanon (1977) employed the following heights for international class long jumpers: 2.5m (8.2 feet) for men, and 2.10m (7 feet) for women. The landing from boxes of these heights was immediately followed by a long jump for distance!!!

As far as the number of repetitions is concerned, plyometric exercises fall into two categories: single-response (SR) and multiple-response (MR) drills. The former represents a single action such as high reactive jumps, shock tension (#1), and drop jumps (#2) where the main purpose is to induce the highest level of tension in the muscles. The objective of such exercises is to develop maximum strength and power. The repetitive exercises such as bounding (#3), low reactive (#4), and low impact (#5) result in the development of power and power endurance. Therefore, as suggested in Figure 78, the number of repetitions can be anywhere between 1 and 30, with the number of sets ranging from 5–25, depending on the scope of training, type of exercise, and the athlete's background and physical potential.

Often, however, especially for MR exercises, it is more convenient and practical to equate the number of repetitions with a distance, e.g. 5 sets of 50 m rather than 5 sets of 25 repetitions. In this way, it is not necessary to constantly count the number of repetitions.

One of the factors for high quality training is adequate physiological recuperation between exercises. Far too often athletes/ coaches either do not pay enough attention to the duration of the RI, or are simply caught-up in the "traditions" of a given sport. Quite often "tradition" dictates that the only RI taken is the time necessary to move from one station to another. There is no question that this is quite inadequate, especially when the physiological characteristics of plyometric training are taken into consideration.

The **fatigue induced by plyometric** exercises is twofold: **local**, and fatigue affecting the **CNS**. Local fatigue is experienced as a result of **depleting the energy** stored in the muscle, the fuel necessary to perform such explosive movements (ATP/ CP), and the production of lactic acid for repetitions longer than 10–15 seconds. But even more importantly, during training, athletes are fatiguing the CNS, the very system which is determinant in sending powerful signals to the working muscle to perform a given amount of quality work. Plyometric training is performed as a result of nerve impulses sent by the CNS to the working muscle. These impulses have a certain speed, power, and frequency. Any high quality training requires that the **speed of contraction**, its power, or frequency, be at the **highest level possible**.

When the RI is short (1–2 minutes), the athlete experiences both local and CNS fatigue. For the working muscle, a short RI means the inability to remove the lactic acid from the muscle, and to replenish the energy necessary to perform the next repetitions with the same intensity. Similarly, a fatigued CNS is no longer able to send the powerful nerve impulses which ensure that the prescribed load is performed with the same number of repetitions and sets before exhaustion is experienced. And from exhaustion to injury is often just a short step! Therefore maximum attention should be paid to the RI!

As suggested in Figure 78, the RI is a function of the load and type of plyometric training performed. **The higher the intensity of the exercise, the greater the RI.** Consequently, for maximum intensity (high reactive jumps) the RI between sets should be 8–10 minutes, or even longer. The suggested rest for intensity #2 is 5–7 minutes, for #3 and #4 between 3–5 minutes, while for low impact activities (#5) around 2–3 minutes.

THE APPLICATION OF POWER TRAINING TO THE SPECIFICS OF SPORTS

As demonstrated in chapter 2, Figure 5, power is not a combined ability which suits the needs of every single sport/ event. On the contrary, it has to be developed in a sport-specific way, so that it meets the needs of a given sport, event, or position one plays in a team.

To further illustrate the needs of sport-specific application of power, specific references will be made below. However, one should keep in mind that many elements of the aforementioned power training methods are highly applicable, and that the following discussion is intended to further explain the needs to develop power according to the specifics of each sport, event, and skill.

LANDING/ REACTIVE POWER. In several sports landing represents an important skill, often being followed by another skill, such as another jump as in figure skating, or a quick move in another direction, such as in tennis, or many team sports. This is why one not only needs the power to control the landing but also the reactive power to quickly perform another move.

The power necessary to control and absorb the shock of landing is related to the height of the jump. Landing (such as in drop or depth jumps) from 80–100cm (32–40 inches) often loads each ankle joint by 6–8 times the athlete's own body weight. Similarly, to absorb the shock from a figure skating jump requires a power of 5–8 times one's own body weight. Therefore, the muscles have to be trained to cope with shock absorbing power, to reduce impact forces at the instant of landing.

Landing involves the muscles into an **eccentric contraction**, which if not trained properly will not just result in incorrect landing, but can be more prone to injuries since there is a higher tension produced for the same amount of muscle fiber activity. As such the elastic tissue of the tendons are placed under greater stress. To overcome that one should apply in training eccentric contractions as well as plyometrics.

Schmidtbleicher (1992) specifies that at the instant of ground contact in landing, the athletes experience an **inhibitory effect**. Well-trained athletes can cope with the impact forces much better, and that **after drop jump training the inhibitory effects were reduced**. He concluded that the inhibitory mechanisms represent a **protection system**, especially for novice athletes, which **shields them against injuries**.

As part of training to enhance landing/ reactive power, one should use both concentric and eccentric contractions. The latter type of contraction can use eccentric strength training, and plyometrics, mostly **drop jumps** which can **mimic the desired landing skill**. Drop/ reactive jumps are performed from a raised platform (box, bench, chair, etc.), landing in a flexed position (knees slightly bent), thus absorbing the shock. Landing is performed on the ball of the feet, without touching the ground with the heels.

During the **dropping phase** the muscles take a reflex, **ready-to-work position** by means of nervous stimulation, which **enhances the tension** and the elastic properties of the muscles involved. At the instant of landing, especially if the athlete is quickly preparing for an other action, **energy is stored in the elastic elements of the muscle**. This readily available energy, at the instant of an ensuing take-off/ quick move in another direction, **releases a stretching reflex which recruits more FT fibers** than under normal strength training conditions. This enables the athlete to **immediately perform another quick and explosive action**. It is rather important for the practitioners to understand that these **reflexes** (including the muscle-spindle reflex) **are trainable**, and that drop/ reactive jumps can be improved as a result of a well periodized training.

THROWING POWER, whether for a pitcher, or thrower in track and field, is served mostly by the FT muscle fibers. The larger the diameter of the individual fiber the faster it contracts. Similarly, the more fibers that are involved in a simultaneous contraction, the higher the performance power.

Throwers, and often athletes from other sports such as fencing, boxing, and baseball, must be able to develop considerable power to accelerate the implement or the equipment they use. Often it is necessary to **overcome the inertia of an implement/ equipment, with the greatest possible speed from the beginning** of the movement, as well as to **increase acceleration** throughout the movement, especially before the release. In order to achieve that, internal strength has to exceed the resistance of the implement. The more one exceeds the weight of the implement the higher the acceleration. This is why, sports where throwing power is utilized **requires a well planned MxS** and **power training**. The higher the difference between MxS of the athlete and the resistance, the higher the acceleration.

Specific power training for throwing events/ movements has to concentrate on the **maximum application of force**, using especially the **isotonic** and **ballistic methods**. For the isotonic method it is not necessary to use the number of repetitions (4–10) in a non-stop manner and with a high rate. For maximum benefit of explosive contraction, where the maximum number of FT fibers are recruited at once, it is more important to perform one repetition at the time, and to achieve the highest mental concentration before each of them.

TAKE-OFF POWER. There are many sport-events or skills where a good performance is possible only if the athlete is capable of performing an explosive take-off (jumping events in track and field, ski-jumping, volleyball, basketball, figure skating, etc.). In many cases the take-off occurs following short, high velocity running, where during the crouch, or preparation for take-off, the muscles pre-stretch, thus storing energy. As the take-off is performed this energy is used as an acceleration thrust, and a powerful jump occurs.

The depth of the crouch performed at the instant of joint flexion depends on the power of the legs. **The deeper the crouch, the greater the force required from the leg extensors.** However, the crouch represents a mechanical necessity, because it puts the muscles in a state of stretch giving them a greater distance to accelerate, culminating in a take-off. To be more effective, the depth of the crouch must be proportional to the power of the legs. If the flexion is too great, the extension (or shortening phase) will be performed slowly, and as a result the jump will be low.

Many jumpers use traditional weight training (e.g. squats or any Olympic lifts) in order to train for this take-off phase of their jumps. This type of weight training places a large load on the leg extensors which will overtime provide an adequate strength training base. The main problem with using only weight training is that it is unlikely that a heavy squat lift will be fast enough to utilize the elastic qualities of the muscles. This is not the case in the single leg take-off, which involves multiple joint movements all happening simultaneously.

Plyometric, and more specifically bounding exercises can be used successfully to simulate an effective take-off and can therefore improve the overall jumping ability of the athlete. Bounding has the potential to possess very similar force-time characteristics to the take-off. Similarly, it allows the athlete to practise resisting large impact loads on the take-off leg and to exert force in an short time interval. The bounding exercises will also involve multi-joint movements and provide the possibility of the development of the required muscle elasticity.

STARTING POWER is essential, often the determinant ability, in sports where the initial speed of action dictates the final outcome (boxing, karate, fencing, the start in sprinting). The ability of the athlete to **recruit the highest possible FT fibers** in order to start the motion explosively is the **essential physiological characteristic** necessary for a successful performance.

Starting power in sprinting is performed with the muscles in a pre-stretch position (both knees being bent), which are able to **generate greater power** than relaxed or even shortened muscles. In this position the elastic elements of the muscles **store kinetic energy which act like a spring at the sound of the gun.** The power used by the national class athletes at the start is very high: 132kg (290lbs) for the front leg and 102kg (225lbs) for the back leg. The higher the starting power, the more explosive and faster the start.

In boxing and martial arts a quick and powerful start of an offensive skill prevents the opponent from using an effective defensive action. The elastic and reactive component of a muscle is of vital importance for delivering quick actions and powerful starts. The more specific the power training during the conversion phase the better one trains the stretch reflex of a muscle, and the greater the power of the FT muscle fibers.

The stretching and reactive components of the muscle, so important for a quick and powerful start of a motion **are trainable** through isotonic, ballistic, and especially through plyometric exercises. They can be performed in a set of repetitive motions or separately. In the latter case, the number of exercises per set are performed one at a time so that the athlete will have enough time to reach a maximum mental concentration in order to perform the exercise as explosively as possible. Under these conditions one is capable of recruiting a high number of FT fibers, and consequently to perform the action with the highest power available to the athlete.

DECELERATION POWER. In several sports, especially tennis and team sports, deceleration is as important as acceleration. In order to overpass an opponent, or make oneself available to receive a pass, a player must accelerate and run as quickly as possible. But team sport athletes also decelerate, decrease the speed, very quickly in order to stop and then quickly change their direction of running, or jump to rebound an oncoming ball.

Often an athlete who can decelerate faster can create a tactical advantage. In order to perform a quick deceleration one needs powerful legs which may require leg power twice as high as one's own body weight.

Deceleration is performed through eccentric contraction of the leg muscles. Biomechanically this is facilitated by placing the feet ahead of the centre of gravity, and by leaning the upper body behind it. Strong legs and good biomechanics enables one to decelerate quickly.

The development of the muscles to successfully decelerate from a fast sprint, relies on the elastic properties of the muscles to **amortize and reduce impact forces**. The ability to amortize these forces requires similar power and degrees of legs flexion as during the actions of absorbing the shock while landing.

To train the muscles to quickly decelerate, an athlete in action requires the employment of several training methods, such as eccentric contraction and plyometrics. As far as eccentric contraction is concerned, one has to apply the MxS method (eccentric) but progressing from medium to supermaximum loads. From plyometrics, after a few years of normal progression from low to high impact exercises, one has to use drop (depth) and reactive jumps. By following the methodology described under the above methods, one will successfully develop the needed deceleration power.

ACCELERATION POWER. Whether in sprinting, swimming, cycling, rowing or in most team sports, the athletes' ability to accelerate, to develop high speed, is crucial in achieving an improved performance. In each of the sports requiring high acceleration, power is an essential attribute. Without it one cannot perform a strong push against the ground (the propulsion phase in running) or to overcome water resistance in sports performed in the water.

In sprinting, for instance, an athlete's force performed against the ground is 2–3 times that of their own body weight, while to maintain a high acceleration in rowing the oarsperson has to use a constant blade pressure of 40–60 kg (88–132 lbs) per stroke. In all the sports requiring acceleration power, power is brought into action repetitively and very rapidly. The higher the difference between MxS and water resistance or the power performed against the ground in high velocity running, the higher the acceleration.

To achieve high acceleration the development of MxS is essential. A relatively large diameter of the contracting muscle filaments represent a key physiological requirement for one's ability to display power. These filaments, mostly the protein-rich crossbridges of the myosins, can increase their size, or hypertrophy, only as a result of using MxS training methods. As this is achieved during the MxS phase, such gains have to be converted into power through specific power training methods. The isotonic, ballistic, power-resisting, and plyometrics methods can assist the athletes to successfully apply a series of muscle impulses that can activate a great number of FT fibers. When this is achieved acceleration power reaches high and desirable levels.

The above methods can be performed in either a short number of repetitions (6–10) performed explosively and with high frequency, or individually, one repetition at a time. In the first case high frequency is the scope, whereas in the second the application of the highest power in one attempt is the objective of training. Since in sports where acceleration power is sought one has to use both high frequency and power, both methods have to be utilized. By applying the concept of periodization of strength one increases the chance of achieving the above, as well as reaching highest acceleration power before the major races/ games.

CHAPTER FIFTEEN

TRAINING METHODS FOR THE CONVERSION PHASE: CONVERSION TO MUSCULAR-ENDURANCE

Strength training, irrespective of how intensive and comprehensive, cannot result in an adequate adaptation, have a positive influence in every sport or event, unless it addresses to the specific, physiological needs of the sport.

Although most training specialists may agree with the above statement, in reality strength training for sports/ events where endurance is dominant, or it is an important component, is still inadequately done. The weight lifting and bodybuilding training methods still influence the training programs of endurance-dominant sports. There are still many researchers and strength training specialists who consider that 15–20 repetitions represent an effective way to train M-E. For sports such as mid and long distance swimming, rowing, canoeing, boxing, wrestling, cross-country skiing, speed skating and triathlon, such a training regimen would be grossly inadequate.

If an athlete from an endurance-dominant sport employs a low repetition strength training program with submaximum or maximum loads, he/ she will adapt the energy supply, recovery and physiological functioning of the organs and the neuromuscular system, to such loading. All these physiological parameters differ fundamentally from those required for an effective physiological behaviour of an athlete involved in an endurance-dominated sport. Such a program would result in strength increments but would inhibit the endurance component of an athlete adaptation for such a sport.

A strength training program for an endurance-dominant sport requires a **load close to the resistance one has to overcome** while competing, with relatively low muscle tension, but with a **high number of repetitions** and approaching the duration of the event. In this way the athlete is trained to cope with the fatigue specific to the sport and utilize simultaneous stimuli for both specific strength and endurance. Adaptation to such training will be very **similar to the competition's physiological requirements.** Luckily, the neuromuscular system is capable of adapting to any type of training. But it adapts only to what it is exposed to.

The importance of MxS for the endurance-dominant sports increases proportionally to the external resistance. A 400 m swimmer, swims with a higher velocity than one involved in a longer event (800–1500 m). In order to create that velocity the 400 m swimmer has to pull with greater force against the water resistance than the 1500 m athlete. Consequently, MxS is more important for the 400 m than for the 1500 m swimmer. But in both cases, one has to improve MxS from year to year if one expects to cover the distance faster. Such an improvement is possible only if the swimmer improves their aerobic endurance and at the same time, pulls against the water with an increased force. Only this increased force will push the body faster through the water.

M-E is best increased through a strength training program that emphasizes a high number of repetitions. Both the selected exercises and the number of repetitions have to result in the desired adaptation according to the physiological requirement of the sport/ event. If during the conversion of MxS to M-E the adequate method is not applied, positive transfer should not be expected from one type of training to a different physiological requirement. In other words, if a bodybuilding/ weightlifting methodology is applied, with 20 repetitions, an improvement can not be expected in a sport where, during the race, 200 non-stop strokes is performed.

In an endurance-dominant sport, aerobic endurance and M-E have to both be trained at the same time. This is possible by either training each of them on separate days, or combined in the same training session. In this case, M-E will be performed at the end of the session since the specific endurance work includes technical training as well. However, for the combined workouts fatigue can represent a limitation. If the total work per day has to be decreased, M-E is normally reduced or decreased.

For athletes, whose technique and aerobic endurance are properly developed, M-E ought to be trained separately. In such a case training benefits are higher.

As per Figure 5, the strength-endurance axis refers to 4 types of combinations between the two abilities: power-endurance (P-E), M-E short, medium and long. Each of these strength combinations are required for certain sports and for a better discussion, training methods for each will be presented separately.

THE POWER-ENDURANCE METHOD

Several sports and positions, from sprinting in track and field and swimming, to a running back, pitcher or wrestler, require the ability of applying a high degree of power not once, but several times in a repetitive manner.

Sprinting, including all the team sports requiring explosive running (football, baseball, ice-hockey, rugby and Australian football), are often misjudged. Because a sprinter covers the classical 100m in 10–12 seconds, one may fail to understand that the athlete has to be trained to perform powerful leg actions not only during the start and the following 6–8 strides, but rather during the entire race. And in a 100 m race an athlete performs . . . 48–54 strides! (depending on one's stride length). Therefore, during the race one has 24–27 ground contacts with each leg. And in each ground contact the athlete applies a force of approximately 2 times their own body weight!

Consequently, an athlete competing in the above sports do not need only a high degree of power output in one or few repetitions, but rather the ability to repeat that 20–30 times! Often, such as in football, rugby and Australian football, to be able to repeat the same repetition after few seconds of game interruption. Therefore, such athletes need not only a very high level of power, but also the ability to repeat the same amount of power 20–30 times. Therefore power-endurance (P-E). An athlete with a high level of P-E will have the capacity to avoid a decrease in stride frequency and loss in speed velocity at the end of the race, or a longer sprint.

PROGRAM DESIGN

From the above discussion it appears that P and P-E are the determinant abilities in several sports. In both kinds of abilities, MxS represents a determinant factor. Power training, or the methods available to train an athlete to perform an explosive action, was discussed earlier. The scope of this section is to refer to the training methodology to develop muscle-endurance in an explosive manner, or P-E.

P-E requires the **application of 70–85% of MxS, rhythmically, repetitively**, but also **explosively**. The above load requires each repetition to be performed not only in a very dynamic manner but more importantly, to explosively execute each repetition in a set, non-stop, 20–30 times. Certainly, such an important training requirement will be achieved progressively, starting with a lower number of repetitions (8–15) and increased over 4–6 weeks time, or the duration of the conversion phase for such sports.

In the early part of the conversion phase, the FT muscle fibers were trained to be recruited at once, in order to display the highest level of power possible. For the purpose of P-E the FT fibers are trained now to resist the fatigue induced by so many repetitions performed dynamically. In doing so, training is now aimed at **developing the endurance component of speed training.** This is achieved by progressively **increasing** both the **number of repetitions and sets.** In doing so the athletes have to appeal to their psychological abilities by calling upon their maximum willpower to overcome fatigue and to be able to reach maximum mental concentration before each set is performed.

In order to perform a high number of sets per each prime mover, the **number of exercises have to be as low as possible (2–3).** At the same time, each repetition of a **set of 20–30 repetitions** has to be performed explosively and the **RI** has to be long: **8–10 minutes.**

During this type of work the athlete will experience a high level of lactic acid build up, which will impair his/her ability to repeat quality work before it will be disposed of. Therefore, the next set has to be performed only after a length of time necessary to remove at least 50% of the total lactic acid. Normally it takes 15–25 minutes to remove 50% of the lactic acid accumulation, but since the athlete is constantly alternating the muscle groups involved in training, by the time the same exercise will be performed again removal will take at least 20 minutes.

The rhythm/speed of performance has to be very dynamic and explosive. If the coach does not strictly observe that, then the outcome of training will not be P-E but rather hypertrophy training. This will not be P-E training but rather bodybuilding! This is why it will take a few weeks before one can perform explosively and non-stop the above number of repetitions. When the athlete is not capable of performing a repetition of a set dynamically he/ she should stop. From that point on, P-E is not beig trained.

No.	Training parameter	Work
1	Load	70–85%
2	# of exercises	2–3
3	# of reps/ set	15–30
4	# of sets/ session	2–4
5	Rest interval	8–10 min.
6	Rhythm/ speed of execution	Very dynamic
7	Frequency/ week	2–3

FIGURE 80. Suggested training parameters for P-E.

THE MUSCULAR-ENDURANCE OF SHORT DURATION METHOD

In the world of sports there are several sports whose duration lasts between 30 seconds and 2 minutes, such as in track and field, swimming, canoeing, speed skating, skiing, or where intensive activity of such a duration is constantly required during the game or match, as is the case in ice-hockey, soccer, rugby, basketball, boxing, wrestling and martial arts. During such an intensive activity, the athlete builds-up a high level of lactic acid, often over 12–15 mmol/ litre, a signal that the lactic acid energy system is either dominant, or represents an important component in the overall performance of the sport/ event. Most of these sports require both a very strong anaerobic power and a very good aerobic endurance.

If an athlete is to be properly trained, strength training must compliment the overall physiological demands, it should address the same physiological needs for a successful competition. One of the key objectives for the above sports is to **train the athlete to be able to tolerate the negative effects of a high lactic acid build-up and strength training should have the same role.** As the competitive phase approaches, strength training ought to **be designed** in such a way that it **challenges the same training weaknesses of the athlete: the inability to tolerate a high build-up of lactic acid.**

Far too often, the athletes involved in the aforementioned sports are trapped in strength programs influenced by bodybuilding and weightlifting, in which an "8–15" repetition is supposed to achieve miracles for everyone and in every single sport. Certainly, this is a fallacy! And to still adhere to such a program means to be caught in the inertia of tradition.

A training program for M-ES should have the objective of improving the athlete's resistance to fatigue, to lactic acid build-up, during a short-term endurance activity performed against a **load of 50–60%** of one's 1RM. With a properly calculated **RI**, such a program should also enhance the capacity to recover following a training of such an intensity.

The **specifics of M-ES is similar to intensive interval training method used in CT,** where during the RI one develops an oxygen debt, typical for activities where the anaerobic energy system prevails. As such, at the end of an activity of 60–90 seconds the heart rate can be as high as 180–200 beats/minute (b/m) and blood lactic acid concentration between 12–15 mmol/ litre, or even higher. The energy source for M-ES is blood and muscle glucose and especially the glycogen stored in the liver.

PROGRAM DESIGN

The structure of a M-ES can follow the format of a CT, where the repetitions are performed in a rhythmical, but fast pace. The **load** is not very high, **50–60%**, but being performed at a high intensity, at or close to the rate of performance. Since the volume of work is not very high one should select the lowest **number of exercises (3–6)**.

The number of repetitions can also be precisely set, but typical of interval training, it is more appropriate to decide the **duration** of each set and the rhythm of performing it **(30–60 seconds)**.

If the number of exercises are low, one can perform **3–6 sets, or circuits**. As usual, the rhythm of performance and especially the duration and number of sets, have to be increased progressively over time, from a lower level to the work suggested by Figure 81. In order to train the athletes to tolerate the lactic acid build-up, the **RI has to be low: 60–90 seconds**.

No.	Training parameters	Work
1	Load	50–60%
2	# of exercises	3–6
3	Duration of activity	30–60 sec.
4	# of sets/ session	3–6
5	Rest interval	60–90 sec.
6	Rhythm/ speed of execution	Medium to fast
7	Frequency/ week	2–3

FIGURE 81. Training parameters suggested for M-ES.

THE MUSCULAR-ENDURANCE OF MEDIUM AND LONG DURATION METHOD

All the sports, whose performance time is well in excess of 2 minutes, ought to regard the development of M-E as one of the main factors of performance improvement. A specific strength training program has to be related to the non-stop duration of activity for sports where aerobic endurance is either dominant or represents a very important component of the final performance.

Sports such as boxing, wrestling, rowing, swimming (400–1500 m), kayak-canoeing (1,000–10,000 m), road cycling, cross-country skiing, biathlon and thriathlon are the main beneficiaries of M-E training. Some team sports, especially rugby, ice-hockey, basketball, soccer and Australian football, could also consider, during the preparatory phase, the incorporation of M-E of medium duration.

M-E training can be performed as a CT, following the principles of interval training of long duration. This is why this training method can also be called "**extensive interval training**", where the term extensive implies a high volume-long duration type of activity.

The main **objective** of training for M-E is to increase the athlete's ability to **cope with fatigue during lengthy work**. Since M-E training employs **long repetitions, often over 100**, it assists the athlete to improve both the anaerobic and aerobic endurance. In the early part of a non-stop set with many repetitions, the energy is provided by the anaerobic system, where the build-up of lactic acid creates physiological and psychological problems for the athlete in his/her quest to continue the activity. As the athlete overcomes these challenges and continues to work, energy is supplied by the aerobic system. Repetitive M-E training results in specific adaptation which improves cardiovascular regulations and the aerobic metabolism.

Among the aerobic adaptation phenomena, there is a clear increase in the density of capillaries and in the number and size of mitochondria (a subcellular structure found in all aerobic cells). These types of adaptations promote a better oxygen and energy supply, increasing at the same time the removal of metabolic wastes. Repetitive M-E training results in a clear increase of the glycogen stores in both muscle and liver. An overall **increase in the athlete's physiological efficiency is the specific benefit of M-E training**.

Since the **load** is around or **below 50%**, the muscles improve their **long-term contracting capability**, without any evident increase in muscle fiber diameter. As M-E employs a relatively low load, only a certain number of motor units are active, the others are at rest and activated only when and where the contracting fibers are fatigued.

As suggested by the periodization of strength, improvement of MxS during that phase is beneficial also for the sports where M-E represents an important training method. If, as a result of MxS, the diameter of an individual muscle fiber has increased, a smaller number of motor units are requested to perform a M-E training task.

This type of strength reserve is critical and adds to the capacity of the muscle to produce work more effectively since less number of fibers are involved to overcome the resistance. Therefore, MxS should not be minimized. On the contrary it should, within limits, be used for the above sports as well. However, for sports of long duration, such as a marathon, or for sports which require less than 30% of MxS to perform the activity, further increments of MxS has negligible, if any, benefits (Hartman and Tünnemann, 1989).

Since the physiological basis for M-E medium and long are similar, the above discussion did not discriminate between the two. However, M-E medium (M-EM) is suggested for sports where the duration of the competition is between 2–5 minutes, while for M-E long (M-EL), the duration is for sports of 6 minutes and longer.

192

This distinction is necessary from the physiological point of view. The M-EM has a stronger anaerobic component, whereas M-EL is clearly aerobic. As such the load, duration of a set and the rhythm/ speed of execution is clearly different. Therefore, the program design will be made separately for each type of M-E.

Program Design for Muscular-endurance of Medium Duration

The M-EM training program can be designed both as a CT or as interval training (IT). The first option is suggested for sports where it is necessary to train more muscle groups (e.g. wrestling, boxing), while the second is advisable for sports where one limb prevails (e.g. speed skating, canoeing). An example will be given for each option.

For M-EM the **load is 50–60%**, performed in a progressively longer duration. As exemplified by Figures 83 and 84, the duration/number of repetitions are increased progressively over a longer period of time. As such the **duration of the conversion** phase for M-E has to be **8–10 weeks**. Such a long period of time is necessary to physiologically adapt for such a high training demand.

Throughout the M-EM phase the load, number of exercises, rest interval and rhythm/ speed of execution remains constant. What changes, however, is the number of repetitions, which increases every second week (Figure 83).

No.	Training parameters	Work
1	Load	50–60%
2	# of exercises	4–6
3	# of sets/ session	2–4
4	Rest interval between sets	2 min.
5	Rest interval between circuits	5 min.
6	Rhythm/ speed of execution	Medium
7	Frequency/ Week	2–3

Figure 82. Training parameters for M-EM.

As can be observed from the above training parameters the rest interval between sets is not too long, therefore the athlete will not have the time to adequately recover from such demanding work. However, considering the physiological characteristics of the sports employing M-EM, the program is designed exactly to constantly expose the athlete to high levels of fatigue, to be able to cope with the hurt and pain of competitions.

No.	Exercise	No. of weeks	2	2	2	2
1	½ squats		30	40	50	60
2	Arm curls		↓	↓	↓	↓
3	Leg curls		↓	↓	↓	↓
4	Bench press		↓	↓	↓	↓
5	"V"-sits		15	20	25	30
6	Dead lift		15	18	20	25

FIGURE 83. A hypothetical CT for a wrestler. Please observe the progression of the number of repetitions per each training phase of 2 weeks.

From examining Figure 83 there is a clear difference between the first 4 exercises and the last 2. The justification is based on the fact that the last exercises are considered a second priority and that "dead lift" involves a "fragile" area of the body, i.e., the low back. To perform more repetitions of the same exercise requires a good training background of several years. In fact, the load for a dead lift has to be lower (30–40%) and not used with beginners.

No.	Exercise	No. of weeks	2	2	2	2
1	½ squats		30	40	50	60
2	Leg curls		30	35	40	50
3	Dead lifts		15	18	20	25

FIGURE 84. A hypothetical M–EM for a speed skater.

Program Design for Muscular-Endurance of Long Duration

Longer duration sports are performed under a different kind of physiological requirement. In most of them the athlete applies force against a given resistance, such as water in swimming, rowing and canoeing, or they have to overcome their own body weight as strength is applied against the pedals in cycling, ice in speed skating, or snow and variations of terrain in cross-country skiing and biathlon.

Since in these sports aerobic endurance is the dominant energy system and since an improved performance is expected to come from increments in aerobic power, strength training has to be designed to enhance that. Therefore in order to increase M-EL, the **key training ingredient is a high number of repetitions** performed, as much as possible, non-stop. The other training parameters remain constant as indicated by Figure 85.

No.	Training parameters	Work
1	Load	30–50%
2	# of exercises	3–4
3	# of sets/ session	2–4
4	Rest interval	see Figure 86
5	Rythm/ speed of execution	Medium
6	Frequency/ week	2–3

Figure 85. Training parameters suggested for M-EL.

Since one of the training goals of M-EL is to cope with fatigue, the RI will not facilitate a full recovery. On the contrary, there will be just a very short rest as the athlete changes the station, usually 2–5 seconds.

A CT designed for M-EL can use either a barbell or any other equipment. The advantage of using a barbell is that, as shown by Figure 86, one can use it for different limbs without taking a rest.

The circuit from Figure 86 has 8 exercises. The athlete takes a barbell of 40% of MxS, places it on the shoulders and performs, say 50 half squats. As the last repetition is finished the athlete sits on a bench (placed there before work started) and performs 40 arm curls. Then the athlete lies down on their back, on the bench, and does 50 bench presses. The barbell is once again placed quickly on the shoulders and the athlete performs 50 half squats, followed by 50 vertical rowing actions. As quickly as possible the barbell is placed on the shoulders to perform 60 toe raises, followed by 50 dead lifts. Now the barbell is left on the floor so that the athlete performs 50 "V-sits" for the abdominal muscles. The total number of repetitions performed by our hypothetical subject is . . . 400!

As demonstrated by past experiments with this method, its advantages is that as one trains by alternating different muscle groups, the cardio-respiratory system is involved throughout the circuit. Therefore two crucial abilities are developed for such sports: M-E and aerobic endurance.

Before referring to the chart, the following comments are necessary:

1. the number of repetitions are progressively increased to reach 40–60 or even higher. To accomplish this 2–4 weeks may be needed;

2. the number of exercises may vary, depending on the needs of the sport;

3. the same exercise can be repeated twice in the same circuit, to illustrate the importance of that group of muscles in a given sport (half squats in our example);

4. the number of exercises may not be the same for every limb. The decision should be made based on the strength and weaknesses of the athletes involved;

5. observe a steady rhythm throughout the circuit; it will be easier on the cardio-respiratory system;

6. set up all the equipment needed before training. In this way the athlete will waste the least possible time to change from one exercise to another;

7. in the second phase one performs 2 exercises non-stop, in the third, 4 exercises, and all of them during the last phase (see Figure 86);

8. it may take 6–8 minutes or longer to perform non-stop an 8 exercise circuit, depending on the classification of the athlete involved;

9. a circuit can be designed to be even longer and as such, to better improve M-EL;

10. since the physiological demand of M-EL is severe, this method should be applied to athletes with a strong background in both strength and endurance training (from national class athletes and up);

11. a less demanding circuit can have 4–6 exercises (for juniors);

12. since, as one performs 2 and then 4 exercises and then all together non-stop, it is advisable to select an even number of exercises;

13. as the athletes adapt to the total number of exercises performed non-stop during the last phase, the coach can also use a stop watch to monitor improvement. As a result of adaptation the time of performance may continuously decrease;

14. this type of M-EL training should not be used for testing purposes, or as a method of comparison between two or more athletes.

Since the anthropometrics (size, length of limbs) differ from athlete to athlete, such an athletic discrimination will not be fair for the atlhletes, especially for the tall ones.

Nr.	Exercise	Nr. of weeks			
		3–4 weeks	3	3	2
1	½ squats	Take a load of 30–50% and progressively aim to perform 50–60 reps non-stop per exercise	Perform 2 exercises non-stop, or 100 reps together. For instance: 50 ½-squats followed by 50 arm curls. Pair together the remaining 6 exercises	Perform 4 exercises non-stop, or 200 repetitions. After a rest interval repeat the other 4 exercises in the same manner	Perform all exercises non-stop: 8 exercises x 50 repetitions = 400 repetitions non-stop
2	Arm curls				
3	Bench press				
4	½ squats				
5	Vertical rowing				
6	Toe raise				
7	Dead lifts				
8	"V"-sits				
	Rest interval between exercises	1 minute	1–2 min. between each group of 2	2 min. between each group of 4	—
	Rest interval between circuits	—	—	—	4–5 minutes

Figure 86. A hypothetical M-EL for a rower

Chapter Sixteen

Strength Training During the Competitive and the Transition Phase

The specifics of Strength Training During the Competitive Phase

Strength training is used in sports because it represents an important physiological contributor to the overall athletic performance. The more explosive a skill, the more important the MxS and P. The longer the duration of an activity the more determinant the role of M-E.

A very good performance cannot be achieved without the vital contribution of strength. **The benefits of strength to athletic performance is felt for as long as the neuro-muscular system maintains the cellular adaptations induced by strength training.** When strength training is ceased the contractile properties of a muscle diminishes and as a direct result, lessens its positive role. The consequence is detraining, or a visible decrease in the contribution of strength to athletic performance. In order to avoid detraining during the competitive phase one has to plan a sport-specific strength program.

Peaking, or the ability of an athlete to perform a peak performance during the main competitions/ games of the year, should also be related to strength training. In several sports, especially in power-dominant sports, a peak performance is often achieved in the early part of the competitive phase. As specific technical/ tactical training becomes dominant the coach tends to overlook strength training. As the season progresses and the coach does not maintain strength training anymore, performance decreases. For as long as the strength benefits were there, as is the case in the early part of the season, one's performance is the expected one. As soon as the ability of a muscle to contract powerfully fades away, so does performance.

According to the concept of periodization of strength, gains in MxS during the MxS phase were supposed to be transformed into either M-E or P during the conversion phase. The purpose of this conversion was to acquire the best sport-specific strength possible to equip the athlete with the physiological needs for a good performance during the competitive phase. In order to maintain a good performance throughout the competition phase, one has to maintain the required physiological base. From the strength point of view, that means that the coach has to **plan a maintenance sport-specific strength program throughout the competitive phase.**

As demonstrated earlier MxS is a crucial ingredient for sport-specific strength programs. There are many sports which require maintenance of some MxS during the competitive season. Sport research confirms that the easiest way to maintain MxS is to increase muscle mass as a result of increments in protein content of the contractile muscle filaments, mostly the myosins. Such increments are possible mostly as a result of employing the "maximum load method" during the MxS phase.

Gains in MxS decline faster if their increase resulted from the processes dependent on the nervous system, such as recruitment of large motor units (Hartman and Tünnemann, 1989). Very often such gains are mostly the result of power training without having a strong MxS base prior to that. In quite a few sports, track and field being one of the culprits, the type of strength being performed is an event-specific power training. Often, MxS using the "maximum load method" is overlooked. As a result, the life of such gains is short. And since strength training is practiced mostly during the preparatory phase, most of its gains fade away as the competitive phase progresses and approaches its peak.

The maintenance of strength during the competitive phase is not a question of **whether** it should be pursued, but rather **how** it should be done. In order to decide, the coach has to once again keep in mind the dominant ability in his/ her sport. As a result of this decision, the coach should not rush to say whether the athletes should maintain just P or M-E. Since most sports require some elements of MxS, P and, M-E, the most important decision the coach has to make is not **which** of the three has to be maintained but rather in what **proportion** and how to best integrate them in training.

In sports where P is the dominant ability both MxS and P should be maintained. However, one should not be performed at the expense of the other. One can not replace the other, but rather they can compliment each other. For instance for throwers in track and field and linemen in football MxS still has to be maintained during the competitive phase. For these athletes the proportion between MxS and P is approximately 50:50. On the other hand most team sport athletes will maintain P and either P-E or M-ES, depending on the position played.

For endurance sports, on the other hand, the proportion between MxS, P and M-E depends on the duration of the event as well as on which energy system is dominant.

Equally important is to acknowledge that the maintenance program and the proportion between different types of strength also depends on the duration of the competitive phase. **The longer the competitive phase, the more important it is to maintain some elements of MxS,** since this type of strength represents an important element which makes up both P and M-E. Overlooking that means that **as MxS is detrained it will affect both P and M-E.** For a better illustration of the proportions between different types of strength to be maintained during the competitive phase the reader is invited to consult table 4.

Table 4
A suggested proportion between different types of strength
to be maintained during the competitive phase

| No. | Sport/event | MxS | | P | P-E | M-E |
		Concen.	Eccen.			
1	Athletics:					
	-Sprinting	20	—	60	20	—
	-Jumping	20	10	70	—	—
	-Throws	30	20	50	—	—
2	Baseball:					
	-Pitcher	40	—	40	20	—
	-Field players	20	—	70	10	—
3	Basketball	10	—	50	20	20
4	Biathlon	—	—	—	20	80
5	Boxing	20	—	20	30	30
6	Canoeing/ Kayaking:					
	-500m	40	—	30	20	10
	-1000m	20	—	20	20	40
	-10,000m	—	—	—	20	80
7	Cycling:					
	-Track 200	20	—	70	10	—
	-4000 pursuit	10	—	30	20	40

No.	Sport/event	MxS		P	P-E	M-E
		Concen.	Eccen.			
8	Diving:	—	10	90	—	—
9	Fencing:	—	—	60	30	10
10	Figure skating:	20	20	40	10	10
11	Field hockey:	—	—	40	20	40
12	Football:					
	-Linemen	30	20	50	—	—
	-Line backers, - run. backs	20	—	60	20	—
	-Wide receivers, -def. back, -tail backs	20	—	60	20	—
13	Football-Australian:	20	10	40	20	10
14	Ice hockey:	10	—	50	30	10
15	Martial arts:	—	—	60	30	10
16	Rowing:	10	—	—	20	70
17	Rugby:	20	—	40	30	10
18	Skiing:					
	-Alpine	20	20	30	30	—
	-Nordic	—	—	—	20	80
19	Soccer:					
	-Swippers/goaly	20	10	60	10	—
	-other positions	—	—	60	20	20

No.	Sport/event	MxS		P	P-E	M-E
		Concen.	Eccen.			
20	Speed skating:					
	-Sprinting	20	—	60	20	—
	-Distance	—	—	10	20	70
21	Swimming:					
	-Sprinting	20	—	50	20	10
	-Mid distance	10	—	10	20	60
	-Long distance	—	—	—	20	80
22	Tennis:	—	—	60	30	10
23	Volleyball:	15	5	50	20	10
24	Waterpolo:	10	—	20	20	50
25	Wrestling:	—	—	30	10	60

During the maintenance phase one should apply the same training methods as suggested in the previous chapters. What is different during the maintenance phase is not the training methodology but rather the volume of strength training as compared to the technical, tactical and different other elements of physical training.

One should never forget that the maintenance of strength is performed in addition to the above types of training, which ought to be dominant during the competitive phase. Therefore, the **number of exercises** have to be the **lowest possible, 2–3(4)** and to specifically address the prime movers. Thus being very specific to the prevailing skills of a given sport. As such one has to spend the least possible energy for the maintenance of strength, since most of it will be used for technical/ tactical training.

The **number of strength training sessions per week should be 2, maximum 3** and as short as possible. Often a good maintenance program can be accomplished in **20–30 minutes** of a very specific work-out. Obviously, the frequency of strength training sessions depends also on the competition schedule. **If no competitions** are scheduled on the weekend, such a micro-cycle may have **2, maximum 3**, strength training sessions. **If a game/ competition** is planned on the weekend then **1 (maximum 2) short** strength training sessions can be planned, normally in the early part of the week.

The **number of sets** is usually **low: 1–4**, depending on whether P or M-E is trained. **For P and MxS 2–4** sets are possible since the number of repetitions are usually low. **For M-E**, on the other hand, **1–2 sets** are suggested as the number of repetitions are higher. However, considering the specific concerns of the competitive phase, the **number of repetitions** for **M-EM** and **M-EL** should not exceed **20–30**, since these two components of M-E are also developed during the technical, tactical or conditioning program specific to the sport.

The **RI** should be **longer** than normally suggested, mostly because the athlete should **recover almost entirely** during the break. The intent of the maintenance phase is **stabilization of performance and not the aggravation** of the state of fatigue. Therefore, a longer RI for an almost full recovery between sets is required.

The planning of a maintenance program per micro-cycle depends on the type of strength sought. For power training one is constantly looking for exercises which **enhance explosiveness** by using resistance close to the one encountered in competitions. Two types of resistance are suggested:

1. **increased load**, or a resistance slightly higher than in competition, which enhances both specific MxS and P. Exercises ought to be very specific to the skills prevailing in a particular sport. This type of exercise is suggested mostly during the early part of the competitive phase as a transition from MxS to P.

2. **decreased load**, or the employment of a resistance below the one encountered in competition. Exercises using such a load **enhances specific power, explosiveness** and prevails in the phase prior to the main competitions.

These two types of loads have a positive effect on the athletes' ability to recruit a high number of FT fibers, as well as improved synchronization of the muscles involved.

The approach regarding the maintenance of M-E is as briefly as described above. However, if the competitive phase is very long, over 4–5 months, 25% of the total work has to be dedicated to the maintenance of MxS, since the detraining of MxS will negatively affect the overall M-E capacity.

The maintenance of MxS has to be more elaborate since its effectiveness depends on the proportions between different types of contractions employed. Often a combination between concentric and eccentric contraction, can be more effective than just using concentric contraction. A 75% concentric, 15% eccentric and 10% P, seem to be the most effective.

CESSATION PHASE, or an end to the strength maintenance program, may be planned 5–7 days prior to the most important competition of the year, so that all the energies are used for the achievement of the best performance possible.

STRENGTH TRAINING DURING THE TRANSITION PHASE

Following a long period of hard work and stressful competitions when the athlete's determination, motivation and willpower were very often challenged and tested, the athletes acquire a high degree of fatigue, physiological and especially psychological. Although the muscular fatigue may disappear in a few days, the fatigue of the CNS and the psyche can be sensed through the athlete's behaviour for a much longer period of time.

The more intensive the training and the higher the number of competitions the athlete is exposed to, the higher the fatigue level. Under these circumstances, it is hard to believe that an athlete may be able to immediately commence a new annual training cycle. Consequently, before training starts again for another season of competitions, the athlete has to rest, so as to physically and especially psychologically refresh himself/herself. When the new preparatory phase commences, the athlete will be completely regenerated and will participate in training with pleasure. In fact, following a successful transition phase the athlete should feel a strong desire to train again.

The transition phase, which is often inappropriately called the "off season", represents a linkage between two annual cycles. Its major objectives are to facilitate psychological rest, relaxation and biological regeneration as well to maintain an acceptable level of general physical preparation. Therefore the duration of this phase cannot be longer than 4–5 weeks because the athletes will detrain visibly, loosing most of their fitness.

During the transition phase the athletes should **train 2–3 times per week,** for the reason of not completely losing the fitness they had before. One should not forget that it takes less effort to maintain 40–50% of the previous level of fitness than to start to redevelop it from zero.

From the strength training point of view, during transition, the athlete should **perform compensation work,** to involve in activity the muscle groups which usually are not in much action through the preparatory and competitive phases. As such, attention should be paid to the **antagonistic muscles and stabilizers.** At the end of some informal physical training, a game or play, 20–30 minutes can be dedicated to activate these two groups of muscles. It is not necessary for the program to be stressful, but rather relaxed, the athlete working at his/ her will and for as much as he/ she desires. **Stress is undesirable during transition!** Therefore, a formal program with specific load, number of repetitions and sets is not necessary. Just for once the athlete should do as he/ she pleases.

Planning the Training Mehtods

During the discussions on planning-periodization and training methods, in all the illustrations a vertical bar was used to separate training phases. As such, the reader could have had the impression that a certain type of training was to be organized in one day and a completely different one the next day. In reality this is not happening in such a drastic manner. There is always an overlapping effect: a training method from one phase is always progressively introduced in the previous phase. Similarly, a type of work dominant in a given training phase is customarily maintained for a short while in the next phase, although its emphasis is progressively reduced.

In each training phase there is a method(s) which is dominant and another one which may be progressively introduced. In this way one plans a more effective transition from one method, or type of training, to another one. For instance, the transition from MxS to P is performed progressively by introducing some elements of power training during the MxS phase and maintaining some MxS training during the conversion phase (Figure 87).

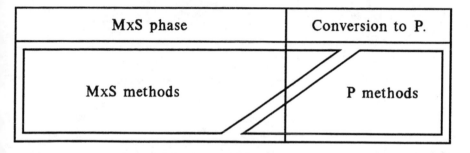

FIGURE 87. An illustration of the transition between two training methods or phases.

A transition between two training methods or phases can take place over 2 micro-cycles (Figure 87). As power is progressively introduced MxS is progressively reduced. This is accomplished by creating different combinations between sets of MxS and P as illustrated by Figure 88. For an easier presentation it is assumed that in each micro-cycle one plans 3 strength training sessions, 5 sets per day.

Micro-cycle	1			2		
Training day	1	2	3	1	2	3
Sets — MxS	5	4	3	2	1	0
Sets — P	0	1	2	3	4	5

Figure 88. The progressive transition from a MxS dominant training phase to P.

Another transition method from MxS to P can be achieved through the number of training sessions dedicated to each ability. Figure 89 illustrates such an example, in which from a micro-cycle (#1) where all 3 training sessions are dedicated to MxS training, to a cycle where only power training is performed (#4).

Micro-cycles	1	2	3	4
Training days — MxS	3	2	1	0
Training days — P	0	1	2	3

Figure 89. A suggested progressive transition from MxS to P.

The transition from one type of training to another can be planned in a more elaborated manner, as illustrated by Figure 90. This chart shows the periodization of strength, the number of workouts/week, duration of each phase in weeks, as well as the transition from one type of strength to another. Please note that for this sport (synchronized swimming) core strength, strength of the core area of the body such as hips, abdominals and low back, was emphasized or maintained throughout the annual plan.

A well organized coach will also try to structure a type of plan which shows how and for how long a certain type of training method should be used. In doing so, the coach will plan for each training phase the most appropriate method, showing not only the duration each method is used for, but also which one is the dominant method.

Figure 91 attempts to illustrated how training method can be planned. The example refers to hypothetical sport where power is the dominant ability. As usual, the top of the chart shows the training phases of a monocycle, while underneath it has the periodization of strength.

The bottom part of the chart lists several methods. Since in a given

DATES		SEPT.	OCT.	NOV.	DEC.	JAN.	FEB.	MAR.	APR.	MAY
	COMPETITIONS	-			PROVINCIAL		DIVISION			NAT. CH.
	TRAIN. PHASE	PREPARATORY			COMPETITIVE					
PERIODIZATION	PERIODIZ OF STRENGTH	A A CORE STR.	MxS MAINT. CORE STR.		CONVERSION -P -M-E -MAINT. CORE STR.				MAINT.	C E S S A
NR. WORKOUTS/WK		3	3 - 4				4		2	
DURATION/WEEKS		5	9		4	4	4	4	4	1
TYPE OF STRENGTH		2 A A 1 CORE	2-3 MxS 1 CORE		2 M-E 1 P 1/2 MxS 1/2 CORE →		3 M-E 1 P	2 M-E 1 P	1 M-E 1 P	·

Figure 90.   An example of transition to different types of strength for synchronized swimming

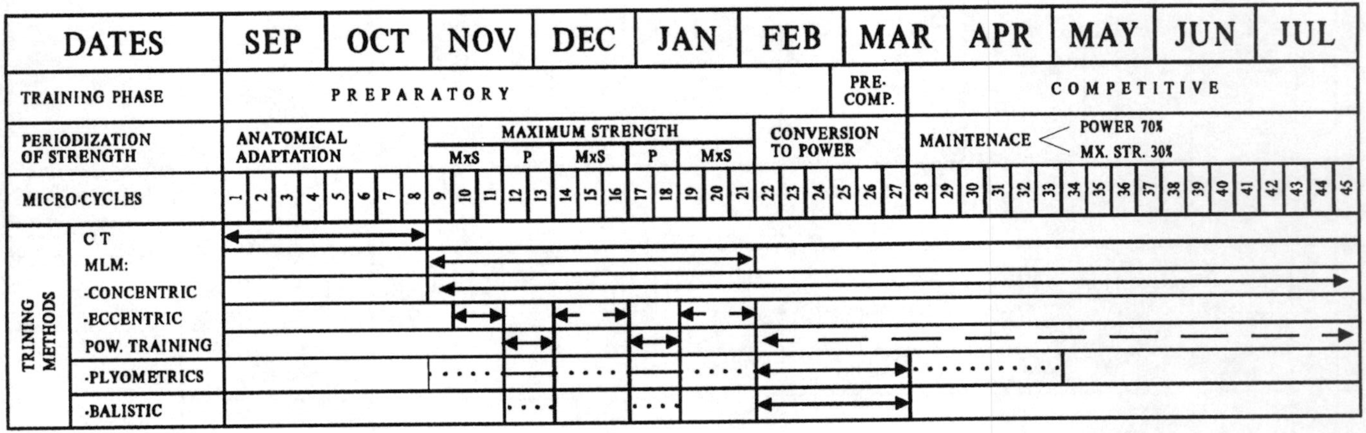

Figure 91. A hypothetical example of planning the training methods for a sport where power is the dominant ability.

training phase a certain method can have the highest priority, as opposed to others, three types of symbols are used. A solid line suggests that a given method has the first priority, as opposed to others, three types of symbols are used. A solid line suggests that a given method has the first priority, the interrupted line the second and the dotted line a third priority. For instance, during the AA, CT is the dominant training method. When the MxS phase begins MLM (maximum load method), concentric, prevails, while the eccentric method is of secondary priority during some segments of the program.

Under power training, presented are only the ballistic method and plyometrics. In some phases, as illustrated by the dotted line, these methods are considered a third priority. Certainly, figure 91 represents just a hypothetical example and does not exhaust all the available methods or possibilities of expressing how they are utilized.

CHAPTER SEVENTEEN

FATIGUE, MUSCLE SORENESS, AND RECOVERY FROM FATIGUE

FATIGUE INDUCED BY STRENGTH TRAINING

Athletes are constantly exposed to various types of training loads, some of which can often exceed one's threshold of tolerance. As a result the athlete's ability to adapt to the desired training load decreases, and as such affects the overall performance.

When athletes drive themselves beyond their physiological limits, there is a risk of going into a state of fatigue. Basically, the greater the level of fatigue the greater the training after-effects such as low rate of recovery, decreased coordination, and diminished power output. Fatigue experienced in training can often be increased if one is exposed to undesirable stressors such as personal, social, and school/ work dissatisfaction.

Muscular fatigue and over-reaching, commonly associated with exercise-induced muscle damage, are very complex physiological and psychological phenomenons. Although much research has been devoted to muscular fatigue, neither the exact sites, nor the exact causes are well known. However, since fatigue affects the force-generating capacity of the athlete, or results in one's inability to maintain a required force, the coach/instructor should know as much as possible in this area so that better plans can be created in order to avoid fatigue and over-reaching. Considering the complexity of this topic, references will be made mostly to fatigue induced by strength training.

In order to improve performance it is important that training loads be as high as necessary to provide a stimulus for adaptation. In order for the adaptation to take place, training programs must constantly incorporate periods of work with rest, as well as alternate different levels of intensities. Large increments in training loads should be avoided as well. Such concerns will result in a good work-rest balance. However, exposing the athletes to heavy loads, far beyond their capacity, or miscalculating the necessary rest, will result in decreased ability to adapt to the new load. Failing adaptation triggers biochemical and neural reactions which will take an athlete from a state of fatigue, to chronic fatigue, ultimately reaching the undesirable state of overtraining.

Irrespective of its definition, it is certain that fatigue is the consequence of physical work, which, as a result, reduces the capacity of the neuro-muscular and metabolic systems to continue physical activity.

Although researchers have attempted to identify sites of fatigue, and consequently of performance failure, through a conventional simplification of a complex phenomenon with many unknown elements, the focus of this section will be on the two main sites: neuro-muscular, and metabolic.

NEURO-MUSCULAR FATIGUE. While it is generally assumed that fatigue originates in the muscles, it is clear that the CNS has an important role in this area, since incentive, stress, temperature, and other psychological factors affect fatigue. Increasing evidence suggests that the CNS may be involved in the limitation of performance to a greater extent than once was assumed.

The CNS has two basic processes: **excitation** and **inhibition**. Excitation is a very favourable, **stimulating** process for physical activity, while inhibition is a **restraining** process. Throughout training there is a constant alternation of the two processes. For any stimulation, the CNS sends a nerve impulse to the working muscle causing it to contract and to perform work. The speed, power and frequency of the nerve impulse directly depends on the state of the CNS.

When (controlled) excitation prevails the nerve impulses are the most effective, which is evidenced by a good performance. When the opposite is the case, namely that as a result of fatigue, the nerve cell is in a state of inhibition, then the muscle contraction is slower and weaker. Thus, the force of contraction is directly related to the electrical activation sent by the CNS and dependable for the number of motor units recruited. **As fatigue increases the recruitment of motor units decreases.**

The nerve cell working capacity cannot be maintained for a very long time. Under the strain of training or competition demand, the working capacity decreases. However, if high intensity is maintained, as a result of fatigue, the nerve cell assumes a **state of inhibition**, protecting itself from external stimuli. Consequently, fatigue should be seen as a self-protecting mechanism against the damage of the contractile mechanism of the muscle.

In speed-power dominated sports, fatigue is visible to the experienced eye by noticing that athletes **react slower to explosive activities**, show a slight **impairment of coordination**, and **increase the duration of contact phase** in sprinting, bounding, rebounding, jumping, and plyometrics. This can be explained by the fact that **FT fibers are more easily affected by fatigue** than ST. Since the above listed activities rely on the activation of FT fibers, even a slight inhibition of the CNS affects their recruitment.

The skeletal muscle produces force by activating its motor units and regulating their firing frequency which is progressively increased in order to enhance force output. Fatigue, which inhibits muscular activity, can be neutralized to some degree by a **modulating strategy**, by responding to fatigue through the ability of the motor units to **alter firing frequency**. As a result, the muscle can maintain force more effectively under a certain state of fatigue. However, if the duration of sustained maximum contraction increases, the frequency of the motor units firing decreases signalling that inhibition will become more prominent (Bigland-Ritchie *et al.*, 1983; Hennig and Lomo, 1987).

Marsden *et al.* (1971) demonstrated that, as compared to the start of a 30 second maximum voluntary contraction, the end firing frequency decreased by 80%. Similar findings were reported by Grimby *et al.* (1992) who stated that **as the duration of contraction increased, activation of large motor units decreased, lowering the firing rate below the threshold level**. Any continuation of contraction beyond that level was possible through short bursts (phasical firing), but not appropriate for a constant performance.

The above findings should send a strong message of caution to those who promote the theory (especially in football and body building) that strength can be improved only by performing each set to exhaustion. The fact that as a contraction progresses the firing frequency decreases, discredits this highly acclaimed method.

As the contraction progresses, fuel reserves deplete, resulting in longer motor unit relaxation time, and the muscle contraction has a lower frequency. Since the cause of such neuro-muscular behaviour is assumed to be fatigue, it should warn the practitioners that short rest intervals (the standard 1–2 minutes) between two sets of maximum load is not sufficient to relax and regenerate the neuro-muscular system in order to expect high activation in the subsequent set(s).

When analyzing the functional capacity of the CNS during fatigue, one must take into consideration the athlete's perceived fatigue and past physical capacity achieved in training. When the athlete's physical capacity is above the level of fatigue experienced in testing or competition, it enhances one's motivation, and as a result the capacity to overcome fatigue. Therefore, the level of motivation has to be related to past experience, and training state.

METABOLIC SOURCES OF FATIGUE. Muscle fatigue may be associated with the mechanism of calcium flux in skeletal muscle, although the interrelationship between them still remains a mystery.

The complex cycle of muscle contraction is triggered by the nerve impulse which depolarizes the surface membrane of the muscle cell, and is then conducted into the muscle fiber. This is followed by a series of events where calcium is bound together with protein filaments (actin and myosin), resulting in contractile tension.

The **functional site of fatigue** is suggested to be the **link between excitation-contraction,** which results in either **reducing the intensity** of these two processes, or in **decreasing the sensitivity to activation.** Changes in flux of calcium ions affects the operation of excitation-contraction (Tesch, 1980).

FATIGUE DUE TO LACTIC ACID ACCUMULATION. The build-up of lactic acid in the muscle results in a **decline of the muscle to contract maximally** (Fox *et al.*, 1989). Any athletic movements requiring quickness or force of contraction must rely on the contraction of FT fibers. However, since such actions are performed anaerobically, they rely on anaerobic types of fuels, resulting in increased production and accumulation of lactic acid. Since for **heavy load sets FT fibers produce high levels of lactates**, these fibers are the first to be affected, **blocking any immediate excitation/ stimulation** coming from the CNS. The next high intensity set will be possible only after a longer resting time (please refer to "rest intervals").

The biochemical exchanges during muscle contraction results in the liberation of hydrogen ions, which in turn produces acidosis, or the not yet clear **"lactate fatigue"**, which seems to determine the point of exhaustion (Sahlin, 1986). The more active a muscle, the greater its hydrogen ion concentration, thus increasing blood acidosis.

An increased acidosis also inhibits the binding capacity of calcium through inactivation of troponin, a protein compound. Since troponin is an important contributor to the contraction of the muscle cell, its inactivation may expand the connection between fatigue and exercise (Fabiato and Fabiato, 1978). The discomfort produced by **acidosis** can also be a **limiting factor in psychological fatigue** (Brooks and Fahey, 1985).

FATIGUE DUE TO THE DEPLETION OF ATP/CP AND GLYCOGEN STORES. From the energy systems point of view, **fatigue occurs** when the creatine phosphate **(CP) is depleted** in the working muscle, when muscle **glycogen is consumed**, or when the **carbohydrate store is exhausted** as well (Sahlin, 1986). The end result is obvious: the work performed by the muscle is decreased, the possible reason being that in a glycogen depleted muscle the ATP is produced at a lower rate than it is consumed. Several studies show that carbohydrate is essential to the ability of a muscle to maintain high force (Conlee, 1987), and that endurance capabilities during prolonged moderate to heavy physical activity is directly related to the amount of glycogen in the muscle prior to exercise. This indicates that fatigue occurs as a result of muscle glycogen depletion (Bergstrom *et al.*, 1967).

For the activities of very high intensity but of a short duration, such as high intensity sets, the immediate source of energy for muscular contraction are ATP and CP. Complete depletion of these stores in the muscle will certainly limit the ability of the muscle to contract (Karlsson and Saltin, 1971).

With prolonged, submaximum work such as muscular-endurance of medium or long duration, the fuel used to produce energy is glucose and fatty acids. Throughout this type of strength training, the availability of oxygen is critical, since when in limited quantities carbohydrates are oxidized instead of free fatty acids. Therefore, the maximum free fatty acid oxidation will be determined by the inflow of the fatty acids to the working muscle, and by the aerobic training status of the athlete since aerobic training increases both the availability of oxygen and the power of free fatty acid oxidation (Sahlin, 1986). The lack of oxygen, the **oxygen carrying capacity**, and inadequate blood flow have an important contribution to **muscular fatigue** (Bergstrom *et al.*, 1967). Hopefully, this demonstrates the needs of a decent aerobic conditioning even for the speed-power dominated sports.

MUSCLE SORENESS

The employment in training of heavy loads for a prolonged period of time, or the exposure of beginners to equally heavy loads with an inadequate adaptation, usually results in the undesirable state of muscle soreness.

There are two basic mechanisms that explains how exercise initiates damage. One mechanism is associated with the **disturbance of metabolic function**, while the other refers to the **mechanical disruption of the muscle cell**. Whenever muscle soreness happens one should immediately alter the training program, because pursuing it at the same level will bring the athlete one step closer to overtraining.

The metabolic mechanism of **muscle damage** occurs during **prolonged submaximum work to exhaustion**, typical of some body-building methods. Direct loading of the muscle, especially during the eccentric contraction phase, may cause muscle damage, and that metabolic changes may aggravate the damage. Disruption of the **muscle cell membrane** is one of the most noticeable damages.

Eccentric contraction is known to produce greater tension in the muscle than concentric contraction. As such, some coaches who want to speed up the process of producing good athletes employ the eccentric method in disregard of whether one is ready for it, has enough strength training background to tolerate it, or whether adequate connective tissue adaptation has occurred. The predictable result could be discomfort and muscle damage.

Eccentric muscle contraction has been shown to produce more heat than concentric contraction at the same workload. The **increased temperatures** can **damage structural and functional components** within the muscle cell (Armstrong, 1986; Ebbing and Clarkson, 1989).

Both mechanisms of muscle damage are related to muscle fibers that have been stressed slightly. When this occurs, the muscle fiber quickly returns to its normal length without injury. However, if the stress is severe, the muscle becomes traumatized. **Discomfort** sets in during the first **24 to 48 hours** following the exercise. The sensation of dull, **aching pain** combined with tenderness and **stiffness** tends to diminish within 5–7 days after the initial workout.

For years lactic acid build-up was considered the main cause of muscle soreness. However, recent research suggests that the actual cause results from an influx of calcium ions into the muscle cell (Fahey, 1985; Armstrong, 1986; Evans, 1987; Ebbing and Clarkson, 1989). Calcium is very important in a muscle contraction. Calcium stimulates the fiber to contract but is rapidly pumped back into the calcium storage area after the contraction has been completed.

When calcium ions accumulate within the muscle fiber, this causes the release of a substance (proteases) that results in **muscle fiber breakdown**. The **soreness** is primarily due to the formation of degraded protein components, or **dead tissue**. The body initiates a "clean-up" phase in order to eliminate muscle cells of dead tissue. A protective mechanism is started by the muscle by **producing stress protein** which stops further damage. This explains why muscle soreness is not felt every day.

However, once the muscle has been traumatized, there is an accumulation of substances (e.g. histamine, serotonin, potassium, etc.) which are responsible for the **inflammation** after the muscle fiber injury (Prentice, 1990). Once the level of these substances has reached a certain degree, they activate the nerve endings. Perhaps the reason why muscle soreness is only felt 24 hours later can be due to the time required for the damaged muscle cells to accumulate all these substances (Armstrong, 1986; Ebbing and Clarkson, 1989).

The discomfort and **soreness** is intensely felt in the region of the **muscle-tendon junction** since the tissue of the tendon is less flexible than that of the muscle tissue, and as such having a higher chance for injury from intense contraction.

As one may expect, **greater damage** is seen in the **FT fibers**, than in the ST, since they participate in a higher proportion in more intense contractions, typical for heavy loads/ high intensity training.

PREVENTION OF MUSCLE SORENESS takes several forms, from training to medication. The most important preventing technique the coach may consider is to use the principle of progressive increase of load in training. Furthermore, applying the concept of periodization will avoid discomfort, muscle soreness, or any other negative training outcomes.

An **extensive**, overall **warm-up** will result in a better preparation of the body for work. Superficial warm-ups, on the other hand, can easily result in strain and pain. A good stretching session at the end of the warm-up, as well as between sets, aids not only in **preventing soreness** but represents also a **relieving** method when muscle damage already exists.

Stretching is also strongly recommended at the end of a training session. As a result of extensive muscle contraction, typical of strength training, muscles are slightly shorter, and it takes some two hours to reach its resting length. **Five to ten minutes of stretching**, facilitates the muscles to **faster reach their resting length**, which is optimal for **biochemical exchanges** at the muscle fiber level. At the same time, stretching also seems to **ease muscle spasm** as well.

It has also been proposed that ingesting 100 milligrams of **vitamin C** per day may prevent or at least reduce muscle soreness. Similar benefits seem to result from taking **vitamin E**. Taking anti-inflammatory medication, such as **Advil or Aspirin**, may help **combat inflammation** of muscle tissue (Fahey, 1985).

Diet is also considered an important element for supplying the athlete with the needed foodstuff but also in helping to **recover** from muscle soreness. An athlete exposed to heavy loads in strength training requires more protein, carbohydrate diets and supplements. It is also suggested that an **inadequate level of carbohydrates** may **delay the recovery** of the muscle from **injury** and **soreness**.

RECOVERY FROM STRENGTH TRAINING

Whether recovering from fatigue or over-reaching, or just recovering from an exhaustive training session, it is important that the athlete/ coach become aware of the various techniques that are potentially available, during the course of training. Understanding the use of these techniques is just as important as knowing how to train effectively. As much as the coach tries to implement new loads to the training program, often recovery methods do not equally match the new training loads. This situation can harbour potential setbacks for the athlete with respect to peaking and regeneration following training. Approximately **50% of an athlete's final performance depends on the athlete's ability to recover** by using recovery techniques. Therefore, without the use of proper recovery techniques, adaptation to various training loads may not be achieved.

It is vital that the coach be aware of the various factors that contribute to the recovery process. Each factor does not affect the athlete's body by itself, but rather, it is the combination of these factors, all at varying degrees, that contribute to the recovery process.

Among the main factors for consideration are the following:

1. The **age** of the athlete has been shown to **affect the rate of recovery**. Older athletes generally require longer periods of recuperation than their younger counter parts.

2. The **better trained**, more experienced athlete generally requires **less time to recuperate**. This is related to a quicker physiological adaptation to a given training stimulus.

3. **Gender** may affect the rate of recovery. **Female athletes** tend to have a **slower rate of recovery**. The reason for this is primarily due to differences in the endocrine systems of male and female athletes.

4. **Environmental factors** such as time differences, altitude and cold climates tend to lessen the affect of the recovery process.

5. **Replenishment of foodstuff** at the cellular level has been shown to affect the recovery process. Proteins, fats, carbohydrates and ATP-CP restoration within the working muscle cell are constantly required for cellular metabolism as well as for the production of energy (Jacobs, 1981; Fox *et al.*, 1989).

6. **Negative emotions** such as fear, indecisiveness, and lack of willpower tend to impair the recovery process.

The process of recovery is a slower process, being directly dependent of the magnitude of the load employed in training. Similarly, the curve of recovery is not linear, and as illustrated by Figure 92, it represents the body's ability to reach homeostasis, or its normal biological state. During the first third, the curve of recovery drops by 70%, while in the second and third 20%, and 10% respectively.

The time interval for recovery depends upon the energy system that is being taxed. Recommended recovery times after exhaustive strength training are presented in table 5.

The effectiveness of recovery techniques are greatly dependent on the time they are employed. It is strongly suggested that they should be performed during and following each training session (Bompa, 1983; Kuipers and Keizer, 1988; Fry *et al.*, 1991).

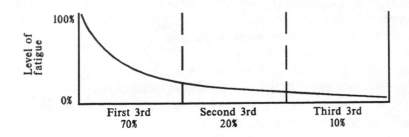

FIGURE 92. The dynamics of the curve of recovery.

RECOVERY TECHNIQUES

ACTIVE RECOVERY refers to the rapid elimination of waste products (i.e. lactic acid) during moderate aerobic recovery exercise. Sixty-two percent of the lactic acid is removed during continuous light jogging during the first 10 minutes. An additional 26% is removed between 10–20 minutes. Therefore, it seems advantageous to maintain an **active recovery period for 10–20 minutes** after strength training (Bonen and Belcastro, 1977; Fox *et al.*, 1989).

TABLE 5

**Suggested recovery times after exhaustive strength training.
(with changes and additions from Fox *et al.*, 1989)**

Recovery Process	Recovery time
Restoration of ATP/CP	3–5 minutes
Restoration of muscle glycogen: - after prolonged exercise - after intermittent exercise (such as strength training)	10–48 hours 24 hours
Removal of lactic acid from muscle and blood	1–2 hours
Restoration of vitamins and enzymes	24 hours
Recovery from overly taxing strength training (both metabolic and CNS to reach overcompensation)	2–3 days
Repayment of the alactacid oxygen debt	5 minutes
Repayment of the lactacid oxygen debt	30–60 minutes

COMPLETE REST or *PASSIVE REST* is perhaps one factor that every athlete requires. Most athletes require up to 10 hours of sleep a day in order to function at full capacity. A portion of this possible 10 hours is usually taken up in the form of naps. The athlete should also have regular sleeping hours and should be in bed no later than 11 p.m. Relaxation techniques should be employed prior to bedtime, allowing the athlete to achieve a mellow state of mind (Bompa, 1983; Gauron, 1984).

THE ATHLETE'S LIFESTYLE almost always has an affect on the rate of recovery. Poor relationships with a spouse, girl/ boyfriend, siblings, parents, teammates and even coaches can have a negative influence on the recovery process. If necessary, the use of a sport psychologist may be an asset to the athlete if he/ she is experiencing some deep emotional problem that has an affect on the development of a strong will and character.

MASSAGE is a systematic manipulation of the soft tissues of the body for therapeutic purposes. Massage is sometimes, more often than not, the treatment of choice by most athletes (Cinique, 1989; Yessis, 1990). For best results, athletes are suggested to use a certified specialist.

The physiological effects of a massage are a result of mechanical intrusion and/ or sensory stimulation.

THE MECHANICAL EFFECTS include:

1. Increased blood circulation. If the muscles are relaxed, squeezing the muscle bodies' helps to empty veins by simple mechanical pressure, in the direction of the applied pressure. The increased emptying of veins stimulates the opening of the small capillaries throughout the massaged area so that blood flow throughout this area is increased. At rest approximately 4% of capillaries are open; this can be increased up to 35% through massage (Bergeron, 1982). The net result is an increased availability of "fresh blood" to the massaged area, making possible greater interchange of substances between capillaries and tissue cells.

2. Increased lymphatic circulation. Massages assist the circulation of the veins in the return of fluid from the tissues. Unlike veins which have one way valves, lymphatic vessels do not have valves and lymph can move in any direction depending on external pressure. Gravity and muscle pump (including breathing activity) are the primary movers of lymph. A massage is the most effective external means of moving the extravascular fluid into the lymph vessels and through the lymph vessels into the circulatory system. This might be described as a cleaning-out action.

3. Stretch muscle adhesion. The mechanical pressure and stretching of the tissue will aid in mobilizing muscle adhesion for removal by the circulatory system.

4. Relieves muscle fatigue by the mechanical effects on the blood stream to promote the removal of lactic acid.

5. Removal of excessive swelling. This is especially beneficial when treating certain types of inflammation.

THE SENSORY EFFECTS of massage are primarily reflexive in nature and are not fully understood.

1. Pain relief. Pain may be relieved by a massage by slowly increasing the sensory input to the CNS, tenderness and pain may be decreased. This necessitates massaging gradually into the painful area.

2. Reflexive capillary dilation. Light stroking of the skin results in a temporary dilation of capillaries. The stronger the stroking the greater and more prolonged the dilation.

3. Relief of muscle spasm. Light stroking of an involuntary muscle contraction such as a muscle spasm may bring about relaxation through reflex mechanisms. Muscle spasms should first be stroked lightly in a direction parallel to the muscle fibers. If this fails, firm pressure should be applied to the muscle belly with both hands. If this fails, deep thumb pressure into the muscle belly may be used. In all cases a gentle stretch of the muscle in spasm is applied. If one begins treatment of a muscle spasm by firm or deep pressure or sudden violent stretching one may simply increase the severity of the spasm.

4. Increased metabolism. The effect of a massage on the metabolism is local, not general, and is due primarily to the increased circulation through the massaged area. Breakdown of waste products and their absorption into the circulatory system may be increased up to 2.5 times above resting levels.

HEAT THERAPY, in the form of steam baths, saunas, and heat packs, can have a relaxation or regeneration effect on the body. Heat packs primarily only heat the skin and not so much the underlying tissues. However this does not mean that this modality is all together useless. If left on long enough (for 20 minutes at least), heat can provide an effective way of increasing the circulation around the muscle. The only problem is that the skin may become too hot before any muscle tissue has actually been heated. The use of heat maybe perhaps best served to help the athlete relax or to heat the surface muscle tissue rather than deep muscle tissue.

COLD THERAPY, such as using ice, ice bath, ice whirlpool, and cold packs for 10–15 minutes may have important physiological benefits for recovery from fatigue. Rubbing ice on an excessively strained muscle may keep swelling down, and in conjunction with heat may create an expansion (heat) or contraction (cold) of the damaged muscle tissue.

Perhaps the best time to use ice would be immediately following an intense training session, where there can be the risk of some micro tearing of the muscle tissue.

CHEMOTHERAPY. Before briefly discussing this topic, a few words should be said regarding food or rather caloric intake. Ideally, an athlete should maintain an energy balance each day. This means that the daily energy expenditure should roughly match the athlete's energy intake. One can judge rather simply whether one's diet is adequate in calories: if the athlete is losing weight while on a rigorous workout schedule, the athlete is perhaps not consuming enough calories.

Despite consuming a "well balanced" diet many athletes should not shy away from taking vitamin and mineral supplements. Even if the diet may be well balanced it usually cannot supply the athlete with all the vitamins and minerals used up during a training session or competition. Athletes typically experience a deficiency in all vitamins except vitamin A (Yessis 1990). Therefore, during periods of heavy training, supplements are as much a part of the training table as any other nutrient.

In **planning a supplement program**, it is vital that the coach/athlete consider different periods of training throughout the annual plan and adjust the supplements accordingly. There will be times, like in the transition phase, where the need for large doses of vitamins, particularly B's, C and certain minerals, will be much less due to the lowered intensity and volume of training. Planning for vitamin and mineral supplements can be made relatively easy provided they are in a chart form representing specific phases during the athlete's yearly training plan.

The time of day when a meal may be consumed can affect the rate of recovery (Clark, 1985, and Yessis, 1990). The above authors feel that developing an eating pattern whereby the athlete consumes his/ her meals at least 4–5 times a day is much better than having 3 large meals. The reasoning behind such a suggestion lies in the fact that there is a greater assimilation and digestion of food stuff when the athlete undertakes such a pattern. With this in mind, about 20 to 25% of the rations are consumed during the early morning meal, 15 to 20% are consumed at the second breakfast, 30 to 35% during the midday meal, and 20 to 25% in the evening meal. The athlete should not allow more than four to five hours to pass between each of the day's meals, and no more than twelve hours between the evening meal and breakfast.

Clark (1985) and Yessis (1990) feel that athletes should not eat immediately before a training session, since a full stomach raises the diaphragm, forcing the cardiovascular and respiratory systems to work harder. The athlete should avoid eating just after training as well. Few gastric juices are secreted during this time. A period of at least 20 to 30 minutes should be allowed prior to the consumption of a post-training meal. During this time the athlete may consume only fluids that contain carbohydrates and mineral supplements. Consumption of carbohydrates as well as foods rich in potassium are vital to normal muscle function (Fox, 1984; Clark, 1985).

PSYCHOLOGICAL RECOVERY. Factors such as motivation and willpower can be affected by the levels of stress from both physical and psychological stimuli. How fast the body reacts to various forms of external and internal stimuli will greatly affect the athlete's performance. The more focused an athlete is, the better he/ she can react to various training stimuli, and as such have a higher working capacity.

The utilization of relaxation techniques, done either by the athlete or with the help of a sports psychologist, can greatly improve the athlete's ability to become more focused. By relaxing the brain, all other parts in the body also assume the same state (Gauron, 1984). Perhaps the best time to employ such methods, would be just before the athlete retires for the evening. A warm bath or shower prior to sleeping, might help induce a more relaxed state.

RECOVERY FROM SHORT-TERM OVERTRAINING should start with the interruption of training for 3–5 days. After this rest period, training can be resumed by alternating each training session with a day off. If overtraining is more severe, and the athlete has to miss more time, for every week of missed training it will require roughly two weeks of training to attain the athlete's previous physical condition (Terjung and Hood, 1988).

Repair of damaged muscle tissue falls under the category of short-term overtraining, requiring at least 5–7 days to complete the process, while the regeneration of muscle tissue takes up to 20 days (Ebbing and Clarkson, 1989).

Recovery from muscle damage during the acute phase would be best treated with ice, elevation, compression and active rest or complete rest (depending upon the extent of damage). Following this, after 3 days, the coach should begin to introduce other modalities such as a massage. Alternation of hot and cold temperatures can also be an effective way of loosening the stiffness associated with exercise induced muscle damage (Arnheim, 1988; Prentice, 1990).

According to Fahey (1991), diet may play a part in muscle tissue recovery. Aside from the obvious need for protein, in particular animal proteins, carbohydrates are also required as well. It has been shown that recovery from muscle injury is delayed when the muscle carbohydrate stores are not adequate. Therefore, it is vital that the athlete also pay strict attention to diet, not only from an energy expenditure point of view, but from a recovery standpoint as well.

The use of some vitamin supplements are generally quite popular when it comes to dealing with muscle damage. Fahey (1991) and Yessis (1990) both feel that vitamin E and C can be of great benefit to the athlete in terms of assisting in the recovery process.

TABLE 6

Daily energy requirements of athletes and main
food substances in periods of heavy and intense training
(per kg of body mass)
(From Yessis, 1990)

Kind of Sports	Protein (g)	Fat (g)	Carbohy-drates (g)	Caloric Value (Cal)
Gymnastics and Figure Skating	2.2–2.5	1.7–1.9	8.6–9.75	59–66
Track and field: Sprints, Jumps	2.3–2.5	1.8–2.0	9.0–9.8	62–67
Middle and long distance running	2.4–2.8	2.0–2.1	10.3–12	69–78
Marathon	2.5–2.9	2.0–2.2	11.2–13	73–84
Swimming and water polo	2.3–2.5	2.2–2.4	9.5–10.0	67–72
Weightlifting and Throwing events	2.5–2.9	1.8–2.0	10.0–11.8	66–77
Wrestling and Boxing	2.4–2.8	1.8–2.2	9.0–11.0	62–75
Rowing and Kayak-Canoeing	2.5–2.7	2.0–2.3	10.5–11.3	70–77
Soccer and Hockey	2.4–2.6	2.0–2.2	9.6–10.4	66–72
Basketball and Volleyball	2.3–2.4	1.8–2.0	9.5–10.8	63–71
Cycling: Track	2.3–2.5	1.8–2.0	10.8–11.8	69–75
Road racing	2.5–2.7	2.0–2.1	12.2–14.3	77–87
Sailing	2.2–2.4	2.1–2.2	8.5–9.7	62–68
Shooting	2.2–2.4	2.0–2.1	8.3–9.5	60–67
Skiing: Downhill	2.3–2.5	1.9–2.2	10.2–11.0	67–74
Cross-country	2.4–2.6	2.0–2.4	11.5–12.6	74–82
Speed skating	2.5–2.7	2.0–2.3	10.0–10.9	69–74

CHAPTER EIGHTEEN

EXERCISE PRESCRIPTION

All athletic skills and actions are performed by muscles, as a result of muscle contraction. The human body has 656 muscles, distributed all over the body and capable of performing a high variety of movements. If one wishes to improve a skill or a physical performance he/ she must concentrate on training the necessary muscles, the muscles performing the athletic action, or the prime movers.

In order to design a good strength program one has to carefully plan, select the necessary training methods and at least equally important is to carefully select the exercise(s). From the previous discussions it was learned that exercise prescription, or the process of selecting an exercise for a given muscle group(s), is phase-specific. During the AA phase exercises have to be selected to develop most muscle groups, both agonistic and antagonistic, in order to build a stronger base for the training phases to follow. As the competitive phase approaches, these exercises become very specific, prescribed specifically for the prime movers.

For an adequate exercise prescription, the coach may consider the following steps:

1. analyze how the skill is performed (direction, angle and the limb's position)

2. figure-out which are the prime movers responsible for the skill performance

3. select the exercises which involve the prime movers, based on their similarity to the direction and angle of contraction for the selected skill(s)

Exercise prescription should be based on the understanding of how the muscles are producing a movement and not based on borrowing exercises from weightlifting or bodybuilding. Almost every athlete does "bench press" and "cleans" irrespective whether they are needed in a given sport or not. The proposed theory that these exercises are good for every sport is a fallacy! An exercise is good for a sport only as long as it involves the prime movers and the synergistic muscles used in the skill performance of a sport/ event.

ANALYTIC VS. COMPOSITE. Quite often some coaches turn to bodybuilding for ideas on exercises to be used in training, without understanding the clear differences between sports and bodybuilding. For best muscle definition, bodybuilders use the "**analytic**" method. They analyze each individual muscle's action and movements, addressing that particular muscle, training it in isolation in order to have the best size development.

In athletics, on the other hand, one should use the "**composite**" method, involving not an individual muscle, but rather all the muscles of a joint, or joints, necessary to produce an athletic skill. Furthermore, for the needs of specific strength development for a sport, as much as possible, a selected exercise should involve the muscles and joints in the specific **chain of action**. This means that the exercise should involve the muscles and joints in a similar sequence as one performs a skill. For instance, if a coach intends to train the muscles involved in starting in sprinting, or in quick-explosive running from a spot, such as in team sports, one should not do knee extension from a seated position, but rather a reverse leg press (using the paddle for the leg press, turn the athlete's back towards the paddle, place the toes on the paddle, hand on the support and press the leg backwards).

There is another difference between the analytic and composite method. In the first case there is only a local adaptation with no cardio-respiratory benefits. In the latter method, on the other hand, by using large muscle groups of 1–3 joints, as in reverse leg press, there is a cardio-respiratory gain as well. And for sports this is a very important training goal.

SPECIFICITY OF EXERCISES FOR STRENGTH TRAINING

As exercises are performed, the position of the body or the grip used on equipment, affects the exercise's effectiveness. However, often body position cannot be duplicated in strength training. To overcome such eventual shortcomings coaches have to do their best to imitate the **dynamic structure** of the skill as well as their **spatial orientation**, or the position of the athlete's body as compared to the surrounding environment. Knowing that, the coach should try to select those exercises which align the position of the body and limbs to the positions used in the competition.

Of similar importance is also the **angle** used in training between body parts or limbs. Both the spatial position of the body, as well as the angle and degrees of contraction, influences how and which parts of a given muscle contracts. And for an improved effectiveness of training the prime movers, one has to be familiar with these aspects. However, a few examples will better demonstrate such theories.

Sit-ups are popular exercises used to develop the abdominal muscles. But the position of the body while performing them, changes their difficulty as well as which segment of the muscles (rectus abdominis) is contracted maximally. For instance, sit-ups performed in a horizontal position involves mostly the upper part of the muscle. If, on the other hand, the same action is performed in an inclined position, the training benefit is mostly on the central section of the muscle since the movement is performed with an almost full range of motion. If the trunk is kept fixed and the legs are lifted then the role of the abdominals decreases and the action is performed mostly by the hip flexors (iliopsoas muscle). Therefore, the best position to activate the abdominals is the one in which the hips are immobilized and the trunk moves as a result of contracting the rectus abdominis muscle (inclined position, or the legs rested on a chair/ bench or against the wall).

Similar concerns should be considered while performing the bench press. If performed on a flat bench the main beneficiaries are the central parts of the pectorals, the triceps and parts of the deltoid muscle. If the same exercise is performed on an inclined bench, the upper part of the pectorals are in full contraction. However, if one would like to stress the lower pectorals then the athlete has to use an incline bench with the head at the lower end.

For the bench press the grip also affects the muscles involved. If the athlete uses a wide grip the exterior part of the pectorals is mostly stressed. A shoulder-width grip will enhance the development of the inner part of the same muscle, while a narrow grip will activate mostly the deeper part of the pectorals and the triceps muscle.

As mentioned earlier, the bench press seems to be the choice of many athletes in several sports, irrespective whether it is essential or not. Often this is true for sprinting. In all the sports performed on the ground, from sprinting to most team sports, high velocity running is unachievable without high leg frequency. Most readers know that the frequency of the legs directly depend on the frequency of arms. In fact, the arm frequency dictates the leg frequency. Being aware of such a reality, coaches' understand that a strong arm drive directly influences the arms' frequency. As such it is quite logical to develop the power of the sprinters' arms. However, in their quest to develop the power of the arms' drive, a coach employs the bench press, but fails to realize that the backward drive of the elbows is the actual force generating a high arm and leg frequency. In order to do that, a program aiming to develop the force of the arms' drive has to include horizontal arm pulls, driving the elbow behind the level of the trunk.

For maximum training specificity, an exercise often has to imitate the angle of the skill performed. Take for instance the action of the arms in shot putting or of a linemen. It is quite simple to conclude that the arm extension used in both cases are performed by the tricep muscles. If a bodybuilder is asked what kind of exercise to use for the development of triceps it is quite likely that the answer will be "bent over" elbow extension, or the same exercise in an erected position, elbow above the shoulder. Such exercises involve the triceps in isolation of the other muscles taking part in the action of shot putting or tackling (the analytic method). Consequently, not very effective for the two groups of athletes in discussion. The best exercise in our case would be the incline bench press, the angle of the bench around 45°, which is similar to the angle used in the above actions. In addition, this exercise involves the other active muscles, such as pectorals and deltoids.

The Development of the "Core" Muscle Area

From the beginning it was stated that this book does not have the objective of discussing or illustrating exercises. However, a brief discussion is necessary for the core muscle groups, some of which are often neglected.

Strength training programs should not revolve only around the legs or arms, but should focus particularly on strengthening the "core" muscles: the abdominals, the low back and the hip musculature. These sets of muscles are crucial because they:

1. act as shock absorbers for jumps, rebounds, or plyometric exercises,

2. stabilize the body so that the arms and legs can perform all kinds of movements having the core muscles as a support, and

3. represent a link, a transmitter, between the legs and arms. Weak core muscles will fail to play the above very essential roles, affecting the overall ability of an athlete to perform effectively. Because of this very important role played by the core muscles (i.e., support for arms and legs), most of these muscles seem to be dominated by ST muscle fibers. They contract constantly, but not necessarily dynamically, to create this solid support for the actions of the other groups of muscles of the body.

Often, both athletes and/ or the general population, complain about low back problems but do not do much for it. However, the best protection for the low back problems is a well developed functioning back and abdominal muscles. A brief discussion regarding the core muscles, as well as the stabilizers, will, hopefully, make the reader direct more attention to this area of the body.

ABDOMINAL MUSCLES. The majority of people, including athletes, have abdominal muscles that are too weak in relation to their back. Therefore, general and specific abdominal muscle training can be recommended for most athletes. The abdominal muscles, made out of rectus abdominis, which runs vertically, and the external and internal obliques. The first muscle pulls the trunk forward when the legs are fixed, as in sit-ups. It has an important role in maintaining a good posture. If the abdominal muscles are poorly developed, the hips are tilted forward, and because the low back muscles are much stronger, one develops lordosis, or a sway back at the lumbar area of the spine.

If an individual intends to train only the abdominal muscles, he/ she has to select an exercise in which the spine bends and not the hips. Any exercise which flexes the hips is performed by iliopsoas, a very powerful hips flexor, and to a lesser degree by the abdominals. Sit-ups are the most popular exercise for the abdominals. The best sit-ups for the abdominals are those in which the athlete lies on the back, legs with calf rested on a chair/ bench. Since in this position the hips are already bent, the sit-ups will be performed only by the abdominals.

The internal and external obliques assist rectus abdominis in bending the trunk forward. If stimulated on one side only, the trunk is bent toward the side. These muscles perform all the twisting, lateral bending, and trunk rotating motions. They are very important for raising up from the floor/ ground following a fall in many sports, especially in team sports, as well as in many actions in boxing, martial arts, and wrestling.

An overview of the anterior and lateral abdominal muscles makes it obvious that these muscles enable the body to perform delicate and precise movements of the trunk. This is made possible because these large muscles run vertically, diagonally, and horizontally.

THE BACK MUSCLES, including the deep back muscles of the vertebral column, are responsible for many exercises, such as back extension and extending and rotating the trunk. Strong back muscles are necessary because the trunk plays the role of the transmitter and support of most exercises performed by the arms and legs. Along with the hips, the vertebral column also plays an essential role as a shock absorber for landing and take-off actions.

Excessive and uneven stress on the spine, or exposing the body to sudden movements while in unfavourable position may result in some back problems. While for the non-athlete back complaints are often due to poorly trained back muscles, and even those of the abdomen and legs, for the athletes they may be due to the wear and tear of improper positions, or when the body is tilted forward.

The pressure on the discs of the vertebral column varies according to the position of the body to the external stress. There is more stress on the spine when one lifts in a standing position or seated position, or when the upper body swings, such as in vertical rowing or in elbow flexions. Of the two positions, a sitting position produces greater disc pressure than standing, with the least stress being if an exertion is performed with the entire body lying down (such as bench press, or bench pulls).

In many exercises that engage the back muscles the abdominal muscles contract in most cases isometrically, thus having a stabilizing effect. This is why the coach should make sure that the low back and abdominals always are properly developed. They play the role of stabilizing one part of the body so that the others can perform the work, absorb the shock, or directly take part in very powerful as well as fine motions.

THE ILIOPSOAS is an essential muscle for any hip flexion or running actions. Although far from being a large muscle, it is the most powerful hip flexor, responsible for swinging a leg forward during running and jumping. Any sport performed on the ground, from team sports to sprinting, should make sure that the iliopsoas is well developed. Exercises, such as leg lifts and knee lifts against a resistance, are well suited for training this important muscle in many sports.

STABILIZERS. If improperly developed these muscles may hamper the activity of major muscles. Similarly, if one reaches the state of chronic stress, it puts the stabilizers into spasm, and as a result restrains the activity of the prime movers. Obviously, under such conditions one's athletic effectiveness may suffer. In discussing this subject reference will be made to 3 major sites of the body:

1. the shoulders, where supra, and infra spinatus muscles are performing inward and outward arm rotations. The best simple exercise to strengthen these two muscles is to perform the above two motions with the arm vertical, fist inside of the palms of a partner held tight together against the performer's fist. The resistance provided by the partner represents the necessary stimulus to strengthen the 2 muscles stabilizing (keeping fixed) the shoulder.

2. the hips, where piriformis muscle performs an outward rotation. Exercise: standing, knees locked, with a partner holding the foot with both hands. The athlete performs inward-outward leg rotations against the resistance provided by the partner.

3. the knees, where popliteus muscle is responsible for the inward-outward calf rotation. Suggested simple exercise: seated on a table/ desk, knee flexed. The athlete performs inward-outward rotations of the calf against the resistance provided by a partner holding the foot.

The stabilizers execute several functions for the human body. In addition to the dynamic actions mentioned above, these muscles contract isometrically to stabilize a joint so that one limb forming a joint is immobilized and thus allows the other to perform a certain move. The stabilizers can also monitor the state of the long bones' interactions in joints and sense injury potential in joints as a result of improper technique, inappropriate strength, and spasms produced by a poor stress management. If one of these three conditions occur, the stabilizers will restrain the activity of the prime movers avoiding strain and injuries.

As already mentioned, not too many coaches dedicate the time for strengthening the stabilizing muscles. There may not be too much time to work on stabilizers during the competitive phase, but this certainly should

229

not be a big problem during the transition and preparatory period, especially the AA phase.

The above groups of muscles, core area, rotators and stabilizers ought to be developed on a long-term progression basis. A casual approach will not do a good service to a serious athlete with chances to succeed in the world of athletics. On the contrary, a long-term progression should be considered for these muscles as well, including the one suggested below (Figure 93):

No.	Stage of development	Program
1	Puberty	- core area
		- intervertebral muscles
2	Post-puberty	- core area
		- stabilizers
		- rotatory muscles for all the limbs
3	Adolescence	- stabilizers
		- annual periodization
4	Maturation	- annual periodization
		- specificity

FIGURE 93. A suggested long-term periodization for basic muscle groups.

CHAPTER NINETEEN

METHODICAL GUIDELINES AND MECHANICAL CHARACTERISTICS OF STRENGTH

METHODICAL GUIDELINES FOR STRENGTH TRAINING

Throughout the pages of this book, numerous methodical suggestions were made, giving several guidelines to follow as one plans and creates their own strength training program. The intent of this chapter is to briefly refer to other methodical guidelines so that each person's strength training needs are best served.

CHECK THE EQUIPMENT. The types of equipment in use nowadays varies so much that if one moves from one gym to another he/she has to get accustomed to a new set of equipment and free weights. Although private clubs have supervisors or instructors, others do not. This is why before using any equipment one has to check it for maximum safety.

Among the most popular equipment used for strength training by athletes are free weights and circuit machines such as those built by Universal Gym Machine. Before using a free weight, secure collars and check, in the case of power racks, to make sure that the barbells are properly placed on supports, and the pins are locked-in properly. As for the circuit machines, the seats should be properly adjusted and secured, as well as any other movable equipment parts prior to training. Similarly, make sure that the weight key used for stacks is locked in its place by inserting and twisting it, or by pressing it to the end.

If other equipment than free weights/ circuit machines are used, the main criteria of selection is its effectiveness. The criteria for deciding the machine's effectiveness are:

1. **to duplicate, reproduce the skills performed by the prime movers**, and
2. **to permit a constant acceleration through the range of motion.**

In the first case this means specificity in training, an important requirement for top athletes during the training phases from the AA phase on. The second criteria is crucial for speed-power sports, especially from the conversion phase on and throughout the competitive phase. If it is not possible to reproduce constant acceleration in training, then there is no positive transfer from strength training to the sport's skills and performance.

In order to ensure safety, strength training equipment must be maintained properly so that wear and rust does not pose any danger to the users. One should constantly check for loose belts and cracks, as well as to periodically lubricate cables, chains, and rods to ensure smooth operation.

USE AND KNOW SPOTTING TECHNIQUES. Advanced strength trainers prefer free weights for the reasons explained above. As such they have training partners who can act as spotters, especially when they use maximum loads or the eccentric method. As already mentioned, the eccentric method employing free weights is both impossible to perform and dangerous without using spotters. To reduce risk, especially for young and inexperienced athletes, the coach could ask for assistance from trained instructors, as well as to use power/ squat racks.

Irrespective of one's experience, for high-risk movements (employing heavy loads) such as squats, military press, cleans, bench press, etc., one must use spotters. Not only that, but a spotter also has the advantage of offering feed-back regarding the technical accuracy of the lifts performed. In order to avoid any problems, including injuries, a spotter should:

1. Before actually spotting:
   - know both the exercise and spotting technique
   - know how many repetitions one performs
   - check the equipment. In the case of free weights make sure that the weights are evenly distributed and the collars properly secured
   - ensure that the performer grips the barbell properly
   - assume a ready position, feet apart for a strong base of support
   - if necessary assist the performer to take the barbell from the rack

2. During performance:
   - be ready, especially for maximum loads, to give a "lift-off" for the beginning of the lift
   - be attentive throughout the lift, and close enough to provide help if necessary
   - count the number of repetitions to make sure that there is a coordinated effort between the performer and spotters
   - if necessary communicate with the performer, giving him/her feed-back regarding performance, and motivation. A technical feed-back is crucial in avoiding eventual injuries (e.g. during bench press if an arm is higher, the weights might fall down from the lower end)
   - stop the exercise if the lift is performed with an incorrect technique

- be attentive during both the concentric and eccentric phase of the lift
- if one fails the attempt, secure the barbell and help the lifter to place it on the rack/ supports

USE CORRECT FORM AND BODY POSITION. A proper lifting technique, especially for free weight exercises, represents an important factor in performance improvements and prevention of injuries. The form, or the technique of lifting, has to constantly be stressed, especially during the early years of involvement in strength training.

Although there are many technical elements to be discussed, reference will be made only to the body position. All exercises, especially those involving lifting and carrying, ought to be performed with a straight upper body, and a flat back. An over arched, hollow back, as well as a round back should be avoided in all circumstances, with maximum attention when the loads are heavier. In both positions the spine, and in particular the intervertebral discs, are under excessive strain. An athlete lifting a 50 kg (110 lbs) weight with a rounded back yields an intervertebral stress of some 65% higher than with a straight back (Hartman, and Tünnemann, 1988).

The back posture is directly dependent upon the position of the head. Take for instance a half squat, with the barbell held on the shoulders. An improper head position may result in an undesirable muscle tension. For instance, an exaggerated and vigorous head extension (backward drop) causes an increased tension on the back extensor muscles, resulting in a hollow back. On the other hand, a forward bend of the head results in a rounded back, stretching the back muscles, and as a consequence the motion is performed by "shooting" the hips. The outcome of such a fault is that the head will follow the hips, rather than lead them. Therefore attention must be paid to the position of the head! The best position for half squats is an erect position of the upper body, with the back straight and the head upright with eyes in front, or slightly upward.

One can also cushion the intervertebral discs of the spine by contracting the abdominals, which creates pressure against the training belt, and as such compensating the back. In many lifting moves the hips and especially the abdominals act as stabilizers, representing a strong support for the working muscles of the arms and legs.

PROPER BREATHING, represents an important concern for anyone involved in strength training, especially for beginners. As beginners learn the technique of lifting, they should also receive instructions regarding proper breathing.

During strength training some breath holding occurs, especially during heavy lifts. If the athlete's breath is held for the duration of the lift there is a noted blood pressure increment, as well as a large increase in intra-thoracic and intra-abdominal pressure caused by the Valsalva maneuvre (the name of an Italian physician). This forced expiration against a closed glottis (the space between the vocal cords) may restrict the return of blood, causing veins to swell and the face to turn red (MacDougall et al., 1985). While the first reaction may be that the Valsalva maneuvre is hazardous, and as such to be avoided in strength training, it also has a beneficial function. This intra-thoracic and intra-abdominal pressure turns the trunk into a rigid body, which stabilizes the vertebral column, thus creating a strong support for the muscles to pull against it.

The Valsalva maneuvre represents a reflex reaction to lifting heavy loads and should not be perceived negatively, only unless breathing is held for a long time. In that case, it can result in fainting. However, since in strength training one rarely holds their breath for longer than 2–3 seconds, such undesirable situations occur very rarely. In any instance, a coach should take any precautions necessary in order to prevent the Valsalva maneuvre, especially for young athletes, by:

1. teaching the athletes correct breathing, and
2. encouraging young athletes to breath naturally during strength training.

The natural pattern for breathing in strength training is to inhale just before and during the lowering phase, or the eccentric segment of the lift, and to exhale during the lifting, or concentric phase. The exhalation part is preceded by a very short Valsalva, releasing most of the air from the lungs at the very end of the lift. In any instance, athletes should be strongly suggested not to maintain breath holding for too long, especially during a MxS training session.

The same suggestions should be given to the athletes performing isometric contractions: do not hold their breath while in contraction, except for a very short time! As the muscles are in contraction, and as the natural tendency is to hold their breath, the athletes should concentrate on breathing throughout the contraction. As for any exercises in regards to doing jumps and throws, one should inhale before the action and exhale while performing the exercise.

STRENGTH TRAINING ACCESSORIES commonly used in strength training are the belt, and eventually the training gloves and shoes.

A strength **training belt** is designed specifically to represent a support for the low back and abdominal muscles. It also represents an aid to counteract weak abdominal muscles for all exercises performed with the lower limbs. As a lift is performed the belt represent a support for the abdominal muscles, to push against it so that there is an approximate balance between the low back and abdominal muscles. Certainly, this should not represent an excuse for not strengthening the muscles of the above two anatomical regions. On the contrary, during the AA phase and even during other phases of training the athletes can dedicate the time to fortify the back and abdominal muscles. Another possible time to address the muscular weaknesses, and to do compensation work is during the transition phase.

Training gloves are used mostly to protect the palms, to prevent them against blistering. The popularity of the gloves is mostly among fitness fans, and are rarely worn by dedicated athletes. The latter often say that their functional calluses take care of the palm's protection.

Training shoes, with higher heels than any normal athletic shoes are used to provide a good support for the arch and to keep the feet tight. The elevated heels, however, have a mechanical advantage. As a barbell is lifted, such as in "cleans", in order to overcome the weight of the barbell, the athlete tends to lean backwards. A slight slip, or fall onto the back, may be dangerous. In order to counteract such inconveniences, a high heel shoe brings the vertical projection of the centre of gravity slightly forward. As the barbell is lifted, the athlete will not be able to lean backwards, and thus balancing out the weight of the barbell and the force and the mass of athlete's body.

Another advantage for wearing strength training shoes refers to the many athletes' lack of decent ankle flexibility. Take for instance the position of half squats (or even a deep squat). Under normal conditions, and for a better balance, a squat should be performed flat footed. However, many athletes lack good ankle flexibility, visible by the fact that as one takes that position he/ she immediately tends to stay on the ball of their foot or toes. This is a clear signal for a lack of a decent flexibility. The strength training shoes with their higher heels compensates for the lack of ankle flexibility, allowing therefore the athlete to take a flat footed and balanced position.

Wrapping or taping vulnerable joints is often used in order to provide additional support for weak joints, or beginners in strength training. If an athlete wraps a given joint (wrist, elbow, ankles, or knees), one should make sure that it is not very tight so that blood circulation is not affected. As much as possible during the rest interval, the wrap should be untightened for both comfort and increased circulation.

MEDICAL CLEARANCE is necessary for anyone involved in sports, and as such essential for strength training as well. Many children have a great desire to take part in sports, which may involve some strength training activities. And yet, without anybody's knowledge some children may have heart conditions, or a cardiovascular disease. Taking such individuals into sports, or even strength training may aggravate their health.

As previously mentioned, strength training employing heavy loads results in the Valsalva's maneuvre, thus allowing for increases in blood, chest and abdominal pressure. These pressures are more than unsuitable stressors for an already weak heart and cardiovascular system. In addition these increased pressures may limit or even restrict blood flow to and from the heart (Compton et al., 1973).

Other youngsters may experience other health problems, such as growth plate problems or orthopedic abnormalities like degenerating arthritis, which, as a result of strength training may increase skeletal and joint stress.

All such individuals, for their own sake, should be restricted by a physician to participate in stressful training in general, and strength training in particular. This is why before taking part in sports and strength training one should have the clearance from a medical doctor. In fact a concerned coach **should** require from the part of every athlete to have a medical clearance.

Force as a Mechanical Characteristic

The function of skeletal muscles is to produce mechanical work through muscle contraction.

From the theoretical viewpoint, force may be referred to as both a mechanical characteristic and a human ability. In the former case force is the object of studies in mechanics, while in the latter it is the scope of physiological and methodical investigation in training.

Force can be determined by direction, magnitude or the point of application. According to Newton's second law of motion force is equal to mass or load (m) times acceleration (a), or:

$$F = m \cdot a$$

Consequently, an increase in strength may be achieved by changing one or both of these factors (m or a). Such changes result in quantitative alterations which must be kept in mind when developing strength. The following two equations utilized in mechanics may illustrate this point:

$$Fmx = mmx \cdot a \ (1)$$
$$Fmx = m \cdot amx \ (2)$$

where Fmx is maximum force; mmx is maximum mass and amx means maximum acceleration.

In the first equation (1) maximum force is developed by utilizing the maximum mass (or load) as high as possible. In the second equation (2) force increments are achieved by utilizing the maximum speed of movement. The force that an athlete can apply and the velocity at which one can apply it maintain an inverse relationship. This is also true for the relationship between an athlete's applied force and the time period over which one can apply it. The gains in one ability is at the expense of the other. Consequently, although force may be the dominant characteristic of an ability, it cannot be considered in isolation because the aforementioned speed and time component will directly affect its application.

The force-velocity inverse relationship was demonstrated a long time ago. An adaptation of Ralston's (1949) force-velocity curve is illustrated by Figure 94 which demonstrates that when the load is low, the acceleration is high, given maximum effort by the participant. As the mass increases (from a baseball throw to shot put and weight lifting) the acceleration decreases, up to no movement at all (or static muscular contraction for a mass heavier than one's maximum force).

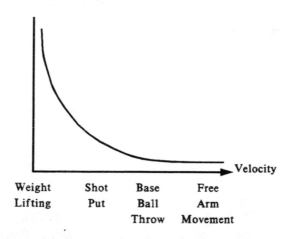

Figure 94. The force-velocity curve (adapted from Ralston et al., 1949).

The magnitude of the force is directly related to the magnitude of the mass. This relationship is linear only at the beginning when the force increases as the mass of the moving object increases. A continuous elevation of a mass will not necessarily result in an equally large increase in applied force. Therefore, the per gram force which the athlete applies against a shot (shot putting in athletics) will be greater than that applied when one lifts a barbell. In order to put a shot of 7.250kg (16lbs) a distance of 18.19m (60ft) an athlete displays a power of 5147 Watts (6.9 horse power (h.p.)) while to snatch a barbell of 150kg (330lbs) in weight lifting requires only 3207 Watts (4.3 h.p.). (Florescu et al, 1969).

From the mechanical point of view, strength can be expressed as:

$$F = R \left(1 + \frac{a}{g}\right)$$

Where: R = the magnitude of the resistance to be overcome
         a = the acceleration of the overcoming resistance
         g = the force of gravity

The relationship between these three elements can result in different types of strengths thus:

1. when R < R max, but a = a max, it results in explosive strength, or power,
2. when R < R max, but a < a max, the outcome is fast strength, or accelerating power, and
3. when R = R max, but a ~ 0 the resultant is strength performed at a low velocity

By using the above three situations one can work on the kind of relationships which will result in the desired type of strength. It is quite obvious that for sports where speed and power are the dominant abilities, one will decrease the resistance in order to increase acceleration (or number 1 or 2).

SOME MECHANICAL CHARACTERISTICS OF PLYOMETRICS

The action involved in a plyometric type of exercise relies mechanically on the stretch reflex which is found in the belly of the individual muscle. The main purpose of the stretch reflex is to monitor the degree of muscle stretch and to thereby prevent overstretching of any muscle fiber which can otherwise be torn. When an athlete jumps off the ground, a large amount of force is required to propel the entire body mass off the ground. The body must be able to flex and extend the body limbs very quickly, in order to leave the ground. A plyometric type of exercise relies on this quick body action, in order to attain the power which is required for the movement.

Mechanically, when the take-off leg is planted, the athlete must lower the centre of gravity, which creates a downward velocity. This "amortization phase" is an important component of any jumping type of activity, for it is during this phase that the athlete prepares for take-off in a different direction. A long amortization phase (also called the "shock absorbing phase"), is responsible for a loss of power. An example of this lower power output is seen in the long jumper who does not plant the take-off leg properly. This

238

mistake by the jumper will result in a loss of both the upward and the horizontal velocity which is required to propel the jumper forward. An athlete who performs a jumping action must work towards a shorter and quicker amortization phase: the shorter this phase, the more powerful the concentric muscle contraction, when the muscle has previously been stretched during the eccentric contraction or the amortization phase (Bosco and Komi, 1980). This action is possible due to the recovery and utilization of all the energy which has been stored in the elastic components of the muscle during any stretching action.

All jumping motion can be improved through the analysis of each individual, biomechanical component of the jump. An example of this is the improvement in a high jumper's technique: enhanced performance of a high jump can be achieved through the elimination of the deep knee bend phase of the jump, and the shortening of the time interval between the eccentric and the concentric contractions. The elimination of a deep flexion utilizes the elastic qualities of the muscle more efficiently.

As mentioned earlier, all jumpers need to first lower their centre of gravity, thereby creating a downward velocity. The athlete must then produce forces which will counter the downward motion (amortization phase), in order to get prepared for the upward, thrusting phase. To look at the jump from a mechanical point of view, it must be remembered that **force equals mass times acceleration** ($F = m \cdot a$). A greater force is required in order to decelerate the body more quickly and therefore will result in a shorter amortization phase. From this a second equation can be created:

$$\text{Average force of amortization} = \frac{\text{body mass x change in velocity}}{\text{time of amortization}}$$

If the athlete wants to decrease the time of amortization, a greater average force is required. If the athlete is not able to generate this force, a longer, less efficient amortization phase will occur which will result in a loss of horizontal velocity, due to the weakened concentric contraction.

This amortization equation also points out the importance of maintaining a low level of body fat and a high power-weight ratio, for even greater average force of amortization will be required if the body mass of the athlete is increased. A greater downward velocity at impact requires an increase in the average force produced during the amortization phase. An example of this is seen in any long or high jumpers who lower their centre of gravity prior to take-off, thereby reducing the impact of the forces.

The entire body of the athlete must be used efficiently in order to maximize jumping ability. The upward acceleration of the free limbs, for example the arms, after the amortization phase acts to increase the vertical forces placed on the take-off leg. A triple jumper, for example, must be able to apply peak force as great as 4–6 times their own body weight in order to compensate for the inability to lower the centre of gravity during the more upward hopping phase. The requirement to exert this large force is due mainly to the inability to lower the centre of gravity during a hop, as compared to a long jumper who can manipulate his/ her body more easily just prior to take-off. An effective take-off will only be achieved if the jumper can apply large forces on impact and produce a shorter, quicker amortization phase.

It is sometimes difficult to train for this specific phase of the jump, as few conventional exercises are applicable. Many jumpers use traditional weight training (e.g. squats or any Olympic lifts) in order to train for this take-off phase of their jumps. This type of weight training places a large load on the leg extensors which will, over time, provide an adequate strength training base. The main problem with only using weight training is that it is unlikely that a heavy squat lift will be fast enough to utilize the elastic qualities of the muscles. Such a lift is also restricted to a single joint movement. This is not the case in the single leg take-off, which involves multiple joint movements all happening simultaneously.

Bounding exercises, on the other hand, can be used successfully to simulate an effective take-off and can therefore improve the overall jumping ability of the athlete. Bounding has the potential to possess very similar force-time characteristics to the take-off. Similarly, it allows the athlete to practise resisting large impact loads on the take-off leg and to exert force in a short time interval. The bounding exercises will also involve multi-joint movement and provide the possibility of the development of the required muscle elasticity.

THE ROLE OF STRENGTH FOR WATER SPORTS

For sports performed in, or on water, such as swimming, synchronized swimming, water polo, rowing, and kayak-canoeing, the athlete's body or the boat moves forward as a result of exerting force. As force is performed against the water, the water exerts an equal and opposite force on the athlete or boat. This force acting against is known as **drag**.

When the boat or the swimmer moves through the water, the drag slows-down the forward motion or glide. To overcome that the athlete has to produce equal, or superior force if he/ she intends to maintain or increase speed.

The magnitude of the drag acting on a body moving through the water can be computed with the aid of the following equation (Hay, 1993):

$$F_D = C_D \, p \, A \, \frac{v^2}{2}$$

Where: F_D= the drag forces
C_D = the coefficient of drag
p = the density of the fluid involved
A = the frontal area exposed to the flow, and
V = the velocity of the body relative to the water

The coefficients of drag are numbers which refer to the nature and the shape of the body, which includes its orientation relative to the water flow. For instance, a long and slender shape, such as in rowing and kayak-canoeing boats, has a smaller value of CD if the long axis of the boat is exactly parallel to the water flow.

A simplified version of the above equation is presented below. This equation is not only easier to understand, but also easier to apply:

$D \sim V^2$

meaning that drag is proportional to the square of velocity.

In the case of water sports the velocity can be increased only if the athlete applies force against the water. As force increases the body is projected through the water faster. However, there is a catch to that: as the velocity of the body increases so does the drag. Therefore, according to the above equation, drag increases proportional to the square of velocity.

An example will easier demonstrate the above equation and assertion. Assume that an athlete swims or rows at 2m/sec. In this case:

$D \sim V^2 = 22 = 4 \text{ kg}$

In other words the athlete pulls with a force of 4 kg per stroke. If the athlete desires to be more competitive he/ she has to swim/ row with 3 m/ sec. As such:

$D \sim V^2 = 9 \text{ kg}$

For an even higher velocity, 4 m/sec. drag will equal 16 kg. Obviously, to be capable of pulling with increased force, one has to increase MxS. A body will not be able to generate increased velocity without increasing the force per stroke unit. To believe otherwise is a fallacy.

Certainly, the above reality has some training implications. In the first case, it is certain that MxS has to be increased. But since all water sports have a strong endurance component the coach should also make sure that the athlete is capable of displaying the same force for all the strokes, throughout the entire duration of race. And that means to incorporate in training not only a MxS phase, but also an adequate M-E phase, as suggested in chapter 15.

APPENDIX 1

Training log.

No.	Exercise	SETS									
		1	2	3	4	5	6	7	8	9	10

Enter: — Exercise
      — Load and number of repetitions per set (ex. 180 x 6)

APPENDIX 2

A MAXIMUM LIFT BASED ON REPETITIONS (Table compiled by Mike Clark, Strength and Conditioning Coach, University of Oregon)

% of 1RM	100	95	90	85	80	75
REPS	1	2	4	6	8	10
lbs. lifted	700.00	665.00	630.00	595.00	560.00	525.00
	695.00	660.25	625.50	590.75	556.00	521.25
	690.00	655.50	621.00	586.50	552.00	517.50
	685.00	650.75	616.50	582.25	548.00	513.75
	680.00	646.00	612.00	578.00	544.00	510.00
	675.00	641.25	607.50	607.50	573.75	540.00
	670.00	636.50	603.00	569.50	536.00	502.50
	665.00	631.75	598.50	565.25	532.00	498.75
	660.00	627.00	594.00	561.00	528.00	495.00
	655.00	622.25	589.50	556.75	524.00	491.25
	650.00	617.50	585.00	552.50	520.00	487.50
	645.00	612.75	580.50	548.25	516.00	483.75
	640.00	608.00	576.00	544.00	512.00	480.00
	635.00	603.25	571.50	539.75	508.00	476.25
	630.00	598.50	567.00	535.50	504.00	472.50
	625.00	593.75	562.50	531.25	500.00	468.75
	620.00	589.00	558.00	527.00	496.00	465.00
	615.00	584.25	553.50	522.75	492.00	461.25
	610.00	579.50	549.00	518.50	488.00	457.50
	605.00	574.75	544.50	514.25	484.00	453.75
	600.00	570.00	540.00	510.00	480.00	450.00
	595.00	565.25	535.50	505.75	476.00	446.25
	590.00	560.50	531.00	501.50	472.00	442.50
	585.00	555.75	526.50	497.25	468.00	438.75
	580.00	551.00	522.00	493.00	464.00	435.00
	575.00	546.25	517.50	488.75	460.00	431.25
	570.00	541.50	513.00	484.50	456.00	427.50
	565.00	536.75	508.50	480.25	452.00	423.75

% of 1RM	100	95	90	85	80	75
REPS	1	2	4	6	8	10
lbs. lifted	560.00	532.00	499.50	471.75	444.00	416.25
	555.00	527.25	504.00	476.00	448.00	420.00
	550.00	522.50	495.00	467.50	440.00	412.50
	545.00	517.75	490.50	463.25	436.00	408.75
	540.00	513.00	486.00	459.00	432.00	405.00
	535.00	508.25	481.50	454.75	428.00	401.25
	530.00	503.50	477.00	450.50	424.00	397.50
	525.00	498.75	472.50	466.25	420.00	393.75
	520.00	494.00	468.00	442.00	416.00	390.00
	515.00	489.25	463.50	437.75	412.00	386.25
	510.00	484.50	459.00	433.50	408.00	382.50
	505.00	479.75	454.50	429.25	404.00	378.75
	500.00	475.00	450.00	425.00	400.00	375.00
	495.00	470.25	445.50	420.75	396.00	371.25
	490.00	465.50	441.00	416.50	392.00	367.50
	485.00	460.75	436.50	412.25	388.00	363.75
	480.00	456.00	432.00	408.00	384.00	360.00
	475.00	451.25	427.50	403.75	380.00	356.25
	470.00	446.50	423.00	399.50	376.00	352.50
	465.00	441.75	418.50	395.25	372.00	348.75
	460.00	437.00	414.00	391.00	368.00	345.00
	455.00	432.25	409.50	386.75	364.00	341.25
	450.00	427.50	405.00	382.50	360.00	337.50
	445.00	422.75	400.50	378.25	356.00	333.75
	440.00	418.00	396.00	374.00	352.00	330.00
	435.00	413.25	391.50	369.75	348.00	326.25
	430.00	408.50	387.00	365.50	344.00	322.50
	425.00	403.75	382.50	361.25	340.00	318.75
	420.00	399.00	378.00	357.00	336.00	315.00
	415.00	394.25	373.50	352.75	332.00	311.25
	410.00	389.50	369.00	348.50	328.00	307.50
	405.00	384.75	364.50	344.25	324.00	303.75
	400.00	380.00	360.00	340.00	320.00	300.00
	395.00	375.25	355.50	335.75	316.00	296.25
	390.00	370.50	351.00	331.50	312.00	292.50
	385.00	365.75	346.50	327.25	308.00	288.75
	380.00	361.00	342.00	323.00	304.00	285.00
	375.00	356.25	337.50	318.75	300.00	281.25
	370.00	351.50	330.00	314.50	296.00	277.50
	365.00	346.75	328.50	310.25	292.00	273.75
	360.00	342.00	324.00	306.00	288.00	270.00

% of 1RM	100	95	90	85	80	75
REPS	1	2	4	6	8	10
lbs. lifted	355.00	337.25	319.50	301.75	284.00	266.25
	350.00	332.50	315.00	297.50	280.00	262.50
	345.00	327.75	310.50	293.25	276.00	258.75
	340.00	323.00	306.00	289.00	272.00	255.00
	335.00	318.25	301.50	284.75	268.00	251.25
	330.00	313.50	297.00	280.50	264.00	247.50
	325.00	308.75	292.50	276.25	260.00	243.75
	320.00	304.00	288.00	272.00	256.00	240.00
	315.00	299.25	283.50	267.75	252.00	236.25
	310.00	294.50	279.00	263.50	248.00	232.50
	305.00	289.75	274.50	259.25	244.00	228.75
	300.00	285.00	270.00	255.00	240.00	225.00
	295.00	280.25	265.50	250.75	236.00	221.25
	290.00	275.50	261.00	246.50	232.00	217.50
	285.00	270.75	256.50	242.25	228.00	213.75
	280.00	266.00	252.00	238.00	224.00	210.00
	275.00	261.25	247.50	233.75	220.00	206.25
	270.00	256.50	243.00	229.50	216.00	202.50
	265.00	251.75	238.50	225.25	212.00	198.75
	260.00	247.00	234.00	221.00	208.00	195.00
	255.00	242.25	229.50	216.75	204.00	191.25
	250.00	237.50	225.00	212.50	200.00	187.50
	245.00	232.75	220.50	208.25	196.00	183.75
	240.00	228.00	216.00	204.00	192.00	180.00
	235.00	223.25	211.50	199.75	188.00	176.25
	230.00	218.50	207.00	195.50	184.00	172.50
	225.00	213.75	202.50	191.25	180.00	168.75
	220.00	209.00	198.00	187.00	176.00	165.00
	215.00	204.25	193.50	182.75	172.00	161.25
	210.00	199.50	189.00	178.50	168.00	157.50
	205.00	194.75	184.50	174.25	164.00	153.75
	200.00	190.00	180.00	170.00	160.00	150.00
	195.00	185.25	175.50	165.75	156.00	146.25
	190.00	180.50	171.00	161.50	152.00	142.50
	185.00	175.75	166.50	157.25	148.00	138.75
	180.00	171.00	162.00	153.00	144.00	135.00
	175.00	166.25	157.50	148.75	140.00	131.25
	170.00	161.50	153.00	144.50	136.00	127.50
	165.00	156.75	148.50	140.25	132.00	123.75
	160.00	152.00	144.00	136.00	128.00	120.00
	155.00	147.25	139.50	131.75	124.00	116.25

% of 1RM	100	95	90	85	80	75
REPS	1	2	4	6	8	10
lbs. lifted	150.00	142.50	135.00	127.50	120.00	112.50
	145.00	137.75	130.50	123.25	116.00	108.75
	140.00	133.00	126.00	119.00	112.00	105.00
	135.00	128.25	121.50	114.75	108.00	101.25
	130.00	123.50	117.00	110.50	104.00	97.50
	125.00	118.75	112.50	106.25	100.00	93.75
	120.00	114.00	108.00	102.00	96.00	90.00
	115.00	109.25	103.50	97.75	92.00	86.25
	110.00	104.50	99.00	93.50	88.00	82.50
	105.00	99.75	94.50	89.25	84.00	78.75

APPENDIX 3

MAXIMUM WEIGHT CHART
(Made by Strength Tech, Inc., Box 1381, Stillwater, OK 74076, U.S.A.)

If for any reason (i.e. equipment) an athlete cannot lift the load necessary to calculate 1RM, but only 3, 4, or 5RM etc., one can still figure out his/her 1RM by using the chart below. In order to calculate it, perform the maximum number of repetitions with the load available (say 4 repetitions with 250lbs), and then:

1.   choose from the top of the chart the column headed "4" (the number of repetitions you did)
2.   find the row with "250" lbs (the maximum load you had available), and
3.   find the number where column "4" and the row "250" meet. This number is your 1RM at that given time.

Pounds	10	9	8	7	6	5	4	3	2
5	7	6	6	6	6	6	6	5	5
10	13	13	13	12	12	11	11	11	11
15	20	19	19	18	18	17	17	16	16
20	27	26	25	24	24	23	22	22	21
25	33	32	31	30	29	29	28	27	26
30	40	39	38	36	35	34	33	32	32
35	47	45	44	42	41	40	39	38	37
40	53	52	50	48	47	46	44	43	42
45	60	58	56	55	53	51	50	49	47
50	67	65	63	61	59	57	56	54	53
55	73	71	69	67	65	63	61	59	58
60	80	77	75	73	71	69	67	65	63
65	87	84	81	79	76	74	72	70	68
70	93	90	88	85	82	80	78	76	74
75	100	97	94	91	88	86	83	81	79
80	107	103	100	97	94	91	89	86	84
85	113	110	106	103	100	97	94	92	89
90	120	116	113	109	106	103	100	97	95

Pounds	10	9	8	7	6	5	4	3	2
95	127	123	119	115	112	109	106	103	100
100	133	129	125	121	118	114	111	108	105
105	140	135	131	127	124	120	117	114	111
110	147	142	138	133	129	126	122	119	116
115	153	148	144	139	135	131	128	124	121
120	160	155	150	145	141	137	133	130	126
125	167	161	156	152	147	143	139	135	132
130	273	168	163	158	153	149	144	141	137
135	180	174	169	164	159	154	150	146	142
140	187	181	175	170	165	160	156	151	147
145	193	187	181	176	171	166	161	157	153
150	200	194	188	182	176	171	167	162	158
155	207	200	194	188	182	177	172	168	163
160	213	106	200	194	188	183	178	173	168
165	220	213	206	200	194	189	183	178	174
170	227	219	213	206	200	194	189	184	179
175	233	226	219	212	206	200	194	189	184
180	240	232	225	218	212	206	200	195	189
185	247	239	231	224	218	211	206	200	195
190	253	245	238	230	224	217	211	205	200
195	260	252	244	236	229	223	217	211	205
200	267	258	250	242	235	229	222	216	211
205	273	265	256	248	241	234	228	222	216
210	280	271	263	255	247	240	233	227	221
215	287	277	269	261	253	246	239	232	226
220	293	284	275	267	259	251	244	238	232
225	300	290	281	273	265	257	250	243	237
230	307	297	288	279	271	263	256	249	242
235	313	303	294	285	276	269	261	254	247
240	320	310	300	291	282	274	267	259	253
245	327	316	306	297	288	280	272	265	258
250	333	323	313	303	294	286	278	270	263
255	340	329	319	309	300	291	283	276	268
260	347	335	325	315	306	297	289	281	274
265	353	342	331	321	312	303	294	286	279
270	360	348	338	327	318	309	300	292	284
275	367	355	344	333	324	314	306	297	289
280	373	361	350	339	329	320	311	303	295
285	380	368	356	345	335	326	317	308	300
290	387	374	363	352	341	331	322	314	305
295	393	381	369	358	347	337	328	319	311

Pounds	10	9	8	7	6	5	4	3	2
300	400	487	375	364	353	343	333	324	316
305	407	394	381	370	359	349	339	330	321
310	413	400	388	376	365	354	344	335	326
315	420	406	394	382	371	360	350	341	332
320	427	413	400	388	376	366	356	346	337
325	433	419	406	394	382	371	361	351	342
330	440	426	413	400	388	377	367	357	347
335	447	432	419	406	394	383	372	362	353
340	453	439	425	412	400	389	378	368	358
345	460	445	431	418	406	394	383	373	363
350	467	452	438	424	412	400	389	378	368
355	473	458	444	430	418	406	394	384	374
360	480	465	450	436	424	411	400	389	379
365	487	471	456	442	429	417	406	395	384
370	493	477	463	448	435	423	411	400	389
375	500	484	469	455	441	429	417	405	395
380	507	490	475	461	447	434	422	411	400
385	513	497	481	467	453	440	428	416	405
390	520	503	488	473	459	446	433	422	411
395	527	510	494	479	465	451	439	427	416
400	533	516	500	485	471	457	444	432	421
405	540	523	506	491	476	463	450	438	426
410	547	529	513	497	482	469	456	443	432
415	553	535	519	503	488	474	461	449	437
420		542	525	509	494	480	467	454	442
425		548	531	515	500	486	472	459	447
430		555	538	521	506	491	478	465	453
435		561	544	527	512	497	483	470	458
440		568	550	533	518	503	489	476	463
445		574	556	539	524	509	494	481	468
450		581	563	545	529	514	500	486	474
455		587	569	552	535	520	506	492	479
460		594	575	558	541	526	511	497	484
465		600	581	564	547	531	517	503	489
470		606	588	570	553	537	522	508	495
475		613	594	576	559	543	528	514	500
480		619	600	582	565	549	533	519	505
485		626	606	588	571	554	539	524	511
490		632	613	594	576	560	544	530	516
495		639	619	600	582	566	550	535	521
500		645	625	606	588	571	556	541	526

Pounds	10	9	8	7	6	5	4	3	2
505		652	631	612	594	577	561	546	532
510		658	638	618	600	583	567	551	537
515		665	644	624	606	589	572	557	542
520		671	650	630	612	594	578	562	547
525		677	656	636	618	600	583	568	553
530		684	663	642	624	606	589	573	558
535		690	669	648	629	611	594	578	563
540		697	675	655	635	617	600	584	568
545		703	681	661	641	623	606	589	574
550		710	688	667	647	629	611	595	579
555		716	694	673	653	634	617	600	584
560		723	700	679	659	640	622	605	589
565		729	706	685	665	646	628	611	595
570		735	713	691	671	651	633	616	600
575		742	719	697	676	657	639	622	605
580		748	725	703	682	663	644	627	611
585		755	731	709	688	669	650	632	616
590		761	738	715	694	674	656	638	621
595		768	744	721	700	680	661	643	626
600		774	750	727	706	686	667	649	632
605		781	756	733	712	691	672	654	637
610		787	763	739	718	697	678	659	642
615		794	769	745	724	703	683	665	647
620		800	775	752	729	709	689	670	653
625		806	781	758	735	714	694	676	658
630		813	788	764	741	720	700	681	663
635		819	794	770	747	726	706	686	668
640		826	800	776	753	731	711	692	674
645		832	806	782	759	737	717	697	679
650		839	813	788	765	743	722	703	684
655		845	819	794	771	749	728	708	689
660		852	825	800	776	754	733	714	695
665		858	831	806	782	760	739	719	700
670		865	838	812	788	766	744	724	705
675		871	844	818	794	771	750	730	711
680		877	850	824	800	777	756	735	716
685		884	856	830	806	783	761	741	721
690		890	863	836	812	789	767	746	726
695		897	869	842	818	794	772	751	732
700		903	875	848	824	800	778	757	737
705		910	881	855	829	806	783	762	742

Pounds	10	9	8	7	6	5	4	3	2
710		916	888	861	835	811	789	768	747
715		923	894	867	841	817	794	773	753
720		929	900	873	847	823	800	778	758
725		935	906	879	853	829	806	784	763
730		942	913	885	859	834	811	789	768
735		948	919	891	865	840	817	795	774
740		955	925	897	871	846	822	800	779
745		961	931	903	876	851	828	805	784
750		968	938	909	882	857	833	811	789
755		974	944	915	888	863	839	816	795
760		981	950	921	894	869	844	822	800
765		987	956	927	900	874	850	827	805
770		994	963	933	906	880	856	832	811
775		1000	969	939	912	886	861	838	816
780		1006	975	945	918	891	867	843	821
785		1013	981	952	924	897	872	849	826
790		1019	988	958	929	903	878	854	832
795		1026	994	964	035	090	883	859	837
800		1032	1000	970	941	914	889	865	842
820		1058	1025	994	965	937	911	886	863
840		1084	1050	1018	988	960	933	908	884
860		1110	1075	1042	1012	983	956	930	905
880		1135	1100	1067	1035	1006	978	951	926
900		1161	1125	1091	1059	1029	1000	973	947
920		1187	1150	1115	1082	1051	1022	995	968

GLOSSARY OF TERMS

Actin A protein involved in muscular contraction.

Action Potential The electrical activity developed in a muscle or nerve cell during activity or depolarization.

Active Transport The movement of substances or materials against their concentration gradients by the expenditure of metabolic energy.

Acyclic A skill made out of actions which are constantly changing, without being similar to others.

Adaptation Persistant changes in structure or function of a muscle as a direct response to progressively increased training load.

Adenosine Diphosphate (ADP) A complex chemical compound which, when combined with inorganic phosphate (Pi), forms ATP.

Adenosine Triphosphate (ATP) A complex chemical compound formed with the energy released from food and stored in all cells, particularly muscles.

Afferent Nerve A neuron that conveys sensory impulses from a receptor to the central nervous system.

Agonistic Muscle A muscle directly engaged in a muscular contraction and working in opposition to the action of other muscles.

All-Or-None Law A stimulated muscle or nerve fiber contracts or propagates a nerve impulse either completely, or not at all (for instance, a minimal stimulus causes a maximium response).

Alpha Motor Neuron A type of efferent nerve cell that innervates extrafusal muscle fibers.

Alveoli (plural); Alveolus (singular) Tiny terminal air sacs in the lungs where gaseous exchange with the blood in the pulmonary capillaries occurs.

Amortization phase The amortization phase is the eccentric or yielding phase of an activity. Amortization occurs just prior to the active or push-off phase of an activity, and includes the time from ground contact to the reverse movement.

Anabolic Protein building.

Anaerobic In the absence of oxygen.

Anaerobic Glycolysis The incomplete chemical breakdown of carbohydrate. The anaerobic reactions in this breakdown release energy for the manufacture of ATP as they produce lactic acid (anaerobic glycolysis is known as the lactic acid system).

Anaerobic Threshold That intensity of workload or oxygen consumption in which anaerobic metabolism is accelerated.

Androgen Any substance that possesses masculinizing properties.

Antagonistic Muscle Muscle that have an opposite effect on movers, or agonistic muscle, by opposing its contraction.

ATP-PC System An anaerobic energy system in which ATP is manufactured when phosphocreatine (PC) is broken.

Axon A nerve fiber.

Back extensor Muscles involved in straightening the back.

Ballistic Dynamic muscular movements.

Barbell A bar to which varying weights are attached; usually held with both arms.

Biceps brachii Elbow flexor of upper arm.

Bilateral exercise Using both arms or legs at the same time to perform an exercise.

Biomotor Abilities The capacity to perform a range of activities, such as strength, speed, and endurance. They are both genetically determined, and influenced by training.

Bodybuilding A sport in which muscle size, definition, and symmetry determines the winner.

Capillary A fine network of small vessels located between arteries and veins where exchanges between tissue and blood occur.

Carbohydrate Any of a group of chemical compounds, including sugars, starches, and cellulose, containing carbon, hydrogen, and oxygen only. One of the basic foodstuffs.

Cardiorespiratory Endurance The ability of the lungs and heart to take in and transport adequate amounts of oxygen to the working muscles, allowing activities that involve large muscle masses (e.g., running, swimming, bicycling) to be performed over long periods of time.

Central Nervous System (CNS) The spinal cord and brain.

Concentric Contraction The shortening of a muscle during contraction.

Conditioning Augmentation of the energy capacity of muscles through an exercise program. Conditioning is not primarily concerned with the skill of performance, as would be the case in training.

Cross-Bridges Extensions of myosin.

Cyclic A skill comprised of motions which are repeated continuously.

Density The mass per unit volume of an object.

Detraining Reversal of adaptation to exercise. Effects of detraining occur more rapidly than training gains, with significant reduction of strength (and work) capacity in two weeks of cessation of training.

Dumbbell Small weights of fixed resistance; usually held with one hand.

Eccentric Contraction The muscle lengthens while contracting (developing tension).

Efferent Nerve A neuron that conveys motor impulses away from the central nervous system to an organ of response such as the skeletal muscle.

Electrical Potential The capacity for producing electrical effects, such as an electric current, between two bodies (e.g., between the inside and outside of a cell).

Endomysium A connective tissue surrounding a muscle fiber or cell.

Energy The capacity or ability to perform work.

Energy System A metabolic system involving a series of chemical reactions resulting in the formation of waste products and the manufacture of ATP.

Enzyme A protein compound that speeds up a chemical reaction.

Epimysium A connective tissue surrounding the entire muscle.

Estrogen The female androgen.

Excitation A response to a stimulus.

Exercise-Recovery The performance of light exercise during recovery from exercise.

Extracellular Outside the cell.

Extrafusal Fiber A typical or normal muscle cell or fiber.

Fasciculus (singular); Fasciculi (plural) A group or bundle of skeletal muscle fibers held together by a connective tissue called the perimysium.

Fast-Twitch Fiber (FT) A muscle fiber characterized by fast contraction time, high anaerobic capacity, and low aerobic capacity, all making the fiber suited for high power output activities.

Fat A compound containing glycerol and fatty acids. One of the basic foodstuffs.

Fatigue A state of discomfort and decreased efficiency resulting from prolonged or excessive exertion.

Fatty Acid (Free Fatty Acid) The usable form of triglycerides.

Flexibility The range of motion about a joint (static flexibility); opposition or resistance of a joint to motion (dynamic flexibility).

Force Deficit The inability of involving all the muscle fibers to perform an athletic action.

Free Weights Weights not part of an exercise machine (i.e., barbells and dumbbells).

Gamma Motor Neuron A type of efferent nerve cell that innervates the ends of an intrafusal muscle fiber.

Glucose Simple sugar.

Glycogen The form in which glucose (sugar) is stored in the muscles and the liver.

Glycogenesis The manufacture of glycogen from glucose.

Glycolysis The incomplete chemical breakdown of glycogen. In aerobic glycolysis, the end product is pyruvic acid; in anaerobic glycolysis (lactic acid system), the end product is lactic acid.

Golgi Tendon Organ A proprioceptor located within a muscular tendon.

Growth Hormone A hormone secreted by the anterior lobe of the pituitary gland that stimulates growth and development.

Hamstring Muscle on the back of the thigh that flexes the knee and extends the hip.

Hemoglobin (Hb) A complex molecule found in red blood cells, which contains iron (heme) and protein (globin) and is capable of combining with oxygen.

Hormone A discrete chemical substance secreted into the body fluids by an endocrine gland that has a specific effect on the activities of other cells, tissues, and organs.

Hyperplasia An increase in the number of cells in a tissue or organ.

Hypertrophy An increase in the size of a cell or organ.

Innervate To stimulate, to transmit a nervous energy to a muscle.

Intensity Refers to the qualitative element of training such as speed, MxS, and P. In strength training intensity is expressed in percentage of 1RM.

Intermittent Work Exercises performed with alternate periods of relief, as opposed to continuous work.

Intermuscular Coordination The interaction of several muscles which cooperate in performing an action.

Interneuron (Internuncial Neuron) A nerve cell located between afferent (sensory) and efferent (motor) nerve cells, It acts as a "middleman" between incoming and outgoing impulses.

Interstitial Pertaining to the area or space between cells.

Interstitial Fluid The fluid between the cells.

Interval Training A system of physical conditioning in which the body is subjected to short but regularly repeated periods of work stress interspersed with adequate periods of relief.

Intrafusal Fiber A muscle cell (fiber) that houses the muscle spindle.

Intramuscular Coordination The ability of coordinating many neuromuscular units to act simultaneously to perform a move.

Isokinetic Contraction Contraction in which the tension developed by the muscle while shortening at constant speed is maximum over the full range of motion.

Isometric (Static) Contraction Contraction in which tension is developed, but there is no change in the length of the muscle.

Isotonic Pertaining to the same tension.

Isotonic Contraction Contraction in which the muscle shortens with varying tension while lifting a constant load. Also referred to as a **dynamic or concentric contraction.**

Kilogram-Meters (kg-m) A unit of work.

Lactic Acid (Lactate) A fatiguing metabolite of the lactic acid system resulting from the incomplete breakdown of glucose (sugar).

Lactic Acid System (LA System) An anaerobic energy system in which ATP is manufactured when glucose (sugar) is broken down to lactic acid. Used in high-intensity work over a short duration (less than 2 minutes).

Lymph A colorless fluid that bathes the body cells.

Machine Resistance training equipment that dictates the direction of the exercise movement and the body position.

Macro-cycle A phase of training of 2-6 weeks long.

Maturation Progress toward adulthood.

Metabolism The sum total of the chemical changes or reactions occurring in the body.

Metabolite Any substance produced by a metabolic reaction.

Micro-cycle Represents a phase of training of approximately one week.

Millimole One thousandth of a mole.

Mole The gram-molecular weight or gram-formula weight of a substance.

Motoneuron (Motor Neuron) A nerve cell, which when stimulated, effects muscular contraction. Most motoneurons innervate skeletal muscle.

Motor End-Plate The neuromuscular or myoneural junction.

Motor Unit An individual motor nerve and all the muscle fibers it innervates.

Multiple Motor Unit Summation The varying of the number of motor units contracting within a muscle at any given time.

Muscle Bundle A fasciculus. A group or bundle of skeletal muscle fibers held together by a connective tissue called the perimysium.

Muscle Spindle A proprioceptor surrounded by intrafusal muscle fibers.

Muscular Endurance The ability of a muscle or muscle group to perform repeated contractions for a longer period of time.

Muscle Receptors Proprioceptors which monitor systems related specifically to skeletal muscles. These receptors include the Golgi tendon organ and muscle spindle, which send information to higher brain centres about muscle tension, static length, velocity of stretch, and pressure.

Myofibril The part of a muscle fiber containing two protein filaments, myosin and actin.

Myoglobin An oxygen-binding pigment similar to hemoglobin that gives the red muscle fiber its colour. It acts as an oxygen store and aids in the diffusion of oxygen.

Myosin A protein involved in muscular contraction.

Nerve Cell See **Neuron**.

Nerve Impulse An electrical disturbance at the point of stimulation of a nerve that is self-propagated along the entire length of the axon.

Neuron A nerve cell consisting of a cell body (soma), with its nucleus and cytoplasm, dendrites and axons.

Oblique Muscles on the side of the abdominal area.

Oxygen Debt The amount of oxygen consumed during recovery from exercise, above that ordinarily consumed.

Oxygen System An aerobic energy system in which ATP is manufactured when food (principally sugar and fat) is broken down. This system produces ATP most abundantly and is the prime energy source during long-lasting (endurance) activities.

Perimysium A connective tissue surrounding a fasciculus or muscle bundle.

Periodization Represents a process of structuring training into phases.

Periodization of strength It structures the strength training program into phases in order to maximize one's capacity to meet the specifics of strength according to the needs of a sport/ event.

Phosphagen A group of compounds; collectively refered to as ATP and PC.

Phosphagen System See ATP-PC system.

Phosphocreatine (PC) A chemical compound stored in muscle, which when broken down aids in manufacturing ATP.

Plasma The liquid portion of the blood.

Plateau Period during training when no observable progress is made.

Plyometrics Drills or exercises aimed at linking sheer strength and scope of movement to produce an explosive-reactive type of movement. The term is often used to refer to jumping drills and depth jumping, but plyometrics can include any drill or exercise utilizing the stretch reflex to produce an explosive reaction.

Power Performance of work expressed per unit of time.

Prime Movers The muscles primarly taking place in performing a technical movement.

Proprioceptor Sensory organs found in muscles, joints, and tendons, which give information concerning movement and position of the body (kinesthesis).

Protein A compound containing amino acids. One of the basic food-stuffs.

Range of motion Movement allowed by the body's joints and body position in a particular exercise.

Receptor A sense organ that receives stimuli.

Reflex An automatic response induced by stimulation of a receptor.

Repetition The number of work intervals within one set.

Repetition Maximum (RM) The maximum load that a muscle group can lift in one attempt. Also called "one repetition maximum" (1RM).

Resistance training The use of various methods or equipment to provide an external force to exercise against.

Rest Resting during recovery from exercise.

Rotator Cuff Group of muscles that rotate upper arm in shoulder joint.

Sarcolemma The muscle cell membrane.

Sarcomere The distance between two Z lines; the smallest contractile unit of skeletal muscle.

Sarcoplasm Muscle protoplasm.

Sarcoplasmic Reticulum A network of tubules and vesicles surrounding the myofibril.

Sensory Fiber See **Afferent nerve.**

Sensory Neuron A nerve cell that conveys impulses from a receptor to the central nervous system. Examples of sensory neurons are those excited by sound, pain, light, and taste.

Set The total number of repetitions performed before a rest interval is taken.

Slow-Twitch Fiber (ST) A muscle fiber characterized by slow contraction time, low anaerobic capacity, and high aerobic capacity, all making the fiber suited for low power output activities.

Spatial Summation An increase in responsiveness of a nerve resulting from the additive effect of numerous stimuli.

Specificity of Training Principle underlying construction of a training program for a specific activity or skill.

Static Contraction See **Isometric contraction.**

Spotter Individual responsible for the safety of a trainee who is performing a lift.

Stabilizers Muscles that are stimulated to act, to anchor, or stablize the position of a limb.

Stimulus (singular); Stimuli (plural) Any agent, act, or influence that modifies the activity of a receptor or irritable tissue.

Strength The force that a muscle or muscle group can exert against a resistance.

Stretch or Myotatic Reflex It refers to a reflex which responds to the rate of muscle stretch. This reflex has the fastest-known response to a stimulus (in this case the rate of muscle stretch). The myotatic/stretch reflex elicits contraction of homonymous muscle and synergist muscles (those surrounding the stretched muscle which produces the same movement), and inhibition of the antagonist muscles.

Synapse The connection or junction of one neuron to another.

Synergist Muscle Muscles that actively provide an additive contribution to the agonist muscle during a muscle contraction.

Temporal Summation An increase in responsiveness of a nerve, resulting from the additive effect of frequently occurring stimuli.

Testosterone The male sex hormone secreted by the testicles; it possesses masculinizing properties.

Tetanus The maintenance of tension of a motor unit at a high level as long as the stimuli continues or until fatigue sets in.

Tonus Resiliency and resistance to stretch in a relaxed, resting muscle.

Training An exercise program to develop an athlete for a particular event. Increasing skill of performance and energy capacities are of equal consideration.

Training Frequency The number of times per week for the training workout.

Triglycerides The storage form of free fatty acids.

Troponin A protein involved in muscular contraction.

Twitch A brief period of contraction followed by relaxation in the response of a motor unit to a stimulus (nerve impulse).

Valsalva Maneuver Making an expiratory effort with the glottis closed.

Variation Process of changing exercise variables to provide a different training stimulus.

Vein A vessel carrying blood toward the heart.

Vitamin An organic material in the presence of which important chemical (metabolic) reactions occur.

Volume A quantitative element of training. In the case of strength training it measures the total work for a given exercise or training phase (sets x repetitions x load).

Watt Absolute unit of power equal to the work done at the rate of one absolute joule per second.

Wave Summation The varying of the frequency of contraction of individual motor units.

Weight Lifting An Olympic competitive sport in which the highest total poundage in two lifts— snatch and clean, and jerk— determine the winner.

Weight Training A strength training program employing the resistance provided by weights, such as barbells and dumbbells.

Work Application of a force through a distance.

Z Line A protein band that defines the distance of one sarcomere in the myofibril.

REFERENCES

Abernethy, P.J.; Thayer, R.; Taylor, A.W. Acute and chronic responses of skeletal muscle to endurance and sprint exercise. A review. Sports Medicine, 10(6):365-389, 1990.

Adrian, M.J.; Cooper, J.M. The biomechanics of human movement. Indianapolis, Indiana. Benchmark Press, Inc. 1989.

Appell, H.J. Muscular atrophy following immobilization: A review. Sports Medicine, 10(1), 42-58, 1990.

Appenzeller, O. Sports Medicine, Baltimore, Urban and Schwarzenberg. 1988.

Armstrong, R.B. Mechanisms of exercise-induced delayed-onset muscular soreness: A brief review. Medicine and Science in Sports and Exercise, 6, 529-538, 1984.

Armstrong, R.B. Muscle damage and endurance events. Sports Medicine, Vol. 3, 370-381, 1986.

Asmussen, E., and Mazin, B. A central nervous component in local muscular fatigue. Europ J Appl Physiol, 38:9-15, 1978.

Astrand, P.O.; Rodahl, K. Textbook of Work Physiology. New York, McGraw-Hill Book Co. 1985.

Atha, J. Strengthening muscle. Exercise and Sport Sciences Reviews, 9, 1-73, 1984.

Baroga, L. Contemporary tendencies in the methodology of strength development. Bucharest. Ed. Fizica Si Sport, 6:22-36, 1978.

Bergstrom, J.; L. Hermansen; E. Hultman and B. Saltin. Diet, muscle glycogen and physical performance. Acta Physiol. Scand., 71:140-150, 1967.

Belcastro, A.N., Bonen, A. Lactic acid removal rates during controlled and uncontrolled recovery exercise. J Appl Physiol, 39(6):932-936, 1975.

Bergeron, G. Therapeutic massage. Canadian Athletic Therapist Association Journal. Summer, 15–17, 1982.

Bigland-Ritchie, B., Jones, D.A., and Woods, J.J. Excitation frequency and muscle fatigue: electrical responses during human voluntary and stimulated contractions. Exper Neurology, 64:414-427, 1979.

Bigland-Ritchie, B.; Johansson, R.; Lippold, O.C.J.; Woods, J.J. Contractile speed and EMG changes during fatigue of sustained maximal voluntary contractions. J. Neurophysiology, 50(1):313-324, 1983.

Bompa, T.O. Theory and Methodology of Training. Dubuque, Iowa. Kendall/Hunt Publishing Inc. 1983.

Bompa, T. Theory and Methodology of Training: The Key to Athletic Performance. Dubuque, Iowa. Kendall/Hunt Publishing Co. Third Edition, 1994.

Bompa, T. Power Training: Plyometrics for maximum power development. Oakville-New York-London, Mosaic Press/Coaching Association of Canada, 1993.

Bompa, T.; Hebbelinck, M.; Van Gheluwe, B. A biomechanical analysis of the rowing stroke employing two different oar grips. The XXI World Congress in Sports Medicine, Brasilia, Brazil, 1978.

Bonen, A., and Belcastro, A.N. Comparison of self-selected recovery methods on lactic acid removal rates. Med Sci Sports, 8(3):176-178, 1976.

Bonen, A.; Belcastro, A. A physiological rational for active recovery exercise. Can. J. of Appl. Sp. Sci., 2:63-64, 1977.

Bosco, C. and P.V. Komi. Influence of countermovement amplitude in potentiation of muscular performance. Biomechanics VII. University Park Press, Baltimore, 129-135, 1980.

Brooks, G.A.; K.T. Brauner and R.G. Cassens. Glycogen synthesis and metabolism of lactic acid after exercise. Am. J. Physiol., 224:1162-1166, 1973.

Brooks, G.A.; Fahey, T. Exercise Physiology: Human Bioenergetics and its Applications. Macmillan Pub. Co. 1985.

Burke, F., Costill, D., and Fink, W. Characteristics of skeletal muscle in competitive cyclists. Med Sci Sports, 9:109-112, 1977.

Bührle, M. (ed.) Grundlagen des Maximal- und Schnellkraft trainings. Hofmann, Schorndorf. 1985.

Bührle, M. and Schmidtbleicher, D. Komponenten der Maximal- und Schnellkraft-Versuch einer Neustrukturierung auf der Basis empirischer Ergebnisse. Sportwissenschaft, 11, 11-27, 1981.

Cinique, C. Massage for cyclists: the winning touch? The Physician and Sportsmedicine, 17, 10:167-170, 1989.

Clamann, H.P., and Broecker, K.T. Relationship between force and fatigability of red and pale skeletal muscles in man. Am J Phys Med, 58(2):70-85, 1979.

Clark, N. Recovering from exhaustive workouts. National Strength and Conditioning Journal, January, 36-37. 1985.

Compton, D.; Hill, P.M.; Sinclair, J.D. Weight-lifters' blackout. Lancet II: 1234-1237, 1973.

Conlee, R.K. Muscle glycogen and exercise endurance: a twenty year perspective. Exercise and Sport Sciences Review, 15:1-28, 1987.

Costill, D.L. Inside running: Basics of sports physiology. Indianapolis, Benchmark Press. 1986.

Costill, D.; Daniels, J.; Evans, W.; Fink, W.; Krahenbuhl, G., and Saltin, B. Skeletal muscle enzymes and fibre composition in male and female track athletes. J Appl Physiol, 40:149-154, 1976.

Costill, D.L.; Coyle, E.F.; Fink, W.F.; Lesmes, G.R.; and Witzmann, F.A. Adaptations in skeletal muscle following strength training. Journal of Applied Physiology, 46, 96-99, 1979.

Costill, D.L.; Sherman, W.M.; Fink, W.J.; Maresh, C.; Witten, M.; and Miller, J.M. The role of dietary carbohydrate in muscle glycogen resynthesis after strenuous running. Am J Clin Nutri, 34:1831-1836, 1982.

Coyle, E.F.; Costill, D.L.; and Lemes, G.R. Leg extension power and muscle fibre composition. Med Sci Sports, 11(1):12-15, 1979.

Dons, B.; Bollerup, K.; Bonde-Petersen, F.; and Hancke, S. The effects of weight lifting exercise related to muscle fibre composition and muscle cross-sectional area in humans. Europ J Appl Physiol, 40-95-106, 1979.

Dudley, G.A.; Fleck, S.J. Strength and endurance training: Are they mutually exclusive? Sports Medicine, 4:79-85, 1987.

Ebbing, C.; Clarkson, P. Exercise-induced muscle damage and adaptation. Sports Medicine, Vol. 7, 207-234, 1989.

Edgerton, R.V. Neuromuscular Adaptation to Power and Endurance Work. Canadian Journal of Applied Sports Sciences, 1:49-58, 1976.

Elder, G.C.B.; Bradbury, K.; and Roberts, R. Variability of fibre type distributions within human muscles. J Appl Physiol: Respirat Environ Exercise Physiol, 53(6):1473-1480, 1982.

Evans, W.J. Exercise-induced skeletal muscle damage. The Physician and Sports Medicine, Vol. 15, No. 1, 89-100, 1987.

Fabiato, A.; Fabiato, F. The effect of pH on myofilaments and the sarcoplasmic reticulum of skinned cells from cardiac and skeletal muscle. J. Physiology, 276:233-255, 1978.

Fahey, T.D. How to cope with muscle soreness. Power-Research. 1991.

Fitts, R.H., and Holloszy, J.O. Lactate and contractile force in frog muscle during development of fatigue and recovery. Am J Physiol, 231(2):430-433, 1976.

Florescu, C.; Dumitrescu, Y.; Predescu, A. The Methodology of developing the motor abilities. Bucharest, CNEFS, 1969.

Fox, E.L. Sports Physiology. New York: CBS College Publishing, 1984.

Fox, E.L. Sports Physiology. 2nd ed. Philadelphia, W.B. Saunders, 1989.

Fox. E.L.; Bowes, R.W.; Foss, M.L. The Physiological Basis of Physical Education and Athletics. Dubuque, Iowa. Wm. C. Brown Publishers, 1989.

Fry, R.W.; Morton, R.; Keast, D. Overtraining in athletics. Sports Medicine, 2(1):32-65, 1991.

Gauron, E.F. Mental training for peak performance. New York. Sports Science Associates, 1984.

Gladden, L.B.; MacIntosh, B.R.; and Stainsby, W.N. O2 uptake and developed tension during and after fatigue, curare block, and ischemia. J Appl Physiol, 45(5):751-755, 1978.

Goldberg, A.L.; Etlinger, J.D.; Goldspink, D.F.; and Jablecki, C. Mechanism of work-induced hypertrophy of skeletal muscle. Med. Sci. Sports Exerc., 7:185-198, 1975.

Gollhofer, A.; P.A. Fujitsuka, N. and M. Miyashita. Fatigue during stretch-shortening cycle exercises: Changes in neuro-muscular activation patters of human skeletal muscle. Journal Sports Medicine, 8:30-47, 1987.

Gollnick, P.; Armstrong, R.; Saubert, C.; Piehl, K.; and Saltin, B. Enzyme activity and fibre composition in skeletal muscle of untrained and trained men. J Appl Physiol, 33(3):312-319, 1972.

Gollnick, P.D., Piehl, K., and Saltin, B. Selective glycogen depletion pattern in human muscle fibres after exercise of varying intensity and at varying pedal rates. J Physiol, 241:45-47, 1974.

Gollnick, P.D.; Timson, B.F.; Moore, R.L.; and Riedy, M. Muscular enlargement and number of fibres in skeletal muscles of rats. J Appl Physiol, 50(5):936-943, 1981.

Gonyea, W.J. Role of exercise in inducing increases in skeletal muscle fibre number. Journal of Applied Physiology, 48, 421-426, 1980.

Gonyea, W.J.; Sale, D.G.; Gonyea, F.B.; and Mikesky, A. Exercise induced increases in muscle fibre number. European Journal of Applied Physiology, 55, 137-141, 1986.

Gordon, F. Anatomical and biochemical adaptations of muscle to different exercises. JAMA, 201:755-758, 1967.

Green, H.J.; Klug, G.A.; Reichmann, H.; Seedorf, U.; Wiehrer, W.; and Pette, D. Exercise-induced fibre type transitions with regard to myosin, parvalbumin, and sarcoplasmic reticulum in muscles of the rat. Pflugers Archives, 400, 432-438, 1984.

Gregory, L.W. Some observations on strength training and assessment. J Sports Med, 21:130-137, 1981.

Grimby, G. Strength and power is sport. In: Komi, P.V. (Ed.). Oxford, Blackwell Scientific Publications. 1992.

Grosser, M.; Neumeier, A. Tecnicas de Entrenamiento (Training Techniques). Martinez Roca. Barcelona. 1986.

Hainaut, K. and Duchatteau, J. Muscle Fatigue. Effects of Training and Disuse, 12:660-669, 1989.

Harre, D. (ed.) Trainingslehre. Berlin, Sportverlag, 1982.

Hartman, J.; Tünnemann, H. Fitness and Strength Training. Berlin, Sportsverlag, 1988.

Häkkinen, K. Personal communications on "Maximum strength Development for Sports." Madrid. 1991.

Häkkinen, K. and Komi, P. Electromyographic changes during strength training and detraining. Medicine and science in Sports and Exercise, 15, 455-60, 1983.

Häkkinen, K. Training and Detraining Adaptations in Electromyography. Muscle Fibre and Force Production Characteristics of Human Leg Extensor Muscle with Special Reference to Prolonged Heavy Resistance and Explosive Type Strength Training. Studies in Sport, Physical Education and Health No. 20. University of Jyväskylä, Jyväskylä, 1986.

Hay, J.G. The biomechanics of sports teqniques. Englewood Cliffs, N.J. Prentice Hall, 1993.

Hennig, R.; Lemo, T. Gradation of force output in normal fast and slow muscle of the rat. Acta Physiologica Scandinavica, 130:133-142, 1987.

Hettinger, T. Isometric Muscle Training. Stuttgard. Georg Thieme Verlag. 1966.

Hettinger, T.; Müler, E. Muskelleistung and Muskel Training. Arbeitsphysiologie, 15:111-126, 1953.

Hickson, R.C.; Dvorak, B.A.; Corostiaga, T.T.; Foster, C. Strength training and performance in endurance-trained subjects. Medicine and Science in Sports and Exercise, 20(2 Supplement):586, 1988.

Houmard, J.A. Impact of Reduced Training on Performance in Endurance Athletes. Sports Medicine, 12(6):380-393, 1991.

Israel, S. The acute syndrome of detraining. Berlin, GDR National Olympic Committee, 2, 30-35, 1972.

Jacobs, I., and Kaiser, P. Lactate in blood, mixed skeletal muscle, and FT or ST fibres during cycle exercise in man. Acta Physiol Scand, 114:461-466, 1982.

Jacobs, I.; Esbornsson, M.; Sylven, C.; Holm, I.; Jansson, E. Sprint training effects on muscle myoglobin, enzymes, fibre types, and blood lactate. Medicine and Science in Sports and Exercise, 19(4):368-374, 1987.

Karlsson, J.; Saltin, B. Lactate, ATP, and CP in working muscles during exhaustive exercise in man. J Appl Physiol, 29(5):598-602, 1970.

Karlsson, J.; Saltin, B. Oxygen deficit and muscle metabolites in intermittent exercise. Acta Physiol Scand, 82:115-122, 1971.

Karlsson, J.; Saltin, B. Diet, muscle glycogen and endurance performance. J Appl Physiol, 31(2):203-206, 1971.

Karlsson, J.; Bonde-Petersen, F.; Henriksson, J.; and Knuttgen, H.G. Effects of previous exercise with arms or legs on metabolism and performance in exhaustive exercise. J Appl Physiol, 38:763-767, 1975.

Kato, M.; Murakami, K.; Takahashi, K.; and Hirayama, H. Motor unit activities during maintained voluntary muscle contraction at constant levels in man. Neurosci Letters, 25:149-154, 1981.

Komi, P.V.; Buskirk, E.R. Effect of eccentric and concentric muscle conditioning on tension and electrical activity of human muscle. Ergonomics, 15, 8, 1972.

Komi, P.; Rusko, H.; Vos, J.; and Vihko, V. Anaerobic performance capacity in athletes. Acta Physiol Scand, 100:107-114, 1977.

Komi, P.V. (ed.) Strength and Power in Sport. Oxford. Blackwell Scientific Publications, 1992.

Kuipers, H.; Keizer, H.A. Overtraining in Elite Athlete: Review and Directions for the Future. Sports Medicine, 6:79-92, 1988.

Larsson, L.; Ansved, T. Effects of long-term physical training and detraining on enzyme histochemical and functional skeletal muscle characteristics in man. Muscle Nerve, 8, 714-722, 1985.

Laubach, L.L. Comparative muscular strength of men and women: A review of the literature. Aviation, Space and Environmental Medicine, 47, 534-542, 1976.

Logan, G.A. Differential applications of resistance and resulting strength measured at varying degrees of knee flexion. Doctoral dissertation, USC, 1960.

Lombardi, V.P. Beginning Weight Training. Dubuque, Iowa. Wm. C. Brown, Publishers, 1989.

MacDougall, J.D.; Sale, D.G.; Elder, G.; and Sutton, J.R. Ultrastructural properties of human skeletal muscle following heavy resistance training and immobilization. Med Sci Sports, 8(1):72, 1976.

MacDougall, J.D.; Ward, G.R.; Sale, D.G.; and Sutton, J.R. Biochemical adaptation of human skeletal muscle to heavy resistance training and immobilization. J Appl Physiol, 43(4):700-703, 1977.

MacDougall, J.D.; Ward, G.R.; Sale, D.G.; and Sutton, J.R. Muscle glycogen repletion after high-intensity intermittent exercise. J Appl Physiol, 42:129-132, 1977.

MacDougall, J.D.; Sale, D.G., Moroz, J.R., Elder, G.C.B.; Sutton, J.R.; and Howald, H. Mitochondrial volume density in human skeletal muscle following heavy resistance training. Med Sci Sports, 11(2):164-166, 1979.

MacDougall, J.D.; Tuxen, D.; Sale, D.G., Moroz, J.R.; Sutton, J.R. Arterial blood pressure response to heavy resistance exercise. J. of Applied Physiology, 58(3):785-790, 1985.

MacDougall, J.D.; Sale, D.; Jacobs, I.; Garner, S.; Moroz, D.; Dittmer, D. Concurrent strength and endurance training do not impede gains in VO2 max. Medicine and Science in Sports and Exercise, 19(2):588, 1987.

Marsden, C.D.; Meadows, J.C.; Merton, P.A. Isolated single motor units in human muscle and their rate of discharge during maximal voluntary effort. Journal of Physiology (London), 217:12P-13P, 1971.

Mathews, D.K.; Fox, E.L. The Physiological Basis of Physical Education and Athletics. Philadelphia, W.B. Saunders Co., 1976.

McDonagh, M.J.N.; Davies, C.T.M. Adaptive response of mammalian skeletal muscle to exercise with high loads. European Journal of Applied Physiology, 52, 139-155, 1984.

Micheli, L.J. Strength training in the youth athletes. In E.W. Bown, and C.E. Branta (eds.) Competitive sports for children and youth (99-105). Champaign, ILL.: Human Kinetics Books, 1988.

Morgan, R.E., and Adamson, G.T. Circuit weight training. London: G. Bell and Sons, 1961.

Nelson, A.G.; Arnall, D.A.; Loy, S.F.; Silvester, L.J.; Conlee, R.K. Consequences of combining strength and endurance training regimens. Physical Therapy, 70(5), 287-294, May, 1990.

Piehl, K. Time course for refilling of glycogen stores in human muscle fibres following exercise-induced glycogen depletion. Acta Physiologica Scandinavica, 90, 297-302, 1974.

Prentice, W.J. Rehabilitation techniques in sports medicine. Times Mirror/ Mosby College Publishing. Toronto. 1990.

Ozolin, N.G. Athlete's training system for competition. Moskow, Phyzkultura i sport, 1971.

Rall, J.A. Energetic aspects of skeletal muscle contraction: implications of fibre types. Exercise Sport Sci Rev, 13:33-74, 1985.

Ralston, H.J.; Rolissan, M.J.; Inman, V.J.; Close, J.R.; Feinstein, B. Dynamic feature of human isolated voluntary muscle in isometric and free contraction. J. of Appl. Physio., 1:526-533, 1949.

Sahlin, K. Metabilic changes limiting muscular performance. Biochemistry of Exercise. Vol. 16, 1986.

Sale, D. Neural adaptation in strength and power training. In L. Jones, N. McCartney & A. McComas (eds.) Human Muscle Power, pp. 289-304. Human Kinetics, Champaign, Illinois, 1986.

Sale, D.G.; MacDougall, J.D.; Jakobs, I.; Garner, S. Interaction between concurrent strength and endurance training. Journal of applied physiology, 68(1):260-270, 1990.

Saltin, B. Adaptive changes in carbohydrate metabolism with exercise. In Howald, H., and Poortmans, J. (eds.): Metabolic Adaptation to Prolonged Physical Exercise. Basel, Switzerland, Birkhäuser Verlag, pp. 94-100, 1975.

Schantz, P.; Randall-Fox, E.; Hutchison, W.; Tydén, A.; and Åstrand, P.-O. Muscle fibre type distribution, muscle cross-sectional area and maximal voluntary strength in humans. Acta Physiol Scand, 117:219-226, 1983.

Scholich, M. Circuit training for all sports. Toronto. Sport Books Publisher (ed. P. Klavora), 1992.

Schmidtbleicher, D. Sportliches Krafttraining. Jung, Haltung, und Bewengung bei Menschen. Berlin, 1984.

Schmidtbleicher, D. Training for power events. In: Komi, P.V. (ed.). Strength and power in sport. Oxford. Blackwell Scientific Publications. 1992.

Schwane, J.A.; Watrous, B.G.; Johnson, S.R.; and Armstrong, R.B. Is lactic acid related to delayed-onset muscle soreness? Physician and Sportsmedicine, 11 (No. 3), 124-131, 1983.

Sharkey, B.J. Physiology of Fitness. Champaign, ILL. Human Kinetiks Publishers Inc. 1984.

Simoneau, J.A.; Lortie, G.; Boulay, M.R.; Marcotte, M.; Thibault, M.C.; and Bouchard, C. Human skeletal muscle fibre type alteration with high-intensity intermittent training. European Journal of Applied Physiology, 54, 250-253, 1985.

Staron, R.S.; Hagerman, F.C.; Hikida, P.S. The effects of detraining on an elite power lifter. Journal of Neurological Sciences, 51, 247-257, 1981.

Staron, R.S.; Hikida, R.S.; Hagerman, F.C.; Dudley, G.A.; and Murray, T.F. Human skeletal muscle fibre type adaptability to various workloads. J Histochem Cytochem, 32(2):146-152, 1984.

Stephens, J., and Taylor, A. Fatigue of maintained voluntary muscle contraction in man. J Physiol (London), 220:1-18, 1972.

Talag, T.S. Residual muscular soreness as influenced by concentric eccentric, and static contractions. Research Quarterly, 44, 458-469, 1973.

Taylor, N.A.S., and Wilkinson, J.G. Exercise-induced skeletal muscle growth: Hypertrophy or hyperplasia? Sports Medicine, 3, 190-200, 1986.

Tesch, P.; Sjödon, B.; Thorstensson, A.; and Karlsson, J. Muscle fatigue and its relation to lactate accumulation and LDH activity in man. Acta Physiol Scand, 103:413-420, 1978.

Tesch, P. Muscle fatigue in man. Acta Physilogica Scandinavica Supplementum, 480:3-40, 1980.

Tesch, P.A., and Larsson, L. Muscle hypertrophy in bodybuilders. European Journal of Applied Physiology, 49, 301-306, 1982.

Tesch, P.A., and Karlsson, J. Muscle fibre types and size in trained and untrained muscles of elite athletes. Journal of Applied Physiology, 59, 1716-1720, 1985.

Tesch, P.A.; Colliander, E.G.; Kaiser, P. Muscle metabolism during intense, heavy-resistance exercise. European Journal of Applied Physiology and Occupational Therapy, in press, 1986.

Terjung, R.L.; Hood, D.A. Biochemical Adaptations in Skeletal Muscle Induced by Exercise Training. Cited in: Layman, D.K. (ed.). Nutrition and Aerobic Exercise. Washington Am. Chem. Soc., 8-27, 1986.

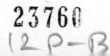

Thorstensson, A. Observations on strength training and detraining. Acta Physiologica Scandinavica, 100, 491-493, 1977.

Thorstensson, A.; Larsson, L.; Tesch, P.; and Karlsson, J. Muscle strength and fibre composition in athletes and sedentary men. Med Sci Sports, 9:26-30, 1977.

Tittel, K. Adolescence and the development of strength. Rivista di cultura sportiva, 9(19) July/Sept. 1990.

Verkhoshanski, Y. Perspectives in the improvement of speed-strength preparation of jumpers. Yessis Review of Soviet Physical Education and Sports, 4(2):28-29, 1969.

Weineck, J. Functional Anatomy in Sports. St. Louis, Mosby-Year Book, 1990.

Wilmore, J.H.; Parr, R.B.; Girandola, R.N.; Ward, P.; Vodak, P.A.; Barstow, T.J.; Pipes, T.V.; Romero, G.T.; Leslie, P. Physiological alterations consequent to circuit weight training. Medicine and Science in Sports, 10, 79-84, 1978.

Wilmore, J.H.; Costill, D.L. Training for sport and activity: The Physiological Basis of the Conditioning Process. Dubuque, Iowa. Wm. C. Brown Publishers, 1988.

Wilson, B.A., and Stainsby, W.N. Relation between oxygen uptake and developed tension in dog skeletal muscle. J Appl Physiol, 45(2):234-237, 1978.

Wirhed, R. Athletic ability: The anatomy of winning. New York. Harpoon Publications. 1984.

Wright, J.E. Anabolic steroids and athletics. In: R.S. Hutton and D.I. Miller (eds.). Exercise and Sport Science Review:149-202, 1980.

Yessis, Michael. Soviet Training Methods. New York: Barnes & Noble Publishing, 1990.

Zanon, S. Reprinted from conference report, Budapest, 1975. Athletics Coach, Dec. 1977.

ORDER FORM

Send to:

Veritas Publishing Inc.
P.O. Box 58031
3089 Dufferin St.
Toronto. ON M6A 3C8
Canada

Please send:

books @ $26.85 _____
Plus P+H $3.00 _____
Total payment enclosed _____

Please Print:

Name/Organization: _____

Address: _____

City: _____Prov./State: _____ Postal/Zip Code: _____

Country: _____

Signature: _____ Date: _____

Payment must accompany order. Please allow 2-3 weeks for delivery.

ORDER FORM

Send to:

Veritas Publishing Inc.
P.O. Box 58031
3089 Dufferin St.
Toronto. ON M6A 3C8
Canada

Please send:

books @ $26.85 _____
Plus P+H $3.00 _____
Total payment enclosed _____

Please Print:

Name/Organization: _____

Address: _____

City: _____Prov./State: _____ Postal/Zip Code: _____

Country: _____

Signature: _____ Date: _____

Payment must accompany order. Please allow 2-3 weeks for delivery.